D093841?

POSITRON ANNIHILATION

POSITRON ANNIHILATION

Proceedings of the Conference Held at
Wayne State University on July 27-29, 1965

Edited by

A. T. STEWART

Department of Physics
University of North Carolina
Chapel Hill, North Carolina

L. O. ROELLIG

Department of Physics
Wayne State University
Detroit, Michigan

ACADEMIC PRESS • New York • London • 1967

ACADEMIC PRESS INC.
111 Fifth Avenue, New York, New York 10003

United Kingdom Edition published by
ACADEMIC PRESS INC. (LONDON) LTD.
Berkeley Square House, London W.1

LIBRARY OF CONGRESS CATALOG CARD NUMBER: 66-26268

PRINTED IN THE UNITED STATES OF AMERICA

List of Contributors

Numbers in parentheses indicate the pages on which the authors'contributions begin.

G. AMBROSINO (345), Institut National des Sciences et Techniques Nucléaires, Saclay, France

J. BELL (393), Department of Nuclear and Radiation Chemistry, University of New South Wales, Sydney, Australia

S. BERKO (61,269), Department of Physics, Brandeis University, Waltham, Massachusetts

W. BRANDT (155), Department of Physics, New York University, New York, New York

C. V. BRISCOE (377, 383), Department of Physics, University of North Carolina, Chapel Hill, North Carolina

J. P. CARBOTTE (265),[1] Laboratory of Atomic and Solid State Physics, Cornell University, Ithaca, New York

G. J. CELITANS (365, 371),[2] New England Institute for Medical Research, Ridgefield, Connecticut

G. CHANDRA (335), Tata Institute of Fundamental Research, Bombay, India

P. COLOMBINO (353), Istituto di Fisica dell'Università, Turin, Italy

H. R. CRANE (321), Harrison M. Randall Laboratory of Physics, The University of Michigan, Ann Arbor, Michigan

N. E. CUSACK (309), Department of Physics, University of East Anglia, Norwich, England

S. DeBENEDETTI (3, 297), Carnegie Institute of Technology, Pittsburgh, Pennsylvania

L. H. DIETERMAN (317), Department of Physics, The University of Texas, Austin, Texas

[1]Present Address: Department of Physics, McMaster University, Hamilton, Ontario, Canada.

[2]Present Address: Department of Physics, The Hiram Scott College, Scottsbluff, Nebraska.

G. FABRI (357, 421), Laboratorio Centro Informazioni Studi Esperienze, Milan, Italy

A. FIORENTINI (81), Gruppo Nazionale Struttura della Materia del
CNR, Istituto de Fisica del Politecnico di Milano, Milan, Italy

B. FISCELLA (353), Istituto di Fisica dell'Università, Turin, Italy

E. GERMAGNOLI (357), Istituto di Fisica dell'Università, Parma,
Italy

V. I. GOLDANSKII (183), Chemical Physics Institute of the Academy
of Science of the USSR, Moscow, USSR

J. H. GREEN (95),[3] Department of Nuclear and Radiation Chemistry,
University of New South Wales, Sydney, Australia

G. IACI (357), Istituto di Fisica dell'Università, Catania, Italy

G. JONES (401), Department of Physics, University of British Columbia, Vancouver, Canada

S. KAHANA (51),[4] Department of Physics, McGill University, Montreal, Canada

T. M. KELLY (387), Department of Physics, Wayne State University,
Detroit, Michigan

T. KOHONEN (277), Institute of Technology, Otaniemi, Finland

V. G. KULKARNI (335), Tata Institute of Fundamental Research,
Bombay, India

J. H. KUSMISS (341),[5] Department of Physics, University of North
Carolina, Chapel Hill, North Carolina

R. G. LAGU (335), Tata Institute of Fundamental Research, Bombay,
India

G. F. O. LANGSTROTH (281), Department of Physics, Dalhousie University, Halifax, Nova Scotia, Canada

J. LEE (365, 371), New England Institute for Medical Research,
Ridgefield, Connecticut

---

[3] Present Address: New England Institute for Medical Research, Ridgefield, Connecticut.

[4] Present Address: Physics Department, Brookhaven National Laboratory,
Upton, New York.

[5] Present Address: Physics Department, Western Michigan University,
Kalamazoo, Michigan.

C. Y. LEUNG (409), Department of Physics, University of Toronto, Toronto, Canada

T. L. LOUCKS (287), Institute for Atomic Research and Department of Physics, Iowa State University, Ames, Iowa

J. D. McGERVEY (143, 305), Department of Physics, Western Reserve University, Cleveland, Ohio

B. T. A. McKEE (281), Department of Physics, Dalhousie University, Halifax, Nova Scotia, Canada

A. R. MACKINTOSH (287), Institute for Atomic Research and Department of Physics, Iowa State University, Ames, Iowa

I. K. MacKENZIE (281), Department of Physics, Dalhousie University, Halifax, Nova Scotia, Canada

C. K. MAJUMDAR (299), Department of Physics, Carnegie Institute of Technology, Pittsburgh, Pennsylvania

H. S. W. MASSEY (113), Department of Physics, University College, London, England

J. MELNGAILIS (297),[6] Carnegie Institute of Technology, Pittsburgh, Pennsylvania

W. E. MILLETT (317, 361), Department of Physics, The University of Texas, Austin, Texas

P. H. R. ORTH (401), Department of Physics, University of British Columbia, Vancouver, Canada

T. M. PATTERSON (349),[7] Department of Physics, University of North Carolina, Chapel Hill, North Carolina

D. A. L. PAUL (409, 417), Department of Physics, University of Toronto, Toronto, Canada

R. PAULIN (345), Institut National des Sciences et Techniques Nucléaires, Saclay, France

G. POLETTI (421), Laboratorio Centro Informazioni Studi Esperienze, Milan, Italy

I. F. QUERCIA (357), Istituto di Fisica dell'Università, Catania, Italy

G. RANDONE (421), Laboratorio Centro Informazioni Studi Esperienze, Milan, Italy

---

[6] Present Address: Centre National de la Recherche Scientifique, France.
[7] Present Address: Physics Department, Wayne State University, Detroit, Michigan.

A. RICH (321), Harrison M. Randall Laboratory of Physics, The University of Michigan, Ann Arbor, Michigan

D. M. ROCKMORE (259),[8] Department of Physics, University of North Carolina, Chapel Hill, North Carolina

L. O. ROELLIG (127, 387), Department of Physics, Wayne State University, Detroit, Michigan

J. B. SHAND (291),[9] University of North Carolina, Chapel Hill, North Carolina

P. C. STANGEBY (417), Department of Physics, University of Toronto, Toronto, Canada

A. T. STEWART (17, 259, 291, 313, 341, 349, 377, 383), Department of Physics, University of North Carolina, Chapel Hill, North Carolina

S. J. TAO (371, 393), New England Institute for Medical Research, Ridgefield, Connecticut

J. H. TERRELL (269),[10] Department of Physics, Brandeis University, Waltham, Massachusetts

J. C. THOMPSON (317), Department of Physics, The University of Texas, Austin, Texas

B. V. THOSAR (335), Tata Institute of Fundamental Research, Bombay, India

L. TROSSI (353), Istituto Nazionale di Fisica Nucleare, Sezione di Torino, Turin, Italy

E. TURRISI (357), Istituto di Fisica dell'Università, Catania, Italy

P. G. VARLASHKIN (313),[11] Department of Physics, University of North Carolina, Chapel Hill, North Carolina

H. L. WEISBERG (269),[12] Department of Physics, Brandeis University, Waltham, Massachusetts

[8]Present Address: Physics Department, University of Maine, Orono, Maine.

[9]Present Address: Department of Physics, University of Georgia, Athens, Georgia.

[10]Present Address: Mithras Inc., Cambridge, Massachusetts.

[11]Present Address: Physics Department, Louisiana State University, Baton Rouge, Louisiana.

[12]Present Address: Lawrence Radiation Laboratory, University of California, Berkeley, California.

R. N. WEST (309), Department of Physics, University of East Anglia, Norwich, England

R. W. WILLIAMS,(287), Institute for Atomic Research and Department of Physics, Iowa State University, Ames, Iowa

E. J. WOLL, Jr. (329),[13] Department of Physics, Carnegie Institute of Technology, Pittsburgh, Pennsylvania

[13] Present Address: Department of Physics, McMaster University, Hamilton, Ontario, Canada.

Preface

This book summarizes the present knowledge of positron annihilation in various environments. The first part of the book presents lengthy review articles based on the invited talks presented at the Positron Annihilation Conference. These papers were coordinated with respect to each other and written to survey the entire field. The second section contains short reports of the most recent developments in the field and illustrates the present direction of research.

The study of the annihilation of positrons has provided valuable information concerning the properties of matter. Positrons make a useful probe, for they can penetrate into liquids and solids without damaging the material. The annihilation gamma rays (which are relatively unattenuated by the usual experimental apparatus, e. g. Dewars, vacuum chamber walls, or high pressure cells) provide information concerning the structure of the material and its interactions with positrons. In recent years several important advances have been made, especially in positron annihilation in gases and metals, and in positronium chemistry. Furthermore, the commercial development of fast and stable electronic apparatus has encouraged many more groups to work in the field so that the rate of progress is increasing rapidly.

A Positron Annihilation Conference was orgainized to help consolidate present progress, to discuss unsolved problems, and to discern new directions of profitable research work for this interesting and unique method. The conference, held at Wayne State University in Detroit, Michigan on July 27-29, 1965, was made possible through the generous support of the Wayne State Fund, University of North Carolina at Chapel Hill, National Science Foundation, United States Army Research Office, Durham, and the Advanced Research Projects Agency (University of North Carolina). The organizing committee, L. O. Roellig (chairman), A. T. Stewart, and P. R. Wallace, is pleased to take this opportunity to thank these organizations for their sponsorship.

The editors are much indebted to their colleagues, for it is they who by contributions and discussions have created this book, a review and guide to positron annihilation in matter.

A. T. STEWART
L. O. ROELLIG

July, 1967

Contents

Part II: RESEARCH DEVELOPMENTS

Review Articles

The Physics of Positron Annihilation
A Survey*

S. DeBenedetti

Carnegie Institute of Technology
Pittsburgh, Pennsylvania

THE ERA OF DISCOVERY AND OF QUANTUM ELECTRODYNAMICAL INVESTIGATION

The opportunity of presenting a historical survey of the developments in the physics of positrons is both an honor and a pleasure. The pleasure, however, is somewhat reduced when I think that such honors are usually conferred on people who are themselves considered as part of history. And though history is concerned with the past, I would like to have the illusion that, for the moment, I still do belong to the present. Do I?

But I am not here to speak of my personal life, but rather about the life of the positrons.

In this connection I discovered a remarkable coincidence. The life of the positrons is about as long as my own scientific life. With this, I do not mean that my scientific life is of the order of 10^{-9} sec; it might well be just as ephemeral, but measured in seconds it is closer to 10^9 than to 10^{-9}. Perhaps this is because I have not yet met my antiself! Had my life been of the order of 10^{-9} sec, I would not have been invited to give this historical introduction.

When I say that my scientific life is as long as that of the positrons, I refer to the fact that the positrons were discovered by Anderson in 1933[1] when I was in the last year of study at the University of Florence.

The news of the discovery did not come to me from Anderson in California, but from a schoolmate of mine a year or so older than myself, whose name some of you may remember. I am speaking about Occhialini who, in 1933, was in England working with Blackett on the construction of the first counter-controlled cloud chamber.

From my friend Occhialini a letter arrived at the Institute of

*Work supported by the National Science Foundation.

Physics in Florence telling about the results of his work. At the Institute—which is located in the lovely hill of Arcetri where Galileo spent the last years of his life under house imprisonment for having dared to support the Copernican system—the letter was passed on to me by Bernardini, whose name you may also have heard. This letter told of the discovery of cosmic ray showers.[2] The pictures of the showers, which we received, contained both positrons and electrons. Not only did they confirm the existence of positrons, which had been established quite convincingly by Anderson, but they proved that positrons were actually produced in the transformation of energy into matter. This interrelation between matter and energy was a new thing at the time, and you might understand how it appealed to the mind of a young student such as I was. It is true that the theory of relativity was known and that Dirac had predicted the existence of some positively charge states of the electron (which he himself found very embarrassing because they had not been found in nature); but, until these pictures showed the actual creation of matter from energy, all the theoretical arguments seemed empty speculations. To see for the first time the creation of particles and antiparticles was an experience which I still remember and which moved me quite deeply.

It is probably from that time on that I fell in love with positrons; in a way I am still in love with them. I must confess, however, that I have not always been faithful to this love. With the discovery of new particles, the object of my intellectual affection has been changing. Some of you might accuse me of being intellectually promiscuous and it is an accusation I will not dispute.

But, going back to positrons, the next step was the discovery that they annihilated. The experimental work was done in France (also published in 1933) separately by Thibaud[3,4] and by Joliot.[5,6] In the meantime Monsieur and Madame Joliot had discovered artificial radioactivity which provided sources of positrons that could be handled with ease.

For this discovery M. and Mme. Joliot were awarded the Nobel prize. When the announcement of the prize came, I was working with them at the Laboratoire Curie, where the occasion was happily celebrated by opening numerous bottles of champagne.

It was at this laboratory, under the direction of Joliot, that I became more directly acquainted with positrons. I had the great satisfaction of seeing how the positrons were actually produced by the materialization of gamma rays. I used the gamma rays from radioactive Thorium C″ , and was able to verify the law predicted by the theory that the materialization cross section goes with the square of the atomic number.[7,8] At about the same time, in 1934, Klemperer was studying some of the features of annihilation, and proved that two gamma rays were emitted in coincidence in approximately opposite directions.[9]

Not much happened in this very interesting field until after Second World War, when new possibilities of experimentation were provided by the discovery of scintillation counters.

In 1949, I was using annihilation radiation to test a coincidence circuit at Washington University in St. Louis. During these tests, I realized that it was possible to measure the anticolinearity of the two annihilation quanta much more carefully than had been previously done. I was asking myself whether this measurement had any significance when Henry Primakoff entered the room, and I directed the question to him. "Yes," said Henry, "it is significant if you can measure angles of the order of 1/137 of a radian; this is about half a degree." Well, it was not difficult to measure half a degree with scintillation counters, and we could show that the gamma-rays of annihilation are not exactly anticolinear and that their angle is determined by the motion of the electrons in the solid matter where the annihilation took place.[10],[11]

About the same time, maybe even a little earlier, DuMond and his associates at California Institute of Technology had proved with very accurate measurements of energy that the width of the annihilation radiation is also affected by the electron motion.[12]

At the time I was not especially interested in solid state, and I abandoned the problem to concern myself with mesic atoms. This work I did together with Martin and Mary Beth Stearns who are now living here in Detroit, where Martin is a dean at this university.

But the problems of positrons were still in the back of my mind, and, at Carnegie Tech, Bob Siegel and I[13],[14] decided to study the three quantum annihilation of triplet pairs with a triple coincidence experiment. But our work was overshadowed by the brilliant results of Deutsch,[15]-[17] which appeared at about the same time, proving the existence of positronium and studying its formation and its properties.

By my standards, the work of Deutsch on the atom of positronium is one of the greatest things that have happened in physics during my thirty years of professional life. These experiments are not only of profound significance for one of the most basic interactions of our universe—as the fine structure of positronium[18]-[20] provides one of the most accurate ways of studying the interaction between electrons and the electromagnetic fields—but they also show that an ingenious man with advanced but not overwhelming instrumentation can still give very significant contributions to our knowledge of the physical world.

In these times when the attention of the physicist is concentrated on the study of strange particles and of interactions which defy our understanding despite the use of gigantic equipment, it is comforting to see that there is a very fundamental subject which can be comprehended with great accuracy and in which significant work has been done with relatively modest means.

It is perhaps because of my abhorrence for the complicated instrumentation of contemporary elementary particle physics that I came
back to positrons. With Lang and Smoluchowski,[21,22] I undertook to
measure more carefully the angles of the two gamma annihilation
radiation, and to study whether there were any differences in different materials. Our results appeared as a Physical Review Letter in
1955, in the same number of the journal where a similar work was
reported by Stewart,[23] with whom we have since maintained a relation of friendly collaboration and consultation.

THE ERA OF APPLICATION

The interaction of electrons and positrons with the electromagnetic field is, at present, very precisely understood up to momentum
transfers of the order of BeV/c and the experimentalist who does
not want to enter the rat race of high energy accelerators, is left
with no problem which cannot be computed very reliably from the
theory. But, with the understanding of the behavior of the positrons
as particles and with the availability of positron sources, it became possible to use positrons for investigation of other problems.

A parallel can perhaps be found in the study of x-rays. After the
initial exciting investigations of the nature of the x-rays and of their
interaction with matter, the x-rays have become a useful tool, very
fruitful in all kinds of other studies.

Thus, the era of quantum electrodynamic investigation with low-
energy positrons was closed, and the era of application was started.

In turn, this second era can be divided into two periods: The first
is the period of hand waving and the second is the period of electronic computing, into which we are entering now. If I speak about
hand waving it is not with the intention of minimizing the importance
of the results of those experiments and of those calculations which
have led to a first, semiquantitative understanding of what goes on in
the process of positron slowing down, thermalization, and annihilation
in matter. It is my feeling, however, that the interest of the semiquantitative studies is now finished, and the problems that remain are
more quantitative in nature. Since they are complicated problems,
they should naturally be attacked with the modern techniques of electronic computing.

There are many people in the audience who could continue this
survey on the behavior of positrons in matter better than myself!
The facts covered in the rest of this survey are well-known even to
people in possession of all their hair!

But, since the job has been assigned to me, I will continue and try
to give you a bird's-eye view of the developments without entering into

those details which properly belong in the papers which will follow. I am sure that the unavoidable omissions will make me many enemies, but this is a risk that I must courageously face.

I will start with a review of the experimental methods which are used in the field.

There are in general three methods which are widely used. I will mention first the measurement of triplet annihilation rate by a triple coincidence counting. Though this method is used less frequently than the others because it is experimentally less practical, it is the easiest to interpret. The measurement of triple coincidence between the annihilation gamma rays tells us the number of annihilations of positrons and electrons in the triplet state. Whenever this rate is larger than the 1/372 ratio that is predicted by the theory for a random orientation of the spins, we assume that there is formation of positronium.

The second method is the measurement of the angular correlation of the two-quantum annihilation radiation. This method actually measures the Fourier transform of the product of the electron and positron wavefunction. A quantitative discussion of the result requires in general the electronic computation of the wavefunctions themselves. We can, however, make a very simple remark. If positronium is formed and if it decays in the singlet state in thermal equilibrium with the surrounding mediums, the angular distribution of the two gamma rays shows a sharp peak, which was first observed by Page[24,25] and collaborators at the University of Pittsburgh in 1955.

The last method is the measurement of the mean life of positrons. The first determinations were made in gases by Deutsch; they were followed by studies in solids at Carnegie Tech,[26] and by the discovery of the two mean lifetimes, τ_1 and τ_2, by Bell and Graham in 1953.[27] It is assumed that the short mean life τ_1 corresponds to annihilation of pairs in the singlet state or to annihilation of unbound positrons, and that the second mean life τ_2 reveals the presence of positronium triplet.

In order to understand the meaning of the results obtained by these three methods in better detail, it is necessary to follow the behavior of the positrons in the last instants of their life. We attempt to describe this behavior in a schematic way with the help of the diagram in Fig. 1.

After the positrons have lost most of their initial energy, they are no more able to ionize the atoms of the medium which they traverse. The remaining energy may be in the range called the "Ore gap" in which positronium formation is the only possible result of an inelastic collision. If positronium is not formed the positron will eventually annihilate freely with a mean life τ_1 of the order of 10^{-10} sec; it is generally assumed that the positron slows down in this time, and that the angular distribution of the annihilation radiation depends mainly on

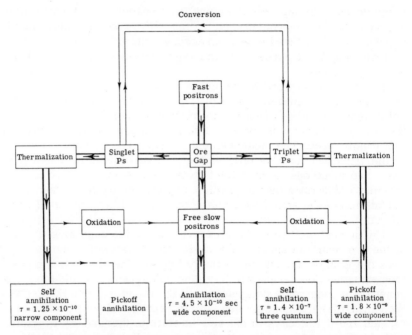

Fig. 1. Flow chart showing the possible reactions of positrons in aqueous solutions.

the wavefunction of the electron in the annihilation medium. If, instead, positronium is formed while the positrons traverse the Ore gap, the positronium atoms (if they do not lose their electrons in a process of oxidation) decrease their energy until they are thermalized and annihilate with their characteristic mean life. The angular distribution of the two-quantum angular annihilation from singlet positronium reflects in this case the kinetic energy of the positronium atom which is very small, and not the momentum distribution of the electrons of the medium.

THE CHEMISTRY OF POSITRONIUM

At present, the applications of positrons cover two important fields: chemistry and solid state.

Let us talk about chemistry first, because this is a meeting of physicists and we do not intend to cover the chemical work in detail.

Positronium is an atom, and some of us had the curiosity of seeing how it behaves as a chemical element. The motivation for these studies was the hope that the chemistry of positronium would be much simpler and easier to understand than that of the other elements; it was conceivable that the study of positronium chemistry could contribute significantly to our knowledge of the chemical bond. This anticipation, however, has been disappointed. Some information has been gathered on the chemical reactions of positronium and on reaction rates, but the results are not easier to understand than the corresponding information for the other elements. It is possible that the difficulty may arise from the fact that these studies have been performed by physicists and not by chemists!

The work on the chemistry of positronium was, of course, initiated by Deutsch. To mention just a few examples of the work which followed, the investigations of the chemical behavior of positrons in gases were pursued by Hughes at Columbia University and by Green at the University of New South Wales; work in benzene solution was carried on by Berko at the University of Virginia, and aqueous solutions were studied by the Canadian group and at Carnegie Tech. An account of these studies has been published in a book by Green and Lee,[28] and whoever is interested is referred to this volume for further information and references.

ANNIHILATION IN NONMETALLIC SOLIDS

Let us now proceed directly to the work on solid state with which the remainder of this talk will be concerned.

Some of the problems of positrons in solids have a chemical flavor. It is in fact possible to form the atom of positronium within solid matter; in certain cases this atom annihilates without decomposing, as is shown by the presence of a long mean life and of a sharp peak in the angular distribution spectrum. A typical substance in which these features are observed is fused quartz[29,30]; since positronium is not found in crystal quartz, it is generally assumed that it is nested in the empty spaces existing between the atoms of the less well-ordered fused samples.

Let us pass to the problems studied with positron techniques which have revealed some properties of the electronic states in regular crystal lattices. Considerable progress has been accomplished in this direction which I regard as the most fruitful of the applications of positron annihilation. The field has been reviewed in 1960 in an article by Wallace.[31]

Data on angular distribution and on mean life have been obtained for a great variety of nonmetallic samples. Evidence of positronium formation is found only in those substances whose complex molecular structure or whose imperfect crystal state make possible the existence of "empty spaces."

Among the nonmetallic elements which have been studied, carbon has been investigated both in the form of diamond and graphite. Considerable differences in the angular distribution of the annihilation

radiation have been reported for single crystal-graphite samples
oriented in different directions.[32]

Whereas graphite and diamonds are typical valence crystals, the
solid noble gases are characteristic van der Waal's solids. In this
kind of solid, the atoms are relatively distant from each other and it
would seem easier to make a satisfactory theoretical model of their
structure. The mean life of positrons in the solid noble gases has
been investigated by Liu and Roberts,[33] and some information on the
angular distribution of the annihilation radiation in argon was obtained at Carnegie Tech.[34] The theoretical analysis of the result is
going to be presented by Woll at another session of this meeting
where several attempts of computation of positron and electron
wavefunctions will be reported and compared with the experimental
data.

It is observed that the angular distribution of the annihilation radiation in sulfur[35] in different crystals and anomolous forms is not
too different from that of argon. This observation might be explained
if we consider that the atom of sulfur is similar to that of argon apart
from two missing electrons in the $3p$ shell.

Some experimental studies have been carried on in semiconductors,
but much remains to be done in this interesting field. The results
have been interpreted in a qualitative way in terms of band structure
but no attempt to develop a quantitative theory has been made to my
knowledge.

Many chemical compounds have also been studied. A simple qualitative interpretation of the data obtained with the alkali halides can
be presented. It is found that the angular distribution of the annihilation radiation of these salts depends almost exclusively on the nonmetallic (negative) ion. This is natural since the positrons are attracted
by negative charges. In particular, the angular distribution of chlorine is very similar to that of argon as seems reasonable when one
considers that the negative chlorine ion, like argon, has a complete
$3p$ shell.

It would be too long to list all the results, and at this point we stop
the survey of nonmetallic substances.

APPLICATIONS TO PHYSICS OF METALS

The study of metals, and particularly of the behavior of the positrons in a gas of conduction electrons, is probably the most fundamental problem of slow positron physics.

In the alkali metals, which are the simplest, the results of the
studies of angular distribution of annihilation radiation[36−43] have provided us with beautiful pictures which present the clearest and most

direct illustration of the Fermi distribution of conduction electrons. But since there were no doubts about the Fermi distribution before these experiments, we cannot say that these results represent any great progress in our knowledge of metals. In some cases, however, such as in bismuth,[44,45] they have served to establish the density of free electrons, or the number of conduction electrons per atom, which was not previously known.

The fact that in the alkali metals, the annihilation takes place almost exclusively with the conduction electrons is easily explained when we consider that the ionic cores are small and, being positively charged, repel the positron.

The behavior of a positron in a Fermi gas of electrons, however, is a many-body problem which is far from being understood.

Significant information comes from the study of positron mean life in the alkali metals. The results show that the mean life is very short and practically the same in all these metals. In my own survey of 1951,[26] I was unable to find any difference between lithium, sodium, and potassium within the experimental error of about 0.5×10^{-10} sec. The results of Bell and Jørgensen[46] in 1960 show a variation from 2.9 to 4.3×10^{-10} sec from lithium to cesium, which is still very small when compared with the difference in the density of conduction electrons. Note that the mean life in lithium is roughly twice as great as the mean life of singlet positronium; since only one out of four positrons in lithium is in a singlet pair, it follows that the electron density at the position of the annihilating positron in metals is larger than the corresponding electron density in the atom of positronium. This density is much larger than the average density of conduction electrons showing the importance of the attraction between the positron and the conduction electron.

This attraction enhances the density of conduction electrons at the position of the positron but does not change the momentum of the annihilating pair. At first sight we might think that these results are contradictory, but it is not difficult to make a model to reconcile them. We are facing a situation somewhat similar to that prevailing in the physics of complex nuclei where the individual particles behave in a certain sense as if they were free (shell model) and in another sense as if they were strongly bound (condensed drop model). This state of affairs has been investigated both by solid state and nuclear theoreticians; as a result of their work we have reached some qualitative understanding, but not yet a complete explanation of the facts. Among the theoretical work specifically connected with positrons we must mention that of Daniel and Friedel[47] and of Kahana.[48,49] This last author has computed, with many-body techniques, a momentum dependent enhancement factor of the annihilation rate from a screened Coulomb attraction between electrons and positrons and succeeds in explaining the value of the positron mean life in the alkali metals. The enhancement is momentum dependent, but it is possible that it affects only slightly the angular distribution.

The behavior of positrons in a Fermi gas is but one of the aspects of the behavior of positrons in metals. The annihilation with the ionic cores cannot be neglected and the periodicity of the lattice must be taken into account for a closer understanding of the electron and positron wavefunction.

These effects can be detected even in the simple alkali metals. Stewart was able to show that the angular distribution of the annihilation radiation depends on the orientation of a lithium single crystal where the positrons are stopped.[50] More conspicuous anisotropic effects have been observed by Stewart[51] and by Berko[52] in beryllium, and are interpreted in terms of the Bloch function of the conduction band.

The results of these and similar experiments are of interest because they may give information on the shape of the Fermi surface. However, the connection between the experimental results and the Fermi surface, is not as direct as some believe. The angular distribution pattern, as previously remarked, reveals the Fourier transform of the product of the wave function of the annihilating particles; as such it is affected not only by the Fermi surface shape, but also by the necessary departure of the conduction electrons from a plane wave.

In transition metals, the angular distribution of the annihilation radiation shows clear evidence that the annihilation may occur with the electrons of the ionic cores. Among the many interesting studies of this effect one must mention the observation of the differences in the angular distribution from solid and liquid mercury,[53] which are probably connected with the change in the probability of annihilation with the ionic core.

Another interesting aspect of positron research in metals is the study of magnetic effects. The field was opened by the discovery of parity violation in β decay, which followed the theoretical work of Yang and Lee. After the Wu-Ambler experiment, which established that electrons from β decay are left handed, i.e., with spin opposite to the direction of motion, Hanna and Preston[54-56] and Page and Heinberg[57] proved that positrons from radioactive sources are right-handed.

The work of Hanna and Preston was based on the fact that the positrons maintain their polarization after slowing down,[58] up to the time of annihilation; thus the two quantum annihilation radiation is emitted only when the annihilating electron has its spin opposite to the initial momentum of the positron. From this remark it is possible to separate experimentally the contribution of polarized electrons to the two quantum annihilation radiation from targets of magnetized materials such as iron. After several published and un-published attempts, accurate results were reported by Mijnarends and Hambro,[59] and by Berko and Zucherman.[60]

These results show that the $3d$ electrons of magnetized iron are polarized, as was already known from neutron diffraction, but they are also "indicative" of an antiparallel polarization of the conduction band electrons.

TOWARDS THE ERA OF COMPUTING

In the course of this survey we have seen that many data have been collected, many suggestions have been advanced, many theoretical models have been discussed, and some semiquantitative theories have been developed. It would seem that, in the year of our Lord 1965, and in the year of Quantum Mechanics almost 40, it should be possible to do better.

Fortunately, the physics of positrons has no practical value; and there is no reason why we should continue studying those aspects of it which are not elegant nor fruitful in an intellectual sense. The mean life of positrons and the angular distribution of annihilation radiation in odd substances is of no commercial interest, and we should not measure it unless it helps us to reach a better understanding of some broader question.

A few years ago I believed that we were near to running out of significant problems, but now, thanks to electronic computers, the situation has changed. I will use these last few minutes to outline what seems to me a significant program for the future.

First we should attack a few simple problems for whose solution we have adequate experimental and theoretical tools. These could include the study of some simple positronium molecules, and, more interesting to me, the investigation of the behavior of positrons in simple nonconducting crystal lattices. These problems present no conceptual difficulty: the interactions are known and the states can be formulated with sufficient accuracy. The problems may be mathematically complicated but should be soluble with the help of fast electronic computers.

We must find the proper procedures, the proper approximations to solve them, and continue to work until our programs give the correct numerical result for both mean lives and angular distributions. The work on argon, presented by Woll, is an attempt in this direction. It is not yet successful, but we should keep improving our methods of calculation until we obtain agreement between theory and experiment.

While we learn to solve these conceptually simple problems we should think about the difficult significant ones. Among these, I consider *par excellence*, the many-body problem of a positron in an electron gas. Typical in this field is the work of Kahana. After these basic questions have been clarified, we may use positron techniques for the investigation of more complicated solids, or more complex molecules.

I hope that this program will be successful and will make the study of positrons a much more powerful tool for the investigation of matter than it has been thus far.

As an example of attempts—possibly premature but in the right direction—to a quantitative explanation of the data, I will mention the work of Berko and Plaskett in aluminum,[61] and the work of Stewart[62] and Melngailis[63] in lithium.

The last work, for which Stewart did the experiment and Melngailis the theory, I will report at another session of this meeting in order to prove that my attention is not exclusively concerned with historical matters . . . and that I still belong to the present!

REFERENCES

1. Anderson, C. D., *Phys. Rev.* **43**, 491 (1933).
2. Blackett, P. M. S., and G. P. S. Occhialini, *Proc. Roy. Soc. (London)* **A139**, 699 (1933).
3. Thibaud, J., *Compt. Rend.* **197**, 1629 (1933).
4. Thibaud, J., *Phys. Rev.* **45**, 781 (1934).
5. Joliot, F., *Compt. Rend.* **197**, 1622 (1933).
6. Joliot, F., *Compt. Rend.* **198**, 81 (1934).
7. DeBenedetti, S., *Compt. Rend.* **200**, 1389 (1935).
8. DeBenedetti, S., *J. Phys.* **7**, 205 (1936).
9. Klemperer, O., *Proc. Cambridge Phil. Soc.* **30**, 347 (1934).
10. DeBenedetti, S., C. E. Cowan, W. R. Konneker, *Phys. Rev.* **76**, 440 (1949).
11. DeBenedetti, S., C. E. Cowan, W. R. Konneker, and H. Primakoff, *Phys. Rev.* **77**, 205 (1950).
12. DuMond, J. W. M., D. A. Lind, and B. B. Watson, *Phys. Rev.* **75**, 1226 (1949).
13. DeBenedetti, S., and R. Siegel, *Phys. Rev.* **85**, 371 (1952).
14. DeBenedetti, S., and R. Siegel, *Phys. Rev.* **94**, 955 (1954).
15. Deutsch, M., *Phys. Rev.* **82**, 455 (1951).
16. Deutsch, M., *Phys. Rev.* **83**, 866 (1951).
17. For reviews see: M. Deutsch, *Progr. Nuclear Phys.* **3**, 131 (1953); S. DeBenedetti and H. C. Corben, *Ann. Rev. Nuclear Sci.* **4**, 191 (1954).
18. Deutsch, M., and S. C. Brown, *Phys. Rev.* **85**, 1047 (1952).
19. Weinstein, R., M. Deutsch, and S. C. Brown, *Phys. Rev.* **94**, 758 (1954).
20. Weinstein, R., M. Deutsch, and S. C. Brown, *Phys. Rev.* **98**, 223 (1955).
21. Lang, L. G., S. DeBenedetti, and R. Smoluchowski, *Phys. Rev.* **99**, 596, (1955).
22. Lang, L. G., and S. DeBenedetti, *Phys. Rev.* **108**, 914 (1957).
23. Stewart, A. T., *Phys. Rev.* **99**, 594 (1955).
24. Page, L. A., M. Heinberg, P. R. Wallace, and T. Trout, *Phys. Rev.* **98**, 206 (1955).
25. Page, L. A., and M. Heinberg, *Phys. Rev.* **102**, 1545 (1956).

26. DeBenedetti, S., and H. J. Richings, *Phys. Rev.* **85**, 377 (1952).
27. Bell, R. E., and R. L. Graham, *Phys. Rev.* **90**, 644 (1953).
28. Green, J., and J. Lee, "Positronium Chemistry." Academic Press, New York, 1964.
29. Page, L. A., and M. Heinberg, *Phys. Rev.* **102**, 1545 (1956).
30. de Zafra, R. L., and W. T. Joyner, *Phys. Rev.* **112**, 19 (1958).
31. Wallace, P. R., *Solid State Phys.* **10**, 1 (1960).
32. Berko, S. E., R. E. Kelley, and J. S. Plaskett, *Phys. Rev.* 106, 824 (1957).
33. Liu, D. C., and W. K. Roberts, *Phys. Rev.* **132**, 1633 (1963).
34. Rose, K. L., and S. DeBenedetti, *Phys. Rev.* **138**, A927 (1965).
35. Colombino, P., I. Degregori, L. Mayrone, L. Trossi, S. DeBenedetti, *Phys. Rev.* **119**, 1665 (1960).
36. Green, R. E., and A. T. Stewart, *Phys. Rev.* 98, 486 (1955).
37. Stewart, A. T., *Canad. J. Phys.* **35**, 168 (1957).
38. Stewart, A. T., *Phys. Rev.* **123**, 1587 (1961).
39. Stewart, A. T., J. H. Kusmiss, and R. H. March, *Phys. Rev.* **132**, 495 (1963).
40. Donaghy, J. J., and A. T. Stewart, *Bull. Am. Phys. Soc.* **9**, 238(A) (1964).
41. Melngailis, J., *Bull. Am. Phys. Soc.* **10**, 22(A) (1965).
42. Stewart, A. T., and J. B. Shand, *Bull. Am. Phys. Soc.* **10**, 21 (1965).
43. Weisberg, H. L., *Bull. Am. Phys. Soc.* **10**, 21 (1965).
44. Dekhtyar, I. Ya., and V. S. Mikhalenkov, *Dokl. Akad. Nauk SSSR* **136**, 63 (1961).
45. MacKenzie, I. K., G. F. O. Langstroth, B. T. A. McKee, and C.G. White, *Canad. J. Phys.* **42**, 1837 (1964).
46. Bell, R. E., and M. H. Jørgensen, *Canad. J. Phys.* **38**, 652 (1960).
47. Daniel, E., and J. Friedel, *J. Phys. Chem. Solids* **4**, 111 (1958).
48. Kahana, S., *Phys. Rev.* **129**, 1622 (1963).
49. Kahana, S., *Phys. Rev.* **117**, 123 (1960).
50. Stewart, A. T., J. J. Donaghy, J. H. Kusmiss, and D. M. Rockmore, *Bull. Am. Phys. Soc.* **9**, 238 (1964).
51. Stewart, A. T., J. B. Shand, J. J. Donaghy, and J. H. Kusmiss, *Phys. Rev.* **128**, 118 (1962).
52. Berko, S., *Phys. Rev.* **128**, 2166 (1963).
53. Gustafson, D. R., A. R. Mackintosh, and D. J. Zaffarano, *Phys. Rev.* **130**, 1455 (1963).
54. Hanna, S. S., and R. S. Preston, *Phys. Rev.* **106**, 1363 (1957).
55. Hanna, S. S., and R. S. Preston, *Phys. Rev.* **108**, 160 (1957).
56. Hanna, S. S., and R. S. Preston, *Phys. Rev.* **108**, 1460 (1957).
57. Page, L. A., and M. Heinberg, *Phys. Rev.* **106**, 1220 (1957).
58. Dufner, A. J., and A. V. Bushkovich, *Bull. Am. Phys. Soc.* **9**, 562 (1964).
59. Mijnarends, P. E., and L. Hambro, *Phys. Letters* **10**, 272 (1964).
60. Berko, S., and J. Zuckerman, *Phys. Rev. Letters* **13**, 339a (1964).
61. Berko, S., and J. S. Plaskett, *Phys. Rev.* **112**, 1877 (1958).
62. Stewart, A. T., *Phys. Rev.* (to be published).
63. Melngailis, J., *Phys. Rev.* (to be published).

Positron Annihilation in Metals

A. T. Stewart

University of North Carolina
Chapel Hill, North Carolina

Present knowledge of the behavior of a positron in a metal has been accumulated over the past 10 or 20 years. Many have contributed by experiment and by calculation. The interactions of a positron in a metal are now known well enough so that the positron can be used as a tool and, in a few cases, it has yielded information about the metals themselves which was not available from other techniques. The hope that positron annihilation would be of wide usefulness in the study of solids and, in particular, in the study of metals, has grown and faded repeatedly as our understanding of this tool has advanced. In this talk I shall review the developing knowledge of this interesting technique and point out the successes and disappointments which have occurred along the way.

HISTORICAL INTRODUCTION

An early step was taken by Beringer and Montgomery[1] who, in 1942, measured the angular distribution of photons from positrons annihilating in copper and lead. Figure 1 shows a schematic drawing of their apparatus, and illustrates the first angular correlation data. From these results Beringer and Montgomery concluded that most of the electrons and positrons which annihilate have a kinetic energy less than a few kilovolts. Previous to this, of course, Klemperer[2] had shown, by absorption measurements, that the annihilation photons were approximately one-half MeV in energy, and also that they were emitted in opposite directions. Alichanian, Alichanow, and Arzimovitch[3] had shown that this "opposite direction" met within 1 sterad at 180°. No further experiments were reported until after the war. Then in 1948 Vlasov and Tsirelson[4] observed that 95% of the photon pairs were emitted within one degree of 180°, and they concluded that the kinetic energy of most of the annihilating positrons was less than 80 eV. Following this, Dumond, Lind, and Watson[5], in 1949, measured precisely the energy of the half-MeV annihilation line in their crystal spectrometer. They obtained a value in agreement with the value of the natural constants in mc^2,

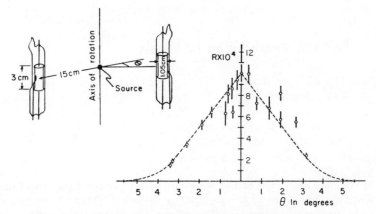

Fig. 1. An early experiment to measure the angular correlation of annihilation photons (Beringer and Montgomery, Ref. 1).

and furthermore they observed that the line had a finite width somewhat greater than the experimental resolution of their gamma spectrometer. This extra width they attributed to a Doppler broadening of the line from motion of the positrons or electrons at the time of annihilation. The energy of the motion required to give this line broadening would average about 16 electron volts. This experiment then confirmed the earlier calculation of Bethe[6] who estimated that most of the positrons would be reduced to very low, that is, atomic,

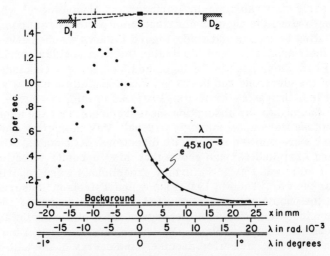

Fig. 2. The angular distribution of annihilation photons obtained in 1949 by DeBenedetti, Cowan, and Konneker (Ref. 7).

energies before being annihilated. In the same year, DeBenedetti, Cowan, and Konneker[7] published a short note showing that the angular distribution of photons from positrons annihilating in copper and lead had a shape at higher momentum characteristic of the momentum of valence electrons in the solid (see Fig. 2). This result was confirmed in 1950 by the nice results of Vlasov and Dzhelepov[8] who measured the angular correlation of positrons annihilating in copper foil surrounded by lead foil. They showed that the width of the angular distribution was much greater than the width expected from the geometrical optics of the apparatus which was about $3\frac{1}{2}$ mrad. They observed, as had DeBenedetti, that this width was characteristic of the motion of valence electrons in the metal. They also first pointed out that under certain conditions the angular distribution of photons from positrons annihilating at rest with the electrons of a free electron metal could be a parabola. Figure 3 shows these results. In the same year, 1950, DeBenedetti, Cowan, Konneker, and Primakoff[9] published a more complete account of the experiment we have just described. In this most important paper they developed the theory of positron annihilation in a crystal. They showed what one could expect from measurements of photon momentum assuming that both positron and electron were described by independent Bloch type waves in the crystal. They formulated clearly the importance of what is called the higher momentum components of the electron and positron wave functions. And furthermore, they anticipated that the positron would be in its ground state. This description is still the framework with which it is easiest to describe most experimental results.

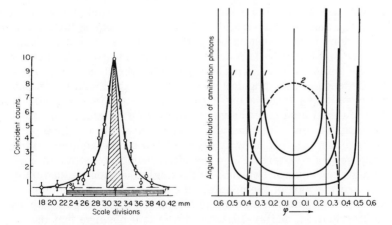

Fig. 3. The angular distribution of annihilation photons obtained in 1950 by the nice results of Vlasov and Dzhelepov (Ref. 8).

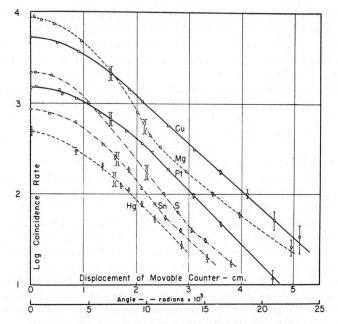

Fig. 4. Angular distributions of annihilation photons.
The distributions are clearly different for the various materials (Warren and Griffiths, Ref. 11).

In the following year two papers appeared by Warren and collaborators.[10,11] In the first one, they showed that positron annihilation
in copper gave an angular distribution of annihilation photons with a
tail at large angles which could be fitted to an exponential as DeBenedetti had done. Their results were similar to his. The other paper
by Warren and Griffiths is notable. Although not explicitly pointed
out by the authors, it showed clearly and for the first time, significant differences in the angular distribution of the annihilation photons for positrons annihilating in different metals (see Fig. 4). Also
in 1951 Maier-Leibnitz[12] arrived at this same conclusion by an ingenious experiment. He mounted various materials in which positrons were annihilating midway between and on the common axis of
two long geiger counters. Since the efficiency of detection of a photon in a geiger counter depends on the angle between the photon direction and the wall of the counter, the efficiency for coincidence
detection of annihilation photons is a function of the angular spread
of the distribution. Maier-Leibnitz did in fact observe that the coincidence counting rate in these two geiger counters (see Fig. 5) was
different for different materials, and thus also showed independently

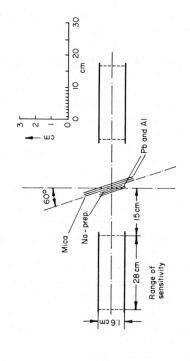

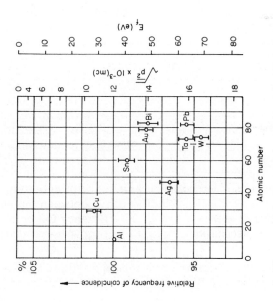

Fig. 5. Apparatus and results of Maier-Leibnitz which showed that the angular distribution of annihilation photons varied with various materials (Ref. 12).

and for the first time that the angular distribution was distinctly and
measurably different in different materials.

The next advance, and one of high importance and enduring per-
plexity, was the measurements by DeBenedetti and Richings,[13] and by
Bell and Graham,[14] of the lifetime of positrons in various metals. In
1952 DeBenedetti and Richings compared the mean life of positrons
annihilating in various metals with aluminum, and discovered that they
were all the same within one twentieth of a nanosecond. In 1953 Bell
and Graham published an important paper which first showed a long
lifetime in amorphous nonconductors. In this paper they also measured the absolute lifetime of positrons in metals. Using DeBenedetti's
relative measurements and several of their own measurements they
found that in about 10 metals the lifetimes were all the same and approximately 1.5×10^{-10} sec. This result was a mystery for, as Bell
and Graham pointed out, the Dirac cross section for annihilation with
electrons whose charge density was uniformly spread out would have
predicted a lifetime of $\tau = 2.2 \times 10^{-10} \, A/\rho N$ sec. (A is the mass
number; ρ, the density; and N, the number of electrons per atom par-
ticipating in the annihilation.) Since it appeared that positrons annihilated only with outer electrons, then the electron density apparently
should be very much lower than the total electron density in the material. For example, in aluminum, this formula would predict a lifetime of $\tau = 7.5 \times 10^{-10}$ sec., five times the observed value. Both
DeBenedetti and Richings and Bell and Graham speculated that a positron must form some sort of a fast decaying state, the formation of

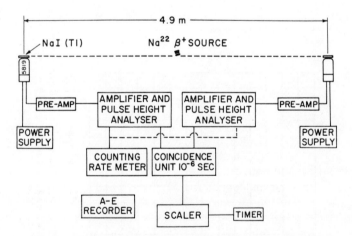

Fig. 6. Early angular correlation apparatus of Stewart
and Green (Refs. 15, 16).

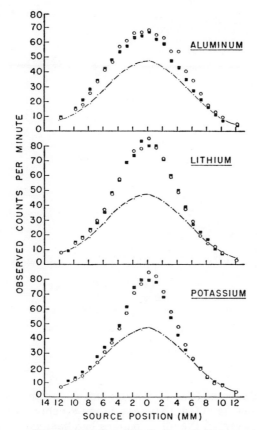

Fig. 7. Angular distribution of photon pairs
from positrons annihilating in Al, Li, and K.
The dotted line represents source annihilation
(Ref. 16).

which was relatively independent of the concentration of electrons in
the metal. There were also suggestions that since the positron and
electron would attract one another, therefore, the electron charge at
the positron would be much greater than the average in the metal,
and hence this would naturally increase the decay rate.

The difficulties of understanding why positrons annihilated so
quickly with conduction electrons was made somewhat more serious
by measurements[15] presented by Stewart and Green at the November,
1954 meeting of the American Physical Society in Chicago, and published more fully in the following year.[16] If I may be allowed to di-
gress a little at this point—I remember the occasion well. It was my

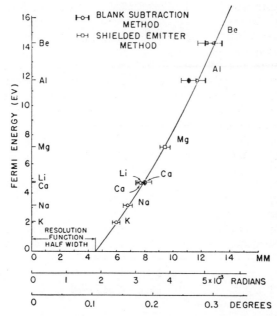

Fig. 8. Width of angular distributions plotted against Fermi energy (Ref. 16).

first visit to an APS meeting and I gave the last paper on a Friday afternoon. There were very few listeners in the steeply sloped University lecture room for all the other papers had been on nuclear physics. However, I remember being questioned most pertinently and persistently at the end of my talk by two men sitting high up in the back row. Later they came down and introduced themselves. It was Professor DeBenedetti and his student George Lang. I gathered that they were trying the same experiment with circular slits.

But to return to physics; the results of Stewart and Green were angular correlation measurements for positrons annihilating in various light metals. The angles were defined by a scintillator which was simply a one-quarter-inch thick slab of sodium iodide mounted on photomultiplier tubes, as shown in Fig. 6. Typical results are shown in the next slide (Fig. 7). We see that they are not as precise as present experiments! The dotted line is the angular distribution of self-absorbed positrons in the sandwich technique. The subtracted data show a half-width exactly what one would expect on the basis of instrument resolution, and the free electron theory as shown in Fig. 8. Now the mystery of understanding both the lifetime of positrons in a metal and the angular distribution is made more perplexing. These data appeared understandable only under the assumptions of (a) thermalized positrons; (b) free electron theory electrons; and (c) the equal probability of annihilation with all electrons. Thus all these assumptions were somewhat substantiated by this measurement. The first of course is hardly an assumption, for in 1954, Garwin,[17] and especially in 1955 Lee-Whiting,[18] had done calculations which showed that a positron would be expected to be thermalized in a time short compared with the annihilation time. How are we then to understand this dilemma? A coulomb field between the positron and noninteracting electrons enhances the density of the electrons very much, an order of magnitude or so, and the lifetime had a chance of coming out approximately correctly. However, in the presence of this coulomb potential between the positron and the electron which annihilates with it, the probability of annihilation is proportional to $1/v$, that is, the slowest electrons would be preferentially annihilated. This conclusion is, of course, contradicted by the angular correlation data just presented. Those results implied that the annihilation probability

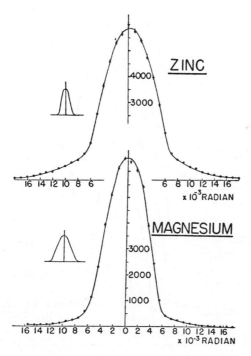

Fig. 9. Angular distribution of photons from positrons annihilating in Zn and Mg (Ref. 20).

could not vary nearly as strongly as $1/v$. So, of course, a compromise was invoked. Calculations were done using a screened coulomb potential, and these calculations regrettably did not agree with either experiment. A screened coulomb potential resulted in a lifetime which was not quite fast enough, and an angular distribution for annihilation photons which also did not agree with the observations.

At about this time two other papers appeared. Ambrosino et al.[19] in 1953 published some measurements in which he observed that the angular distribution of photons from positrons annihilating in copper and in copper compounds was different.

Now the subject became more exciting. The literature suggests that a friendly competition began between the Carnegie group, De-Benedetti, Lang, and Smoluchowski, and Stewart at Chalk River. The July 1955 issue of the Physical Review presents two letters,[20,21] one from each of these groups. By now both groups have attained much better resolution in their angular correlation apparatus, and the data

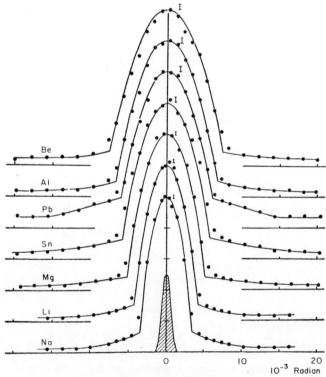

Fig. 10. Angular distribution of photons from positrons annihilating in several metals (Ref. 21).

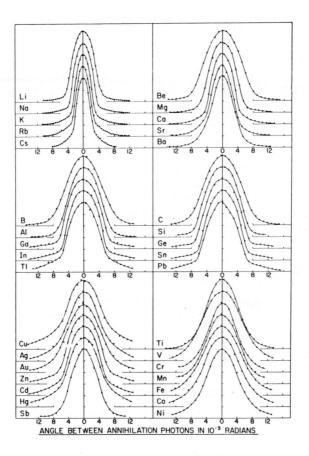

Fig. 11. Collection of distributions of photons from positrons annihilating in 34 metals (Ref. 22).

obtained by both appears to be very much alike. Figure 9 shows some of these data for magnesium and zinc, and illustrates the typical parabolic distribution of momentum anticipated by Vlasov. Figure 10 shows similar data from DeBenedetti's group which illustrates the same thing for about seven metals. Since these data are so alike from the two groups, I will show in the next slide (Fig. 11) a complete collection[22] of angular correlations of annihilation radiation from positrons annihilating in 34 different elements. These show the wide range of shapes obtained, ranging from the parabolic distribution to a much more bell-shaped distribution in the transition metals.

WHAT IS MEASURED?

Photon Momentum Distribution

Let us define $\rho(\mathbf{k})$, the distribution of probability of finding a pair of photons with momentum $\mathbf{k}$ in $d\mathbf{k}$. The long slit type of apparatus measures the coincidence counting rate $N(k_z)$ where

$$N(k_z) = \int_{-\infty}^{\infty} \int_{-\infty}^{\infty} \rho(\mathbf{k})\, dk_x\, dk_y$$

The x-integral occurs because the detector is insensitive to the small Doppler energy shift caused by the motion of the annihilating pair. The y-integral arises from the assumption that the detectors are long compared with the spatial spread in the distribution of photons at the detector. The integral is taken over the plane of constant k_z where

$$k_z = \frac{mc}{\hbar}\,\theta$$

and θ is the z-component of the angle between photon directions. If $\rho(\mathbf{k})$ is an isotropic function $\rho(k)$ it can be easily shown[22] that it is given by

$$\rho(k) = \text{const}\,\frac{1}{k_z} \cdot \frac{dN(k_z)}{dk_z}$$

and that the momentum distribution $n(k)$, $n(k) = 4\pi k^2 \rho(k)$, is thus

$$n(k) = \text{const}\, k_z\, \frac{dN(k_z)}{dk_z}$$

Note that the experimental observation, the function $N(k_z)$, is very simply related to the density in momentum space. Thus experimental data are often presented in the form $\rho(k)$ or $n(k)$ or simply as the slope, $dN(k_z)/dk_z$, of the angular distribution. The derivative is most often taken directly from the difference of adjacent measurements

$$\frac{dN(k_z)}{dk_z} \sim \frac{N(k_z') - N(k_z'')}{k_z' - k_z''}$$

In the data which follows we shall use various forms of presentation.

Figures 12 and 13 show $\rho(k)$ and $n(k)$ obtained from the data of Fig. 11. These results are remarkable for they show that the photons have the momentum distribution of free electrons superimposed upon a broader momentum distribution. This implies that indeed a major number of positrons annihilate with free electrons and do so with approximately equal probability. Also these data suggest to us

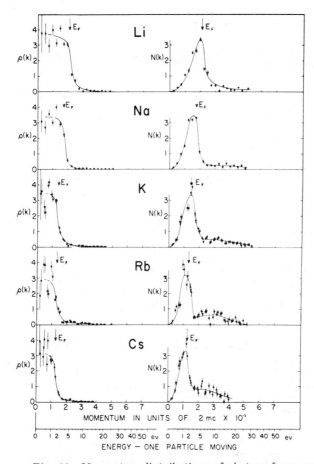

Fig. 12. Momentum distributions of photons from positrons annihilating in the alkali metals (Ref. 22).

that positrons annihilate as one might expect with electrons of the ion cores when these cores occupy a large fraction of the volume of the metal. These data also provide some experimental confirmation of Lee-Whiting's thermalization calculation, for the sharp discontinuity at the Fermi momentum could not occur unless the positron had less energy than about 1 eV. Most important, these experiments showed that indeed the positron was a useful tool for exploring the electron structure of metals; and, although it was not understood at that time, the assumption that the positrons sampled all electrons equally appeared a valid working postulate. The validity of this assumption was immediately substantiated by Ferrell,[23] who pointed

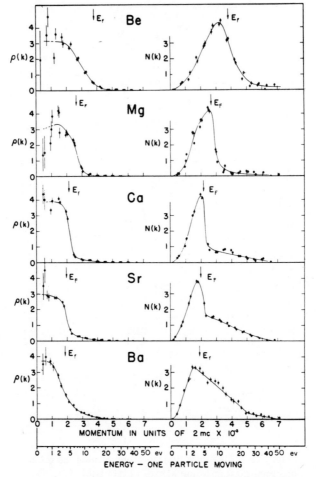

Fig. 13. Momentum distributions of photons from positrons annihilating in two electron metals (Ref. 22).

out that the annihilation probability was approximately equal for all electrons. These many-body effects will be mentioned again later.

The results just discussed illustrate many of the qualitative features of electrons in metals and are useful for various reasons:
(a) The obvious grouping between metals which have a clear parabolic central portion superimposed upon a broader distribution, and those which do not show the central parabolic section is the same classification which now distinguishes the simple OPW metals and the not-so-simple metals. It is very easy to see that the transition series, for example (Fig. 14), are not simple in the sense that it is not easy

to distinguish between core and conduction electrons on the basis of momentum distribution; (b) In the simple metals, the width of the parabola is directly determined by the density of conduction electrons, thus yielding this number experimentally. For example, aluminum has three conduction electrons and lead, four, as deHaas-van Alphen studies have also shown; and (c) Although not research, I find that these data are useful for pedagogic purposes, as are soft x-ray experimental results, for teaching the free electron theory of metals.

Single Particle Wavefunctions

Many of the results of positron annihilation research can be described with single particle wavefunctions. If $\psi(r)$ is the wavefunction of the electron and $\psi_+(r)$ of the positron, then the momentum amplitude of the annihilating pair is[9]

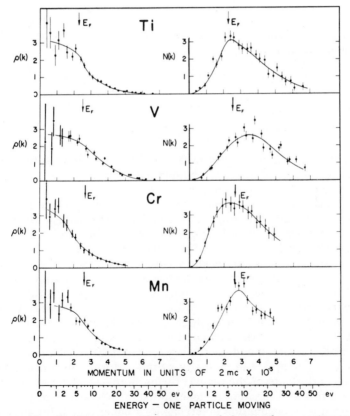

Fig. 14. Momentum distributions of photons from positrons annihilating in some transition metals (Ref. 22).

$$\chi(K) = \int \psi \ \psi_+ \ e^{-iKr} \ d\tau$$

The resultant momentum space density of photons is therefore

$$\rho(K) = \sum_{\text{all electrons}} |\chi(K)|^2$$

This is the connection between measurement of photon momentum and knowledge of electrons in metals. If we suppose that the positron wavefunction can be written as a Block wave, the first term is

$$\psi_+ = e^{ik_+ r}$$

Similarly, if we suppose that the electron can be described by an OPW type wave, the lowest component of it can be written

$$\psi = A \left[e^{ikr} - \sum_s b_{sk} \ \phi(r-s) \right]$$

where $\phi(r-s)$ is an orbital wavefunction of the sth ion core. The coefficient b_{sk} is given by

$$b_{sk} = \int e^{ikr} \ \phi^*(r-s) d\tau = e^{iks} b_{ok}$$

The momentum amplitude wavefunction then has the form

$$\chi(K) \sim \delta_{K, k+k_+} \ [1 - 0(n|b_{ok}|^2)]$$

where n is the atomic density in the crystal. This expression can be easily extended to any of the higher momentum components of the electron or positron wavefunction.

The first term gives the expected intensity of the plane wave components and spreads this over all the higher reciprocal lattice zones that are required to give a Block description of the positron and to give a Block description to the "smooth part" of the electron wavefunction. Note that the part of the electron wavefunction which is plane wave-like yields the central parabolic section of our measurements plus all their higher momentum components. The part of the electron wavefunction which has wiggles at ion cores does not appear in this; it appears in the second term which is essentially the Fourier transform of the core orbitals sighted at as many points of the reciprocal lattice as the positron and electron wavefunctions have higher momentum components. The intensity of this orbital component depends upon the coefficients of the orbital terms in the electron wavefunction. With this single particle description of the results of positron annihilation with conduction electrons as a background, let us now examine what experiments have been done, and what physics has resulted.

MORE RECENT RESULTS

Single Crystals and Fermi Surface Studies

The angular correlation of annihilation radiation has been measured for several single crystals. Berko and Plaskett observed this for aluminum, copper,[24] and I think also indium and cadmium. Lang and Hein did experiments with cadmium.[25] Stewart made these measurements in tin and possibly zinc. I have now forgotten. None of these experiments were very interesting from the point of view of single crystal examination. The data for different directions were only slightly different reflecting the near spherical nature of all simple metals. A most spectacular result was obtained, however, for graphite[26] by Berko et al. (Fig. 15), and accounted for, in terms of electron orbitals in the plane of the graphite and along the c axis.

Two hexagonal close-packed metals have shown considerable asymmetry. In 1962, Berko found strong anisotropy in beryllium and magnesium,[27] and Stewart, Shand, Donaghy, and Kusmiss obtained the

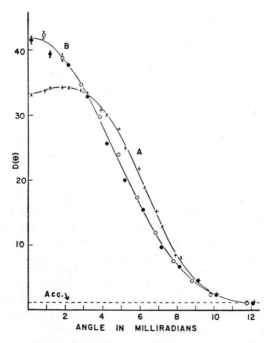

Fig. 15. Angular correlation results for (A) oriented graphite with hexagonal planes parallel to detector slits and (B) polycrystalline graphite (Ref. 26).

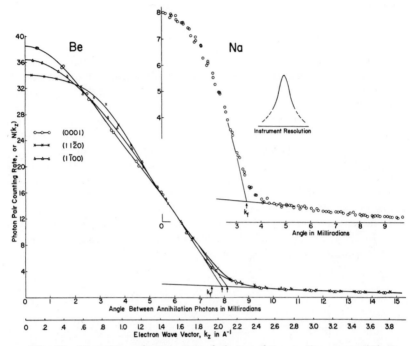

Fig. 16. Momentum distribution of photons from positrons annihilating in oriented beryllium crystals. In each case the indicated direction was parallel to the z-axis of the apparatus. The data for sodium are also shown (Ref. 28).

same results for beryllium,[28] shown in Fig. 16. These data certainly show anisotropy but how much they advance our understanding is less certain. It is much too complicated to obtain a Fermi surface from these measurements. The best that can be done is to postulate a Fermi surface and all band gaps, and calculate the angular correlation curve. This has been done for beryllium by Shand,[29] who used Watts' Fermi surface[30] and calculated higher momentum components to reproduce the experimental data quite satisfactorily. One interesting thing should be pointed out from these data. Note that the free electron Fermi surface is always much inside the endpoint of the "parabolic" portion. This is direct evidence for the existence of the higher momentum components of electron wavefunctions which have been discussed since the nearly free electron description was invented and which Berko and Plaskett[24] worked out in some detail for one dimension. In one favorable case this tail has been analyzed by Shand,[29] and his work has yielded directly a value for the energy gap at the [0002] zone boundary. He will discuss the calculation later at this meeting.

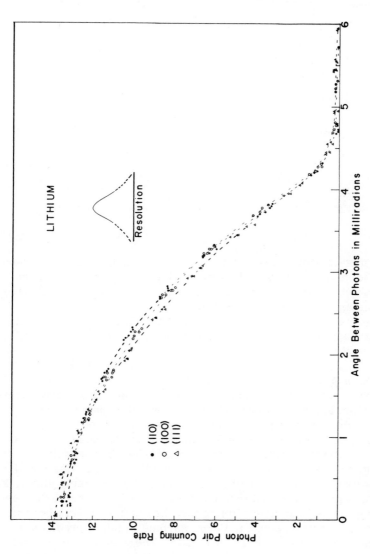

Fig. 17. The angular correlation of positron annihilation photons from single crystal lithium (Ref. 31).

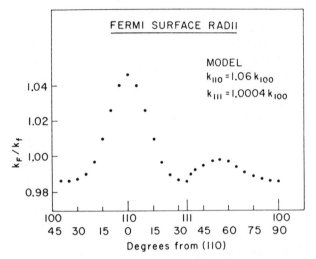

Fig. 18. Radii to the Fermi surface of lithium (Ref. 31).

The metals sodium and lithium have nearly spherical Fermi surfaces and small ion cores. This makes them very suitable for the technique of positron annihilation. The Fermi surfaces of both have been determined by Donaghy.[31] Sodium has been shown to have a Fermi surface which is spherical to $1\frac{1}{2}\%$. This is in agreement with the much more accurate measurements of Shoenberg and Stiles[32] who estimate sphericity to about 0.1%. The angular correlation data for lithium are shown in Fig. 17. They are clearly different for different directions. Donaghy[31] has analyzed these data in terms of a model with bumps in the expected [110] directions. If the parameters of the model are determined by the data near the center of the distribution, i.e., near 180°, the higher momentum components do not enter to first order. Also by using differences between the data obtained for different directions, Donaghy avoided the necessity of considering the enhancement factor since the difference in this factor for the small variations of Fermi surface radii is presumably small. Following this procedure, and then including the effect of higher momentum components in an approximate way, he obtained a very good fit to the data. A phenomenological Fermi surface which is predicted from these measurements is shown in Fig. 18. There is no other direct experimental data on the Fermi surface of lithium at present. Melngailis[33] has done a thorough calculation based upon modern band gap calculations and dispersion relations for lithium, and has also obtained good agreement with Donaghy's data. This beautiful calculation will be discussed later at this meeting.

Rare Earths

Two papers have appeared recently showing the use of positron annihilation as an efficient tool to give semiquantitative answers. The question: What is the valence of certain rare earth elements? Gustafson and Mackintosh[34] answered this question by measuring the two-photon angular correlation, as shown in Fig. 19. It is clearly possible to distinguish between a value of 2 and 3 for the valence of a metal by the width of the central parabolic portion. A similar result was obtained by Rodda and Stewart[35] who measured the lifetime of positrons in a complete series of rare earth elements. Their results (Fig. 20) show clearly that when the conduction electrons are scarce (2 and not 3) the lifetime is longer.

Alloys

Because the techniques of measuring electron momentum by positron annihilation does not require specimens of high purity or long electron mean free path, it will probably become one of the useful techniques for examining Fermi surface and electron structure of alloys. Not much use has been made of this feature to date. Dekhtyar, Litovchenko and Mikhalenkov[36] examined two or three alloy

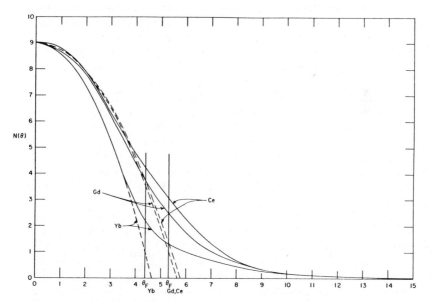

Fig. 19. Positron annihilation in Gd, Yb, Ce. It is clear that the "2 electron parabola" fits only Yb and the "3 electron parabola" only Ce and Gd (Ref. 34).

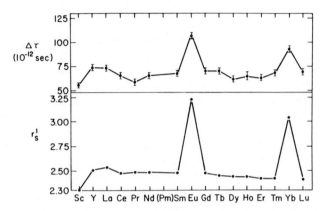

Fig. 20. Positron annihilation lifetime measurements
on a series of rare earth metals. It is easy to identify the
valence 2 elements (Ref. 35).

systems by positron annihilation. They sought to determine if the
order-disorder transformation of Cu_3Au and Ni_3Mn alter the momentum distribution of valence electrons. They saw no large changes.
More recently, Dekhtyar, Levina, and Milhalenkov[36] have observed
a change in the angular correlation of photons from positron annihilation in Ni and NiFe alloys before and after plastic deformation.
They attribute the narrowing of the angular correlation results to
an enhancement of s-type electrons at dislocation sites.

The alloy LiMg is more suitable and very interesting. Magnesium dissolves in lithium up to about 70 at.% with no change in
structure and essentially no change in lattice parameter. Presumably, the alloying does little except add electrons to the Fermi sea.
An experiment to test this hypothesis was done in Chapel Hill and
the results[37] are shown on Fig. 21. The drawing in the lower right-
hand corner shows a section of the first Brillouin zone, and on it we
have drawn free electron spheres corresponding to lithium and to the
two alloys used. The other three sketches show the slope of the
angular correlation data for the specimens. Recalling that this slope
is the average density in k-space times k we see that these measurements do indeed show a steadily expanding Fermi surface, as magnesium concentration is increased. However, there is still a mystery here. The data depart from the line which is drawn on the basis
of single-simple free electron theory and instrument resolution in
a strange way. It appears that the occupied states are less dense for
k greater than approximately $2/3$ of the distance to the nearest zone
boundary. Does the alloying cause a decrease in the density of states
in this region or is this some effect of the heaping up of charge around
the Mg^{++} ions?

Some measurements have also been made in the alloy system copper - aluminum by Mr. Kim. The results for alloys of concentration up to 5 at.-% aluminum agree well with semiquantitative estimates based on a rigid band model, bearing in mind always that in these metals the higher momentum components of the electron wavefunction are quite important.

Liquid Metals

Positron annihilation should be a valuable tool for exploring the electron structure of liquid metals. The disorder and short mean free path is no hindrance at all, in fact, it might be expected that the positron annihilation data could, with sufficient precision, show the blurring of the Fermi surface due to electron scattering. One might expect a smearing of the Fermi surface of the order of the reciprocal of the mean free path of the electrons. To this end I made a few measurements using my old apparatus at Chalk River in about 1957. Sodium showed, as expected, no change. The mean free path in both liquid and solid sodium is too long. On the other hand, we observed,

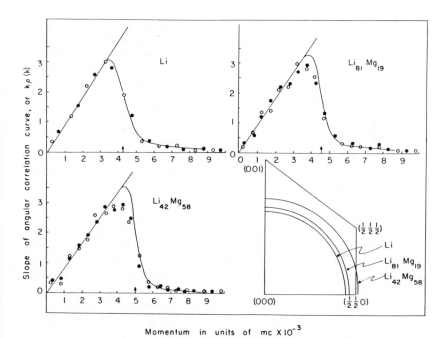

Fig. 21. Slopes of angular correlation data plotted against electron momentum for lithium and two alloys (Ref. 37).

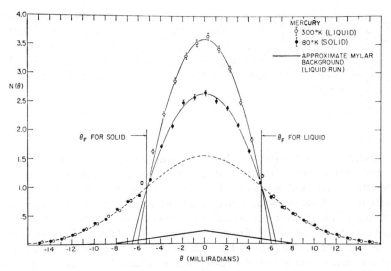

Fig. 22. Photon momentum distribution from positrons annihilating in mercury (Ref. 39).

as did Gustafson and Mackintosh,[38] a large change in the angular distribution for gallium. The first papers on the subject by Gustafson, Mackintosh, and Zaffarano[39] showed two principal effects. These are illustrated in Fig. 22 for mercury. The most startling effect is the change in the ratio of the two portions of the momentum distribution. Upon liquefying the metals, positrons appear to prefer to annihilate more with the conduction electrons and less with core electrons. This was attributed by the authors to the fact that disordered structure of the liquid allowed the positron to "sit" in holes and better avoid the repulsive ions. They also saw a change in the sharpness of the data at the point where the parabolic portion joins the broader distribution. They attributed this smear to change in the mean free path of electrons in mercury, and obtained a value in fair agreement with simple electrical conductivity theory. The results for gallium were similar to those of mercury, but showed a much greater smear in the Fermi surface. The data and results of Stewart, Kusmiss, and March,[40] published later, are shown in Fig. 23. The extreme change of sharpness of the cutoff in Ga implies that free electron theory is not at all a good description of the motion of conduction electrons in that metal. Possibly the electrons are better described as molecular orbitals for the diatomic liquid which has been proposed. But what about more normal metals like indium and tin also shown here? Notice that in tin the Fermi surface appears to smear a little on melting just as expected. However, in indium, on the other hand, the change occurs upon heating up to the melting point and nothing more happens upon melting. Data on cadmium[41] (Fig. 24) shows the same effect. The momentum distribution departs from a good parabola and the tails become more smeared below the melting point. The effect is even more pronounced in aluminum[41] which is shown in Fig. 25. It is clear that the hot solid and the liquid are alike and differ much from the room temperature solid. The more expected result of a change at the melting point is shown in Fig. 26 for tin.[41] Here indeed the momentum distribution changes most at the melting point. However, note that the change is probably only poorly described by a scattering theory. The slope results seem to have a flat top. This is also observed in many other metals. Kusmiss has summarized these data in a table (Fig. 27) grouping the elements into three categories depending upon their behavior. We cannot yet account for these observations. A simple comparison with mean free path from resistivity shows almost no correlation with our data. Even when the change

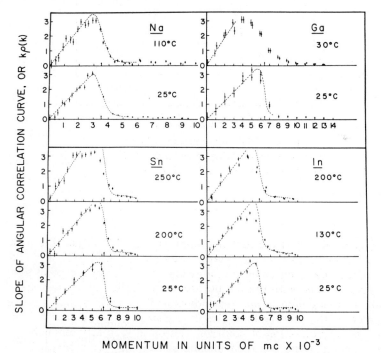

Fig. 23. Slopes of angular correlation data for Na, Ga, In, and Sn. The dashed curves have been calculated on the basis of the free electron theory taking positron temperature and optical resolution into account (Ref. 40).

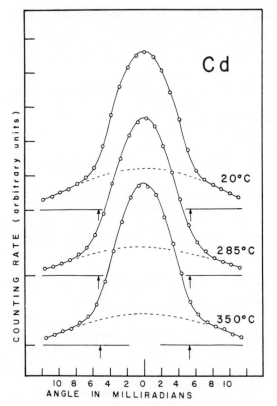

Fig. 24. Photon momentum distributions for positrons annihilating in cadmium at 20°C, 285°C (solid), and 350°C (liquid) (Ref. 41).

of density of states at the melting point was used to adjust the mean free path values, no real correlation was noted. Similarly, the change which occurs between room temperature and the melting point seems to be uncorrelated with the temperature coefficient of resistance. The meaning of these data is not yet understood. Certainly, many more factors enter the picture than simply a change of mean free path of electrons. The question of positron motion is virtually untouched. How important is the positron-phonon scattering, for example? There seems to be no need for positron and electron to have even similar scattering elements. How much smearing this factor can cause has not been calculated. We shall return to this discussion of positron motion in a moment.

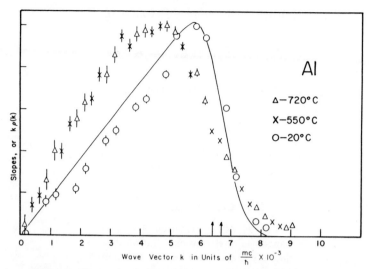

Fig. 25. Slope of angular distribution of photons from positron annihilation in aluminum at 20° C, 550° C (solid), and 720° C (liquid) (Ref. 41).

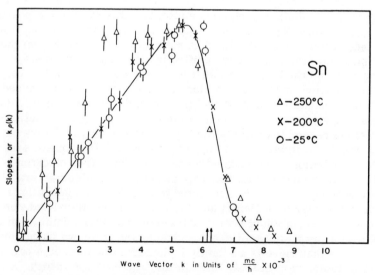

Fig. 26. Slope of angular distribution of photons from positron annihilation in tin at 25° C, 200° C (solid), and 250° C (liquid) (Ref. 41).

GROUP I - change upon melting:

Bi, Ga, Hg, K(?), Sb, Sn, & Te.

GROUP II - change below m.p.
           and little or no further change:

Al, Cd, In, Pb, & Zn.

GROUP III - no change:

Na, Li, Se, & Tl.

Fig. 27. Classification of metals by
changes in positron annihilation results
when the metals are heated and melted
(Ref. 41).

Many-Body Effects; Enhancement

Finally, let us consider the effect of many-body interactions in the
metals. Ferrell's[23] early estimate of the effect of all coulomb interactions was that the electron density at the positron would increase
about an order of magnitude over the average density in metals. The
momentum distribution of photons emitted by this system — a positron
plus an electron cloud — should be quite similar to the free electron
distribution but increased a little at momentum near the Fermi momentum. This result has been verified by detailed calculations of
Kahana[42,43] and Carbotte and Kahana.[44] They showed quantitatively
that the electrons in the charge cloud around a positron are indeed
an order of magnitude more dense than in the rest of the metal. However, strangely enough, the momentum distribution of the electrons
in the cloud resembles closely the simple free-electron theory of
Sommerfeld. To illustrate: the upper part of Fig. 28 shows the occupied distribution in k-space according to simple free electron
theory. It is compared with that calculated when coulomb interactions between electrons are accounted for. This is a schematic
sketch of the results of Daniel and Vosko.[45] On the other hand, the
momentum distribution of photon pairs from positron annihilation in
the electron gas is quite different in shape, and is shown in the lower
figure. Note that there is a slightly higher fraction of photon pairs
with total momentum near k_f than in the free electron theory. A test
of this calculation has been made by Donaghy,[31] and is shown in Fig.
29. The line through the data points was calculated from Kahana's

formula for an enhancement factor with a slightly different value of r_s than for sodium. An exact determination of the shape of the enhancement factor awaits a sure method for separating the core and conduction components in the angular correlation data.

Another test of the many-body theory of positron interaction in a free electron gas comes from observations of the thermal motion of positrons in metals. We should understand first of all that the thermal smearing of the Fermi surface is given by

$$\frac{\Delta k}{k_f} \sim \frac{kT}{2E_f} \sim \frac{1}{400}$$

which is much too small to be observed with present experimental techniques. On the other hand, the thermal motion of the positron being its total kinetic energy is of the order

$$\frac{k_+}{k_f} \sim \left(\frac{3kT}{2E_f}\right)^{1/2} \sim \frac{\sqrt{3}}{20}$$

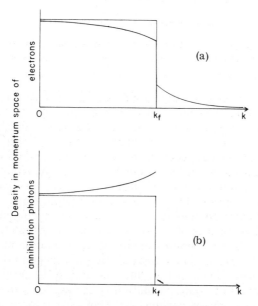

Fig. 28. Schematic sketches of: (a) Density in k-space of electrons following Daniel and Vosko (Ref. 45) compared with simple free electron theory. (b) Density in k-space of electrons at the positron or of annihilation photon pairs, from Kahana (Refs. 42, 44).

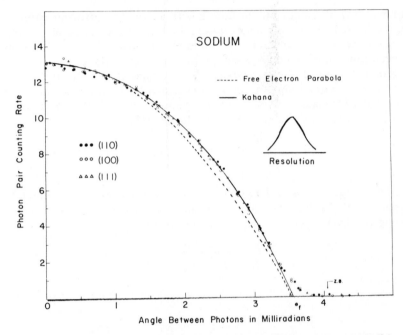

Fig. 29. Angular correlation measurements from positrons annihilating in sodium. The effect of enhancement can be clearly seen (Ref. 31).

which is certainly observable with good resolution instruments at the present time. We thus determined to do an experiment to attempt to measure this thermal motion of a positron. We selected sodium as the material with which to do it for several reasons. First of all the Fermi surface is spherical; second, the higher momentum components of the electron wave functions should be less important in sodium than in most other metals; and third, the mean free path of electrons in sodium is very long even at high temperature so that smearing of the Fermi surface due to electron scattering should not be appreciable. The results obtained by Shand[29] in measurements of the angular correlation of photons annihilating in sodium at four different temperatures from approximately liquid nitrogen temperature up to $600°K$ are shown in Fig. 30. These results show quite clearly that the effect of positron motion is the same as the effect of worsening the instrument resolution. That is, since the experiment measures the z - component of total wave vector $k_z = (\mathbf{k} + \mathbf{k}_+)_z$, the cutoff at k_F is smeared by positron motion. We have analyzed the curvature at the cutoff by the slope method. The analysis was made by assuming that the data could be described by a convolution of the distribution of electron momenta of the free electron theory with a function describing instrument resolution. The instrument resolution is itself a convolution of two functions: one, the optical resolution of the apparatus, and two, the Boltzman distribution of positron velocities. Using the positron temperature as the single variable to find a fit to experimental data we obtained results as shown in Fig. 31. This slide shows a plot of the specimen temperature versus the effective temperature obtained for the positron by this technique. We should note that the effective temperature is almost twice the temperature of the specimen. This parameter could as well have been called an effective mass for the positron. The mass and temperature, of course, appear together in the Boltzman description of the distribution of velocities. Thus one might assume that since the positron is fairly certainly thermalized in the metal that we would better characterize these results by an effective mass. What causes an effective mass of order 2 ? There are probably two principal causes. First, the band mass of positrons, that is, the curvature at the bottom of the dispersion relation. Mr. Kim has made some calculations of the positron mass in sodium and other elements and his preliminary results show that its band mass does not change by more than a few per cent from the free electron mass. Another cause of smearing of the cutoff might possibly be the positron phonon scattering. This is certainly temperature dependent. If this is not the cause of the observed smearing we conclude that this

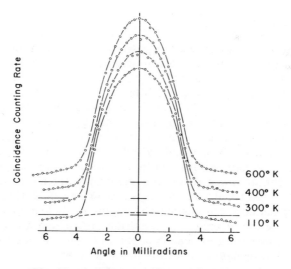

Fig. 30. Angular correlation of radiation from positrons annihilating in sodium at various temperatures (Ref. 29).

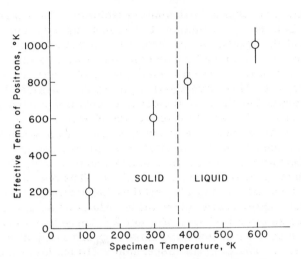

Fig. 31. The effective temperature of positrons
in sodium obtained from the analysis of the data in
Fig. 30 (Ref. 29).

experiment has probably measured the positron effective mass in a
sea of interacting electrons. The measured value of such an effective
mass is 1.9 ± 0.4 for a positron in sodium.

CONCLUSION

We have traced the history of positron annihilation in metals from
its beginning to quite recent developments. What conclusion may be
drawn and what is the outlook?

The technique of positron annihilation in metals has now proven
itself: it has been shown that results of general interest to physicists
working with metals can be obtained. The capacity of this technique
will be found, and will be developed too, as it is used. Yet it is already clear that it will probably yield results of general interest in
disordered systems — alloys and liquid metals — and in special situations like lithium for which other techniques are not so useful. The
usefulness of the results of any experiment or calculation will, of
course, depend upon the system chosen for study and upon our understanding of the technique. Transition metals and metals with large
ion cores appear to offer less opportunities for increasing our understanding of the technique or of the metal studied.

The study of positrons in metals is also of intrinsic interest. Understanding this system is, of course, a prerequisite for much use
of the technique for the study of metals. The most recent advances

in this exploration have been Carbotte and Kahana's calculation of the enhancement factor and lifetime for positrons in an interacting gas of electrons, and the experimental observation of the motion of the positrons. The problem of a positron in an interacting gas of electrons in a periodic potential has not yet been explored. The answers to this problem could be used now. The enhancement factor calculation still needs testing by accurate experiments and in various densities of electrons. The many-body effective mass of the positron has not been calculated. It should be somewhat dependent upon electron density. Perhaps this can be observed. The possibility of some bound state formation in a dilute metal is known to exist, but how dilute and under what conditions? Varlashkin is presenting at this meeting some results on one very dilute metal, Li-NH$_3$ solutions. Some complex seems to be found but is it positronium or what? The behavior of a positron in a hot crystalline metal and in a liquid metal is mysterious. When it is understood we may be able to extract density of electronic states from the data now available. There seem to be endless possibilities for imaginative, interesting, and useful work in the subject of positron annihilation in metals.

REFERENCES

1. Beringer, R., and C. G. Montgomery, *Phys. Rev.* **61**, 222 (1942).
2. Klemperer, O., *Proc. Cambridge Phil. Soc.* **30**, 347 (1934).
3. Alichanian, A. I., A. I. Alichanow, and L. A. Arzimovitch, *Nature* **137**, 703 (1936); *Akad. Nauk. S. S. S. R. Dokl.* **10**, 287 (1936).
4. Vlasov, N. A., and E. A. Tsirelson, *Akad. Nauk. S. S. S. R. Dokl.* **59**, 879 (1948).
5. Dumond, J. W. M., D. A. Lind, and B. B. Watson, *Phys. Rev.* **75**, 1226 (1949).
6. Bethe, H. A., *Proc. Roy. Soc. (London)* **A150**, 129 (1935).
7. DeBenedetti, S., C. E. Cowan, and W. R. Konneker, *Phys. Rev.* **76**, 440(L) (1949).
8. Vlasov, N. A., and B. S. Dzhelepov, *Akad. Nauk. S. S. S. R. Dokl.* **70**, 207 (1950).
9. DeBenedetti, S., C. E. Cowan, W. R. Konneker, and H. Primakoff, *Phys. Rev.* **77**, 205 (1950).
10. Argyle, P. E., and J. B. Warren, *Canad. J. Phys.* **29**, 32 (1951).
11. Warren, J. B., and G. M. Griffiths, *Canad. J. Phys.* **29**, 325 (1951).
12. Maier-Leibnitz, H., *Z. Naturforsch.* **6a**, 663 (1951).
13. DeBenedetti, S., and H. J. Richings, *Phys. Rev.* **85**, 377 (1952).
14. Bell, R. E., and R. L. Graham, *Phys. Rev.* **90**, 644 (1953).
15. Stewart, A. T., and R. E. Green, *Phys. Rev.* **98**, 232(A) (1955).
16. Green, R. E., and A. T. Stewart, *Phys. Rev.* **98**, 486 (1955).
17. Garwin, R. L., *Phys. Rev.* **91**, 1571 (1953).
18. Lee-Whiting, G. E., *Phys. Rev.* **97**, 1557 (1955).

19. Ambrosino, G., J. Houbaut, and P. Maignan, *Compt. Rend.* **237**, 708 (1953); J. des Cloizeaux and G. Ambrosino, *Compt. Rend.* **237**, 1069 (1953).
20. Stewart, A. T., *Phys. Rev.* **99**, 594(L) (1955).
21. Lang, G., S. DeBenedetti, and R. Smoluchowski, *Phys. Rev.* **99**, 596(L) (1955).
22. Stewart, A. T., *Canad. J. Phys.* **35**, 168 (1957).
23. Ferrell, R. A., *Rev. Modern Phys.* **28**, 308 (1956).
24. Berko, S., and J. S. Plaskett, *Phys. Rev.* **112**, 1877 (1958).
25. Lang, L. G., and H. C. Hein, *Bull. Am. Phys. Soc.* **2**, 173 (1957).
26. Berko, S., R. E. Kelly and J. S. Plaskett, *Phys. Rev.* **106**, 824 (1957).
27. Berko, S., *Phys. Rev.* **128**, 2166 (1962).
28. Stewart, A. T., J. B. Shand, J. J. Donaghy, and J. H. Kusmiss, *Phys. Rev.* **128**, 118 (1962).
29. Shand, J. B., Ph.D. Thesis, University of North Carolina 1964 (to be published).
30. Watts, B. R., *Phys. Letters* **3**, 284 (1963).
31. Donaghy, J. J., Ph.D. Thesis, University of North Carolina 1964, and Proceedings of XIth International Low-Temperature Meeting.
32. Shoenberg, D., and P. J. Stiles, *Proc. Roy. Soc. (London)* **A281**, 62 (1964).
33. Melngailis, J., Ph.D. Thesis, Carnegie Institute of Technology, 1965.
34. Gustafson, D. R., and A. R. Mackintosh, *J. Phys. Chem. Solids* **25**, 389 (1964).
35. Rodda, J. L., and M. G. Stewart, *Phys. Rev.* **131**, 255 (1963).
36. Dekhtyar, I. Ya, S. G. Litovchenko, and V. S. Mikhalenkov, *Akad. Nauk. S. S. S. R. Dokl.* **147**, 1332 (1962); I. Ya Dekhtyar, D. A. Levina, and V. S. Mikhalenkov, *Sov. Phys. Dokl.* **9**, 492 (1964).
37. Stewart, A. T., *Phys. Rev.* **133**, A1651 (1964).
38. Gustafson, D. R., and A. R. Mackintosh, *Phys. Letters* **5**, 234 (1963).
39. Gustafson, D. R., A. R. Mackintosh, and D. J. Zaffarano, *Phys. Rev.* **130**, 1455 (1963).
40. Stewart, A. T., J. H. Kusmiss, and R. H. March, *Phys. Rev.* **132**, 495 (1963).
41. Kusmiss, J. H., Ph.D. Thesis, University of North Carolina, 1965.
42. Kahana, S., *Phys. Rev.* **117**, 123 (1960).
43. Kahana, S., *Phys. Rev.* **129**, 1622 (1963).
44. Carbotte, J. P., and S. Kahana, *Phys. Rev.* **139**, A213 (1965).
45. Daniel, E., and S. H. Vosko, *Phys. Rev.* **120**, 2041 (1960).

On the Theory of Positron Annihilation in Metals

S. *Kahana*

McGill University, Montreal, Canada

What I will discuss here has by now mostly appeared in print. I will be referring mainly to work by Carbotte and myself,[1] because this is the material I know best, but I will make some reference to the work of Bergersen,[2] Majumdar,[3] and Melngailis.[4] The theory of positron annihilation in metals is, at present, a theory of annihilation in the conduction electron gas. I say this because, although attempts have been made to calculate annihilation rates in the ion cores and, in addition, to include the effects of the lattice, these attempts proceeded on the assumption that one could ignore the electron-positron and electron-electron interactions. The results in a translationally invariant gas, which indicate that the large enhancement in annihilation rates is not accompanied by an appreciable distortion of the momentum distribution, provide some justification for treating the lattice in a noninteracting approximation. I will have something to say about the core and lattice later.

Since I will be discussing electron gases I should probably limit myself to the "good" metals, with relatively small ion cores. Let me briefly review some of the early thinking on positron annihilation. There are two features of the experimental data which are of broad importance. First, the annihilation rates[5] are considerably larger than predicted by a free-electron (Sommerfeld) theory. Second, the angular correlation experiments of Lang, De Benedetti, and Smoluchowski,[6] Stewart et al.,[7] Berko,[8] and others, agree remarkably well with the Sommerfeld theory.

The electron-positron attractive Coulomb interaction surely has some relevance to the first point. In fact, if one went to the opposite extreme of naive theories and imagined the annihilation took place from an isolated scattering state, then the Sommerfeld rate would be enhanced by a Coulomb "penetration" factor. This leads to annihilation rates at all times larger than the experimental values. Figure 1 indicates this bracketing of the experimental rates by the Sommerfeld theory and the isolated-interaction theory.

Unfortunately, the isolated-interaction theory predicts a dependence of the partial annihilation rate $R(p) \sim 1/p$ violently in contradiction with the angular correlation experiments.

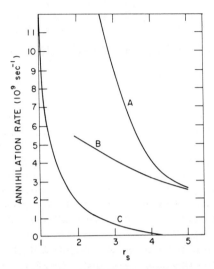

Fig. 1. Annihilation rates as a
function of density. (A) Isolated-interaction theory. (B) Experimental
(see Fig. 4). (C) Sommerfeld model.

If the rest of the electron gas, other than the annihilating electron,
is allowed to play a role we should be able to improve on the above
theories. A reduction of the isolated-interaction rates will result
from the screening of the electron–positron interaction produced by
the background gas. An introduction of the exclusion principle will
flatten the $1/p$ dependence in the isolated-interaction partial rates
by preferentially inhibiting electron–positron interactions for electrons deeper within the Fermi sea. (We are, of course, assuming
that the positron is thermalized.)

To get a quantitative theory of annihilation in an electron gas one
can use a second-quantized many body formalism. The electron-positron interaction may then be discussed in terms of a Green function
(or correlation function) $G_{ep}(xy, x'y')$ describing the propagation of
an electron from (xt_x) to $(x't_x')$ and the positron from (yt_y) to
$(y't_y')$. The partial annihilation rate, or probability of annihilation
per unit time with the emission of a photon pair of total momentum
p is then given by

$$R(p) = \frac{\lambda_0}{\eta_0} \cdot \frac{(-i)^2}{V} \cdot \int d^3x \, d^3y \, e^{-ip \cdot (x - y)} \, G_{ep}(xt \; xt; yt^+ yt^+) \quad (1)$$

where $4\lambda_0$ and n_0 are, respectively, the total annihilation rate and
the electron density at the positron position in singlet positronium.
The total annihilation rate is simply

$$R = \sum_{p} R(p)$$

$$= \frac{\lambda_0}{n_0} (-i)^2 \int d^3x \ G_{ep}(xt \ xt; \ yt^+ \ yt^+) \tag{2}$$

The many-body formalism specifies a set of rules for determining G_{ep} as a perturbation series in terms of the electron–positron and electron–electron interactions. It is natural to parallel the development of the theory of the electron gas, and hence to employ a modified perturbation theory based on the high-density limit for this gas. Let me insert the warning that there is no guarantee that such a perturbation treatment will converge. Nevertheless, if the earlier few paragraphs on the electron–positron interaction are to be believed, we might expect certain well defined terms in the perturbation theory to dominate a calculation of the annihilation rate. If we sum the series of diagrams indicated in Fig. 2a we will obtain the electron-positron effective interaction in the high density limit. If, consequently, we sum the series of diagrams in Fig. 2b we will have accounted for the electron particle–positron interactions and will have effectively reduced the many-body problem to a two-body problem.

The dangers of a selective summation of terms in perturbation theory were realized by many persons and, in particular, let me refer you to the theses of Bergersen[2] and Majumdar,[3] wherein particular weaknesses of my earlier work are criticized. In addition, Carbotte and I have examined in a more or less consistent fashion, low-order corrections to the ladder approximation which are displayed

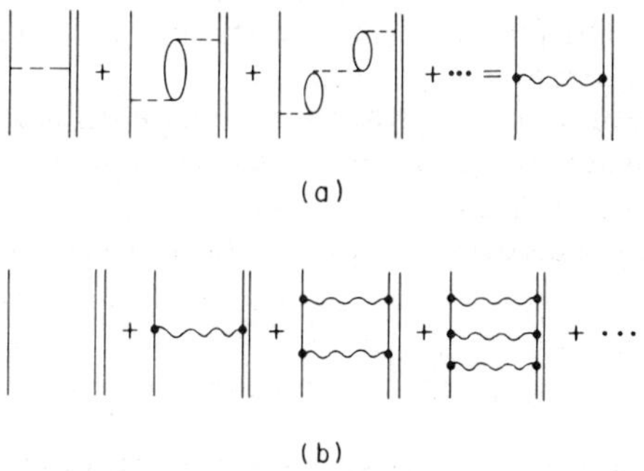

(a)

(b)

Fig. 2. (a) The dynamic effective interaction in the high-density limit. The dotted line represents a bare Coulomb interaction. The single solid line is an electron, and the double solid line, a positron. (b) The ladder approximation to G_{ep}.

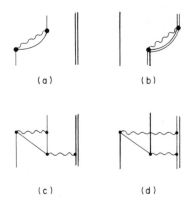

Fig. 3. Corrections to the ladder approximation. (a) Electron self-energy. (b) Positron
self-energy. (c) Electron hole-electron interaction. (d) Electron hole-positron interaction.

diagrammatically in Figure 3. Although qualitatively new features
occur for partial rates in the region $p > p_F$, the general picture is
little changed.

I should like, at this point, to insert an example of an important
result which has been proved for the entire perturbation series. Majumdar,[3] a student of Kohn, has demonstrated that the break in the
angular correlation curve is not shifted by the interactions, and occurs at $p = p_F$. This is analogous to the similar result obtained by
Luttinger[9] for a normal electron gas.

Let me now return to a somewhat more detailed outline of the
ladder approximation. The effective interaction $u(q,\omega)$ suggested by
the high-density limit, may be obtained from the RPA approximation
to the longitudinal dielectric constant $\epsilon(q,\omega)$ for an electron gas in
the fashion

$$u(q,\omega) = \frac{\upsilon_c(q)}{\epsilon(q,\omega)} \tag{3}$$

where $\upsilon_c(q)$ is the electron–positron Coulomb interaction.

It is possible in the high-density limit, in which $u(q,\omega)$ is treated
in first order, to cope with the frequency dependence of the interaction. In fact, one obtains the by-now classical split of the interaction
into a continuum or short-range force, and the plasmon mediated
force. I had noted that the frequency dependence of the effective interaction could be eliminated by the approximation

$$u(q,\omega) \approx u(q,0) = u^{static}(q) \tag{4}$$

the latter quantitatively reproducing the continuum contribution to the annihilation rate.

I should mention at this point that the work of Ferrell[10] on annihilation in metals, which recognized the importance of the electron-positron correlation, was equivalent to a high-density limit calculation.

If a static interaction is employed the ladder approximation reduces to a Schrödinger-like equation. The solution $\Psi_p(r)$ of this equation can then be used to describe the annihilation of the positron, assumed thermalized, with an electron of momentum $p < p_f$. The results of the ladder approximation are summed up in Fig. 4, where there is displayed a comparison of the predicted annihilation rates and the experimental rates taken from Bell and Jørgensen,[5a] as well as from Weisburg and Berko.[5b] In Fig. 5 the predicted photon angular correlation distribution is compared to results of Stewart for Na.

Now I would like to discuss attempts by Carbotte and myself to put the predictions of the ladder approximation on a sounder footing. As I have previously mentioned, Fig. 3 contains some of the low-order diagrams not included in the ladder approximation.

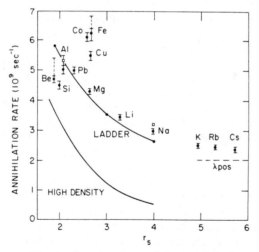

Fig. 4. A comparison of the predicted annihilation rates for the ladder approximation and the high density limit with experiment. The solid dots are those of Weisburg and Berko.[5b] The open squares are taken from Bell and Jørgensen.[5a] The error bars are those of the former experimentalists.

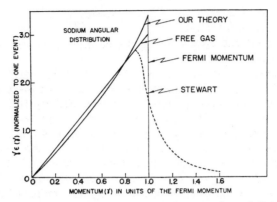

Fig. 5. The derivative of the partial annihilation
rates. This figure is taken from Reference 1a.

I will sum up the results briefly. We can dispose of the electron-
electron hole and positron–electron hole contributions first. The diagrams in Fig. 3c and d are similar in structure but opposite in phase.
Individually, they contribute 5–10% of the Sommerfeld rate (R_0).
There is, however, an almost complete cancellation between the two,
leaving a contribution of less than 2%. One expects this cancellation
will still occur if, after a single hole-particle process has taken
place, ladder-type interactions of the electron particle–positron are
allowed. This cancellation is an indication that care must be taken
in adding corrections to the ladder approximation. The cancellation
of diagrams shown in Figs. 3c and d occurs equally well for annihilation with momentum above or below p_F.

A discussion of the self-energy diagrams, Fig. 3a and b, is best
carried out separately for the regions $p < p_F$ and $p > p_F$. Daniel
and Vosko[11] have indicated how one can deduce, using the RPA effective interaction, the momentum distribution for the interacting electron gas (and hence also for the positron "gas"). A sketch of their
results is shown in Fig. 6. Electron states below p_F are depopu-
lated, resulting in a reduction in partial annihilation rates within
the Fermi sea. In fact, Carbotte found that the proper dynamic high-
density limit varied more rapidly over the Fermi sea than did its
static replacement. When the self-energy effects were included in
the region $p < p_F$, however, the final result was a partial rate
which paralleled the variation of the static rate but was some 4–5%
less in magnitude.

Let me now turn to the annihilation with total momentum $p > p_F$.
One would think, naively, that the tails in the photon correlation distribution should bear the same relation in magnitude to the central
parabola as do the tails in Fig. 6 to the population of states below

p_F. This line of reasoning is based on the expectation of equal enhancement of rates for momenta below or above p_F. Consider the effective interaction displayed in Fig. 2a. For electron momenta $p > p_F$ there is *no* contribution to the annihilation rate from the first diagram in Fig. 2a, while the second diagram produces a negative contribution relative to the self-energy terms. Thus, in the high-density limit the same polarization, which screens the interaction of the positron with an electron of momentum $p < p_F$, considerably reduces the size of the tails expected from self energy effects alone. Here again the cancellation is remarkably exact and tails of magnitude less than 1% of the height of the main parabola result. Let me emphasize that we are limited to zero temperature. If electron–positron states possessing momenta above p_F are populated by temperature fluctuations, one might expect comparable enhancement to that in the main parabola. This point will be discussed by Majumdar later with an interesting result.

One type of correction which we have not mentioned is an improvement in our effective interaction. This has been avoided to some extent because of its complexity and should provide an interesting point for further research parallel to similar investigations in the electron gas itself. Any attempt to include internal changes in the effective interaction, such as is represented by the exchange correction in Fig. 7, must necessarily also take into account the true dynamic nature of

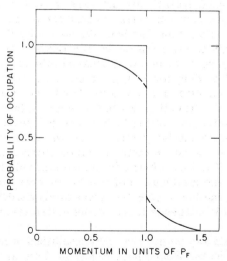

Fig. 6. The electron–momentum distribution calculated in the high–density limit by Daniel and Vosko.[11] This figure is taken from Reference 1b.

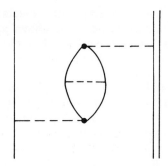

Fig. 7. Low-order exchange correction to
the effective interaction.

the interaction. Bergersen[2] has made an attempt to estimate the effects of the diagram in Fig. 7, based on a suggestion of Hubbard.[12]
The exchange correction reduces the correlation between electrons
in the polarization cloud around an electron–positron pair and accordingly reduces the degree of screening. This results in an increase in the enhancement of some 3–5% in the high-density limit
for Na. To be balanced against this increase, however, is the presence of an excess polarization charge around the positron in the ladder approximation. This point has been discussed by Bergersen,[2]
and was first brought to my attention by Mottelson.

Carbotte and myself have in fact discussed this balancing in a
different fashion. The diagram in Fig. 3c can be viewed as a "ver-
tex" connection to the effective interaction and embodies the lowest
(2nd) order exchange correction, while the diagram in Fig. 3d is a
crossed diagram which, according to Bergersen,[2] reduces the excess
polarization charge around the positron. As we have seen, the latter
two diagrams almost cancel in their combined contribution to the
annihilation rates. The total charge in the polarization cloud is
rather sensitive to the distribution of charge at large distances
from the positron, and hence does not necessarily directly affect the
annihilation rate which depends more on the distribution at short
distances.

I said that I would say something about annihilation in the ion cores
and about lattice effects. What I have to say is, I am afraid, rather
vague. The annihilation rate in the core can be calculated on the basis
of no enhancement using a Wigner-Seitz approximation for the positron
wavefunction. Carbotte has noticed that if this "Sommerfeld" rate is
enhanced by about a factor of 3 in Na, then one can explain both the

broad tails of the angular correlation curve, as well as the discrepancy between the ladder approximation prediction and the experimental annihilation rate. This result is, however, rather sensitive to the positron wavefunction, due to the high-electron density in the core, and should probably not be taken too seriously.

I have mentioned that the lattice effects, which are of great interest, might be calculated ignoring the electron–positron interaction in the fashion suggested by Berko and Plaskett.[13] Such a calculation has been carried out for lithium by Melngailis.[4] I do not feel qualified to discuss his results except to say that he seems able to explain the anisotropy in the experimental results by using an O.P.W. approximation and the momentum dependent enhancement factor of the ladder approximation.

Let me finish with the warning that one must eventually investigate the effect of the lattice on electron–positron interaction, at least in the high-density limit, before feeling completely happy about any calculation which includes the lattice.

REFERENCES

1a. Kahana, S., *Phys. Rev.* **117**, 123 (1960).
1b. J. Carbotte and S. Kahana, *ibid.* **139**, 213 (1965).
 2. Bergersen, B., Ph.D. Dissertation, Brandeis University, May, 1964.
 3. Majumdar, C. K., Ph.D. Dissertation, University of California, San Diego, Feb., 1965.
 4. Melngailis, J., Ph.D. Dissertation, Carnegie Institute, Feb., 1965.
5a. Bell, R. E., and M. H. Jørgensen, Can. J. Phys. **38**, 652 (1960).
5b. Weisburg, H., Ph.D. Dissertation, Brandeis University, 1965.
 6. Lang, G., S. DeBenedetti, and R. Smoluchowski, *Phys. Rev.* **99**, 596 (1955).
 7. Stewart, A. T., J. B. Shand, J. J. Donaghy, and J. H. Kusmiss, *Phys. Rev.* 128, 118 (1962); *ibid.* **128**, 1587 (1961).
 8. Berko, S., *Phys. Rev.* **128**, 2166 (1962).
 9. Luttinger, J. M., "The Fermi Surface," Wiley, New York and London, 1960.
10. Ferrell, R. A., *Rev. Mod. Phys.* **28**, 308 (1956).
11. Daniel, E., and S. H. Vosko, *Phys. Rev.* **120**, 2041 (1960).
12. Hubbard, J., *Proc. Roy. Soc. (London)* **A243**, 336 (1958).
13. Berko, S., and J. S. Plaskett, *Phys. Rev.* **112**, 1877 (1958).

Positron Annihilation in Ferromagnetic Solids[*]

Stephan Berko

Brandeis University, Waltham, Massachusetts

In the two preceding papers Stewart and Kahana have thoroughly reviewed the field of positron annihilation in metals. As we have seen, the experimental work performed to date has been designed to further the understanding of positron behavior in metals and, more recently, to use positron annihilation as a tool to study various aspects of electron physics of metals. The typical experiments consist of two-photon angular correlation measurements, of the studies of positron lifetimes in the respective metals, and, more rarely, of the measurements of three photon vs. two photon annihilation yields. The theoretical problems encountered in explaining and correlating these various experiments were reviewed in Kahana's article.

Our paper is concerned with experiments on polarized positron annihilation in ferromagnets and their theoretical interpretation. After a discussion of the few published experiments we shall concentrate on recent measurements, and present a new detailed theoretical analysis of the general problem, and a model calculation for polarized positron annihilation in magnetized iron. Briefly, the experiments to be discussed measure the change in the two-photon angular correlation curves, when the saturated spins in a ferromagnet are reversed with respect to the spin direction of polarized positrons by an applied external magnetic field. It is hoped that the analysis of the resulting change can provide a measure of the momentum distribution of the spin aligned electrons in the solids studied, thus yielding important information for the study of ferromagnetism.

Annihilation experiments in magnetized media were first performed to prove that in beta decay, positrons, like electrons, are longitudinally polarized due to nonconservation of parity. In a beautifully conceived experiment, Hanna and Preston[1] observed indeed that the angular correlation of annihilation radiation produced by Cu^{64} positrons annihilating in saturated iron changed with the direction of magnetization, thus confirming one of the predictions of

*Work supported by the National Science Foundation and the U.S. Army Research Office, Durham, North Carolina.

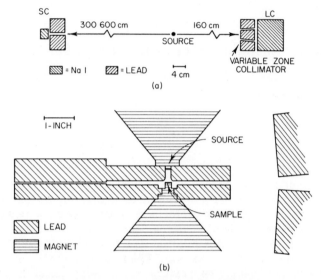

Fig. 1. Angular correlation apparatus of Hanna and Preston[6] for measuring two-photon distributions from magnetized solids.

the then recent parity nonconserving theory of nuclear beta decay.[2] They summarize a plausible explanation of their observed results as follows: (1) Positrons emitted from a Cu^{64} source (spin change $1 \to 0$) are partially polarized parallel to their direction of motion, i.e., opposite to the direction observed for negative electrons; (2) At the time of their annihilation the positrons still retain a substantial amount of this polarization; (3) Annihilation takes place predominantly in the region midway between nuclei where the d electrons mainly responsible for ferromagnetism have higher momentum than the s electrons; and (4) Thus, when the field is parallel (electron spin antiparallel) to the positron spin, two quantum annihilation is enhanced in the high-momentum region of the angular correlation, and when the field is reversed it is diminished.

It is interesting to note at this stage that at that time there was no agreement as to the reason for the high-momentum component in the angular distribution of annihilation radiation, as observed from many metals. For example, Ferrell[3] attributed the high momentum "tail" to high Fourier components in the positron wavefunction due to a postulated very sharp change in its shape at the ionic radii of the metal cores. On the other hand, Berko and Hereford,[4] by analyzing the trend in the angular distributions from Ni, Cu, Zn, and Ga, pointed out that at least part of the high-momentum component should

come from annihilation with "core" electrons, particularly with "d"
electrons. Hanna and Preston's result in iron proved independently
that indeed some positrons must annihilate with the ferromagnetic
"d" electrons. The conclusion of core annihilation was reached also
by Berko and Plaskett[5] from a theoretical analysis of the angular correlation curves for oriented single crystals of aluminum and copper.
Hanna and Preston[6] followed up their original measurement in iron
with a set of more refined experiments on several ferromagnetic
solids. They observed their two-photon angular correlation with an
apparatus having cylindrical symmetry about the two photon axis.
The schematic of their experimental arrangement is shown in Fig. 1;
the figure also presents an enlarged view of their source and sample
placement between the pole pieces of an electromagnet used to saturate the sample. The small counter (SC) subtended a cylindrical
aperture of 3.3 mrad for most measurements. The large counter was
eclipsed by a variable zone collimator, limiting the acceptance angle

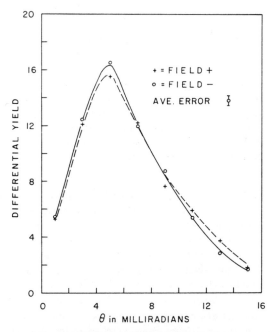

Fig. 2. Differential angular correlation for annihilation in iron for a magnetic field parallel (+)
and antiparallel (−) to the direction of motion of
the positrons, i.e., to the positron polarization,
measured by Hanna and Preston with cylindrical
geometry.[6]

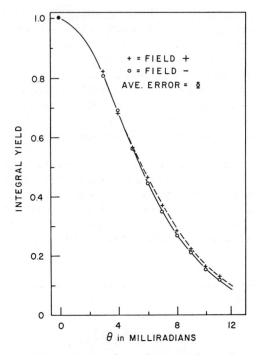

Fig. 3. Integral angular correlation for annihilation in iron for a magnetic field parallel (+) and antiparallel (−) to the direction of motion of the positrons, by Hanna and Preston.[6] Measurements are normalized to the total coincident yield.

to quanta between θ and $\theta + \Delta\theta$. A few differential angular correlations were taken with this setup, but most of the data were obtained in the integral form, i.e., counting all photons emerging at an angle higher than θ; this was accomplished by removing the outer lead collimator in front of the large counter (LC). Figure 2 shows the differential angular correlation obtained in iron for a magnetic field parallel (+) and antiparallel (−) to the direction of motion of the positrons, with $\Delta\theta$ being two milliradians. Figure 3 represents the respective integral correlation curve. Average measurements were performed on several ferromagnetic samples and the data are compiled in Table I. Various absorbers were used to improve the net polarization of the positrons reaching the target. It is to be noted that a null effect was observed in copper, as expected; no effect was observed in nickel, nor in gadolinium below its Curie point. The result in gadolinium was perhaps expected, since the deep lying f shell will overlap little with the positron wavefunction; the null result in nickel was somewhat more puzzling. Hanna and Preston did not attempt a theoretical discussion of their data.

It is of some interest to mention that annihilation in iron was not the only angular correlation technique used to prove positron polarization. Page and Heinberg[7] developed a completely different spin-analyzing technique. They used the fact that in some materials (such as in Teflon) positronium can be formed prior to the annihilation of the positrons, unlike in metals, where it is generally assumed that positrons annihilate in collisions without forming positronium. Page found theoretically that for polarized positrons the formation of either the singlet or triplet state is favored in the presence of a magnetic field, depending on whether the spin of the positrons is parallel or antiparallel to the applied field. The angular correlation technique was then used to differentiate between singlet positronium annihilation and annihilation from the triplet state via "pickoff," i.e., annihilation by overlap with other molecular electrons. The theory of these experiments, as well as a complete review of various other electron and positron polarization experiments, can be found in a review article by Page.[8] In the same article Page compares the two different techniques using the same

TABLE I

Values of $(N_+ - N_-)/N_-$ in per cent, for various samples and several thicknesses of absorber. The symbols N_+ and N_- represent the integral yield over angles greater than 8 mrad, for a field parallel (+) and antiparallel (−) to the direction of motion of the positrons.[a]

Sample	Thickness of aluminum absorber in mils				
	0	4	8	12	16
	Average energy of positrons in Mev				
	0.33	0.38	0.43	0.47	0.50
Fe—Co	5.4 ± 0.8	6.0 ± 1.0	9.4 ± 1.2	11 ± 1.9	11 ± 2.5
Fe—Co (thin source)	4.4 ± 1.2				
Fe (steel)	4.2 ± 0.8	6.0 ± 1.1			
Fe (rectangular)		9.0 ± 1.2			
Fe (Armco)			8.0 ± 1.4		
Ni	−0.3 ± 0.9	−0.1 ± 1.0			
Cu	0.2 ± 0.9		0.1 ± 1.2		
Gd (20°C)			2.2 ± 3.0		
Gd (−100°C)			0.0 ± 1.8		

[a]See Reference 6 (Hanna and Preston).

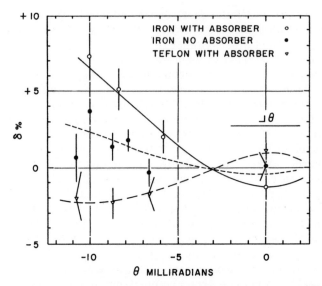

Fig. 4. Response of iron annihilator to polarized Na^{22} positrons compared to the response of a plastic, as measured by Page[8]. Measured δ on reversing magnetic field is opposite in sign for the two materials. Positive δ means higher coincidence rate for H parallel to the positron polarization.

angular correlation setup (the more standard parallel slit geometry, instead of Hanna and Preston's cylindrical geometry). Figure 4 shows Page's comparison curves for iron vs Teflon, using the rather wide angular resolution of 4 mrad. It is interesting to note that, for theoretical reasons described in Page's article, the two methods result in effects with opposite signs. Note also the clear demonstration of the reversal in sign of the effect at small angles. The same positronium formation technique, using, however, lifetime measurements instead of angular correlations, has been used more recently for detailed positron spin analysis experiment.[9]

Using parallel slit geometry, Lovas[10] has remeasured the angular correlation and its change upon magnetic field reversal in iron. The radioactive source used was again Cu^{64}. His angular resolution was rather wide (5 mrad), and the total counting rates did not allow a careful analysis of the shape of the change in the angular distributions. Lovas presented an attempt to predict theoretically the change in the angular correlation curves by using a modification of Ferrell's model.[3] The positron wavefunction $\varphi(r)$ is assumed to be spherically symmetric with a radial wavefunction that goes to zero rapidly in the neighborhood of the ionic radius, and stays constant in the neighborhood of the ionic radius, and stays constant in the in- terionic volume. Since the radial d functions $R_d(r)$ become small in the interionic volume (radius a), Lovas replaces the overlap func- tion $R_d(r)\varphi(r)$ by a delta function $\delta(r - a)$, and then corrects for the error due to this approximation by a cutoff of the overlap in- tegral at high values of k. Thus he predicts an angular distribution from "d" electrons with a variable parameter a. His theoretical computation does not predict a reversal in sign in $(N_+ - N_-)/(N_+ + N_-)$, since he neglects the normalization problem which we shall discuss later. Assuming a positron polarization of 0.6, Lovas concludes that only 5% of all annihilations come from the $3d$ band. We shall see that our theory predicts a much larger percentage of $3d$ annihilation. Lovas also measured the distribution from ferromagnetic magnetite, obtaining a null effect.

In a theoretical paper, McGlinn[11] presented a treatment of the problem based on the computation of the positron wavefunction in the Wigner Seitz approximation, analogous to the theory outlined for copper and aluminum by Berko and Plaskett.[5] The positron radial wavefunction is numerically computed for $k = 0$ by invert- ing the effective ionic potential for iron and satisfying the proper Wigner-Seitz boundary conditions. Overlaps with atomic $3d$ elec- trons are then computed and used to predict the angular distribu- tion. For the $4s$ electrons, a free electron gas model is assumed. Unfortunately, McGlinn computes the integral angular distribu- tions, instead of the differential ones, so that much of the detail of the model is lost; in spite of this, McGlinn is able to point out that a comparison between the theoretical curve and Hanna's experi- mental results are sufficient to rule out the assumption of two, rather than the usual six or more electrons in the d shell, as im- plied by some early x-ray experiments of Weiss and DeMarco.[12]

Having greatly improved our angular distribution setup, we de- cided in 1964 to undertake a new set of measurements, hoping to obtain more detailed information about the momentum distribution of ferromagnetic electrons. The first results were reported in an abstract,[13] and were followed up by a paper.[14] In the experiments we used two seven-in. long by two-in. diameter NaI detectors, shielded from the sample by seven-in. long, parallel-slit lead collimators. The angular resolution was adjustable, most of the data having been taken with slits subtending 0.75 mrad. The sam- ples were zone refined polycrystalline rods, $\frac{3}{8}$ in. in diameter, placed in a vacuum chamber between the pole pieces of an elec- tromagnet. Magnetic fields of 18 Kgauss were used to saturate the samples; the same field served to focus the positrons onto the samples, from a 10 mc. Na^{22} source placed outside the vacuum chamber, with a 2×10^{-4} in. stainless steel window between the source and the sample. The system was fully automated, reversing the magnetic field at each angle every 30 min., before moving one of the slit-counter assemblies to a new, predetermined angle. The data for iron and nickel are presented in Figs. 5 and 6, in the form of $P(\theta) = [N_\uparrow(\theta) - N_\downarrow(\theta)]/[N_\uparrow(\theta) + N_\downarrow(\theta)]$, where $N_\uparrow(\theta)$ is the angular distribution for field parallel, and $N_\downarrow(\theta)$ the distribution for field antiparallel to the positron polarization. $N_\downarrow(\theta)$ is also plotted on the same graphs. θ_f represents the angle corresponding to the free Fermi momentum based on one electron per atom in the "s" band. The size of the effect at large angles was in good agreement with the early experiments of Hanna. We note the clear reversal in sign of $P(\theta)$ between 6 and 7 mrad for iron, and 7 and 8 mrad for nickel. Unlike in Hanna and Preston's experiments, a small polarization effect was found in nickel also, which appeared, however,

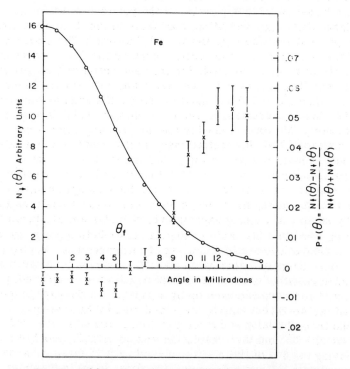

Fig. 5. $N\downarrow(\theta)$, the angular distribution for polycrystalline iron, with magnetic field opposite to the positron polarization (left-hand scale), and $P(\theta)$ (right-hand scale), measured by Berko and Zuckerman.[14]

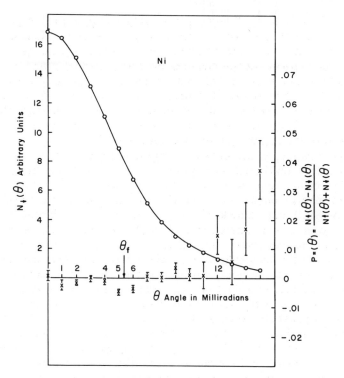

Fig. 6. N ⧫(θ), the angular distribution for polycrystalline nickel, with magnetic field opposite to the positron polarization (left-hand scale), and P(θ) (right-hand scale),
measured by Berko and Zuckerman.[14]

only at quite large angles. It is obvious that nickel needs further
extensive study. A slight indication for a minimum around θ_f is
also to be noted in $P(\theta)$. In the same paper we presented a purely
phenomenological theoretical decomposition of the angular correlation curve for iron into an s band, and a $3d$ band contribution. The
theoretical formulas presented in the paper were based on a model
in which the time dependence of the positron polarization has been
neglected. The correct equations, taking into account their dependence for a partially polarized positron beam has been presented in a note,[14] and their derivation and justification will be
presented at the end of this article.

Independently, Mijnarends and Hambro[15] announced recently new
measurements on polarized positron annihilation in iron. Their experimental technique, described previously in connection with angular correlation experiments from liquids,[16] used a multicounter

parallel slit geometry. They achieve higher counting rates by using multiple, but rather small NaI detectors, instead of the longer slit geometry used by us. Their method has the clear advantage of improving the stability of the counting procedure, which, for the short-lived Cu^{64} source used in their experiments is of great importance. It is not clear to what extent, however, the data obtained with such a geometry can be used without appreciable corrections, since the rather short slits used cannot be considered essentially infinite, compared to the angular distribution measured.

In their paper, Mijnarends and Hambro interpreted the change in the effect for small angles as definite proof for the negative polarization of conduction electrons. Such a negative conduction band polarization was observed in polarized neutron diffraction experiments by Shull and Yamada.[17] As pointed out by us,[14] however, such a sign reversal is a consequence of the large two photon vs three-photon annihilation cross section, rendering the total two-photon yield practically independent of the field direction. One thus needs a more careful model computation in order to infer from the data a possible negative conduction band polarization. In a follow-up paper, presented at the 1964 Nottingham Conference on Magnetism,[18] Mijnarends presented further data on iron, and also new data from a single crystal of $Co_{0.91}Fe_{0.09}$. These data are reproduced in Fig. 7, in the form of $n(\theta) = N_+(\theta) - N_-(\theta)$, where $N_+(\theta)$ corresponds to the angular distribution measured with the electron *spins* parallel to the positron spin, i.e., with the saturating magnetic field antiparallel to the positron spins. Thus $N_+(\theta)$, in their case corresponds to $N_\downarrow(\theta)$ of our measurements—explaining the different sign between the curves of Fig. 7 and those of Figs. 5 and 6. In this paper Mijnarends also reexamined the problem of the interpretation of these experiments in the light of our theoretical discussion,[14] regarding the normalization question mentioned above. The curves obtained by Mijnarends (Fig. 7) have a more pronounced variation for angles smaller than θ_f, than the curve of Fig. 5. Mijnarends pointed out that the *shape* rather than the sign reversal of $n(\theta)$ could be indicative of a negative conduction band polarization. The reason for the difference between Figs. 5 and 7 has not yet been cleared up. The angular resolution of both experiments was comparable. Possible reasons, to be decided by further experiments, could be: (a) A genuine difference between single crystal and the polycrystalline measurements; (b) annihilation in oxide layers, thus forming positronium;[8] (c) the importance of the different geometry between the two experimental setups. For $\theta > \theta_f$, however, there is general agreement between the curves.

Having finished the discussion of the pertinent experimental data,

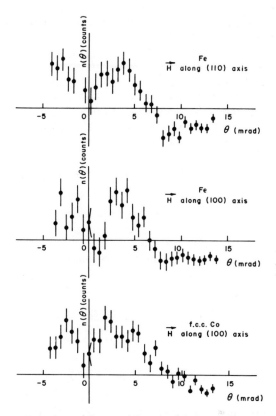

Fig. 7. $n(\theta) = N_+(\theta) - N_-(\theta)$ for oriented single crystals of iron and of fcc. $Co_{0.91}Fe_{0.09}$, measured by Mijnarends and Hambro.[15,18] $N_+(\theta)$ represents the angular distribution with magnetic field antiparallel (+) and parallel (−) to the positron polarization. Note change in sign convention.

we shall now present the theoretical aspects of the problem of partially polarized positron annihilation in magnetized media.* Let the positrons slow down to their ground state $\psi_p(\mathbf{r})$ in the metal lattice, prior to annihilation, with a partial spin polarization $P_p = n_p^+ - n_p^-$; n_p^+ and n_p^- are the probabilities of finding the spin up (+) or down (−), with respect to an axis of quantization z. As we have seen in the previous papers by Stewart and Kahana, the matrix element for

---

*Our derivation follows closely the notation of H. Weisberg, Ph.D. Dissertation, Brandeis University, 1965.

two-photon annihilation with an electron e, the two photons having net momentum $\mathbf{p}$, is proportional to

$$\rho_e(\mathbf{p}) = C \left| \int \psi_e(\mathbf{r}) \psi_p(\mathbf{r}) e^{-i\mathbf{p}\cdot\mathbf{r}} \, d\mathbf{r} \right|^2 \tag{1}$$

Here $\psi_e(\mathbf{r})$ is the eth electron's Bloch function, where e stands for all band quantum numbers except spin, and C is a constant, depending on the units used. Screening due to positron–electron interaction is neglected by using product wavefunctions. Since the parallel slit geometry measures only one momentum component, we introduce

$$\eta_e(p_z) = \iint \rho_e(\mathbf{p}) \, dp_x \, dp_y \tag{2}$$

and

$$w_e = \int \eta_e(p_z) \, dp_z \tag{3}$$

The angle between the two counters is $\theta = p_z/mc$. For a positron with spin + (up) or − (down) the two photon rate, due to spin singlet overlaps is given by

$$\lambda_\pm^{2\gamma} = \tfrac{1}{2} \lambda_s \sum_e n_e^{\mp} w_e = (\lambda_s/4) \sum (1 \mp P_e) w_e \tag{4}$$

The three photon rate, due to spin triplet overlap is

$$\lambda_\pm^{3\gamma} = \tfrac{1}{2} \lambda_t \sum_e (1 + n_e^{\pm}) w_e = \frac{\lambda_t}{4} \sum_e (3 \pm P_e) w_e \tag{5}$$

In formulas (4) and (5) $\lambda_s = 4\pi r_0^2 c$, where r_0 is the classical radius and c the velocity of light, is the singlet 2γ annihilation rate, and $\lambda_t = \lambda_s (4\alpha/9\pi)[\pi^2 - 9] = (1/1115)\lambda_s$ is the basic triplet 3γ annihilation rate; $P_e = n_e^+ - n_e^-$ represents the partial polarization of the e-type electron. We used the selection rule that, for the low velocities involved, singlet collisions result in two-photon annihilation, and triplet collisions have to annihilate via three photons.[19] The total annihilation rate $\lambda_\pm$ is $\lambda_\pm = \lambda_\pm^{2\gamma} + \lambda_\pm^{3\gamma} \cong \lambda_\pm^{2\gamma}$, since $\lambda^{3\gamma} \ll \lambda^{2\gamma}$.

Given a partially polarized positron, the number of photon pairs observed within p_z and $p_z + dp_z$ during the time interval dt, at time t, is given by

$$N^{2\gamma}(p_z,t) \, dp_z \, dt = \tfrac{1}{2} n_p^+ e^{-\lambda_+ t} \lambda_s \sum_e n_e^- \eta_e(p_z) \, dp_z \, dt$$
$$+ \tfrac{1}{2} n_p^- e^{-\lambda_- t} \lambda_s \sum_e n_e^+ \eta_e(p_z) \, dp_z \, dt \tag{6}$$

Since our measurements do not detect the time dependence, we integrate Eq. (6) over the time, to obtain the p_z (angular) distribution

$$N^{2\gamma}(p_z)\,dp_z = \tfrac{1}{2}n_p{}^+\lambda_s \sum_e n_e{}^-\eta_e(p_z)\frac{dp_z}{\lambda^+}$$

$$+ \tfrac{1}{2}n_p{}^-\lambda_s \sum_e n_e{}^+\eta_e(p_z)\frac{dp_z}{\lambda^-} \tag{7}$$

Reversing the saturating magnetic field has the effect of inter-changing $n_e{}^+$ with $n_e{}^-$. Denoting the field along (opposite to) the positron's net polarization with ↑ (↓), we obtain, within the good approximation that $\lambda_\pm = \lambda_\pm{}^{2\gamma}$, the normalization condition we mentioned several times before in the text, i.e.,

$$\int N_\uparrow{}^{2\gamma}(p_z)\,dp_z = \int N_\downarrow{}^{2\gamma}(p_z)\,dp_z \tag{8}$$

Note that in our sign convention, P_e for the d electrons is a negative number for field up ↑, (electron spin down). From (7), using the same approximation, one finds, for the polarization measurement,

$$P(\theta) = \frac{N_\uparrow(\theta) - N_\downarrow(\theta)}{N_\uparrow(\theta) + N_\downarrow(\theta)} = P_p\frac{\Sigma\eta_e\Sigma P_e w_e - \Sigma P_e\eta_e\Sigma w_e}{\Sigma\eta_e\Sigma w_e - \Sigma P_e\eta_e\Sigma P_e w_e} \tag{9}$$

Equation (9) can be simplified by introducing an effective total electron polarization as seen by the positron, $P_{\text{eff}} = (\Sigma P_e w_e/\Sigma w_e)$

$$P(\theta) = P_p\frac{P_{\text{eff}}\,\Sigma\eta_e - \Sigma P_e\eta_e}{\Sigma\eta_e - P_{\text{eff}}\,\Sigma P_e\eta_e} \tag{10}$$

From the above equations we can also express the total three photon yield and its change upon field reversal, obtaining

$$\frac{N_\uparrow{}^{3\gamma} - N_\downarrow{}^{3\gamma}}{N_\uparrow{}^{3\gamma} + N_\downarrow{}^{3\gamma}} = P_p\frac{4P_{\text{eff}}}{3 + P_{\text{eff}}^2} \tag{11}$$

From the basic Eqs. (10) and (11) we can notice the following physically interesting facts: (a) If the electrons would all be of the same kind, $P(\theta)$ would be zero, i.e., identical electrons would lead to a null effect in the angular correlation, even if strongly polarized; Equations (4), of course, indicate that we would, however, observe a change in lifetime upon field reversal. (b) In the general case of a partially polarized positron, we predict a *double* lifetime λ_+ and λ_-. The intensities for the two lifetimes can be obtained by integrating Eq. (6) over all p_z (angles θ). (c) The area under $N_\uparrow(p_z)$ and $N_\downarrow(p_z)$ have to be equal. If we thus observe a positive effect for $P(\theta)$ for a certain region of angles, we are bound to observe a *negative* effect at some other angles. This explains the reversal in sign of $P(\theta)$ for $\theta < \theta_f$. (d) The three-photon yield and the lifetimes depend only on P_{eff}.

We are now ready to demonstrate the use of the above expression with a model computation for the case of polycrystalline iron, due to Terrell. Details of the computation will be presented elsewhere.[20]

The positron wavefunction $\psi_p(r)$ was computed in the Wigner-Seitz approximation, following the prescription of Berko and Plaskett,[5] from a Hartree-Fock-Slater self-consistent potential for Fe$^+$, and a uniform potential due to one electron per atom. The positron wavefunction was found rather insensitive to the exact shape of the potential used. For the $3s$ and $3p$ electrons atomic wavefunctions were used in the tight binding approximation. The $4s$ electron was also computed in the Wigner-Seitz approximation. Instead of using tight binding for the $3d$ electrons, the complete APW band computation of Wood[21] was used to ascertain the average width of the "d" like band. This "d" band wad divided into three representative regions and a $\psi_e(r)$ was computed for each region. Figure 8 shows the positron wavefunction $\psi_p(r)$, and the three radial wavefunctions, marked $d^{(3)}$ "top," $d^{(2)}$ "middle," and $d^{(1)}$ "bottom." The resulting angular distributions obtained are shown in Fig. 9. Note that the top of the band contributes higher momenta corresponding to more tightly bound electron wavefunctions. In Fig. 10 we have plotted the total angular distribution for the $3s$ and

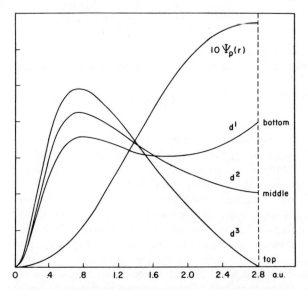

Fig. 8. The normalized positron wavefunctions corresponding to the top, middle, and bottom of the "d" band, by Berko and Terrell[20]. The radial distance is in atomic units.

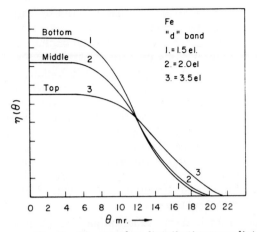

Fig. 9. The angular distributions predicted for the three wavefunctions shown in Fig. 8, by Berko and Terrell[20].

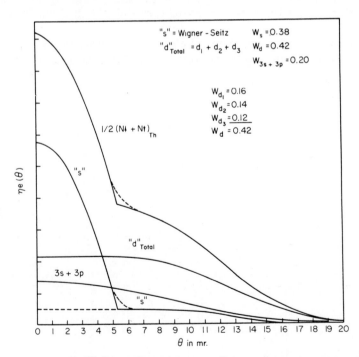

Fig. 10. The predicted total angular distribution for the model calculation discussed in the text.[20]

3p electrons, the conduction 4s "band," and the sum of the three typical "d"-like wavefunctions. The sum was obtained by distributing 7 electrons among the three levels according to a histogram approximating crudely Wood's density of state curves.[21]

The only allowance made for a possible higher positron–electron correlation effect for the "conduction" (4s) band, was to multiply the conduction band contribution by a momentum independent "enhancement" factor chosen so as to give the best total fit to the experimental data. Note that this numerical factor is the only adjustable parameter in the theory. We have used in equation (1) $C''4s'' = 1.8\ C''3d''$, thus enhancing the "s" electrons 1.8 times more than the rest. For a more thorough discussion of the enhancement problem, see the papers of Kahana, Carbotte, and Terrel et al., in this volume.

The resulting angular distribution has the general shape of the experimental distribution, but the high-momentum components are over-emphasized. More complete A.P.W. computations will be needed to test whether the discrepancy is due to poor wavefunctions, or to actual momentum dependent correlation terms.

Finally, Fig. 11 shows the experimental points for $P(\theta)$ in iron, compared with the following three model computations, using Eq. (10):

Model A. One unpolarized electron per atom in the s band; d polarization placed at the top of the d band, (d^3), 2.18 μ_B/atom.

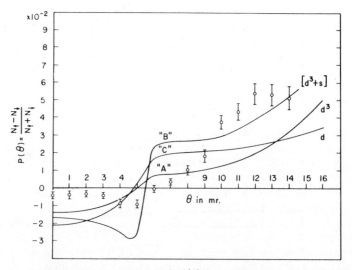

Fig. 11. The experimental $P(\theta)$ from Fig. 5, compared with the theoretical curves for the three models discussed in the text.[20]

Model B. One electron per atom in the *s* band, but assuming 0.2 μ_B/atom, *negative* conduction band polarization.[17] Two spheres are assumed, one holding 0.6 electrons, for spin down, the other holding 0.4 electrons with spin up. The excess spin is thus concentrated on the periphery of the Fermi distribution. The majority spins are placed in the $d^{(3)}$ level, the top of the "*d*" band, 2.38 μ_B/atom.

Model C. No conduction polarization, 2.18 μ_B/atom for the *d* band, but the spins distributed evenly throughout the band. For all three models, the value of P_p = 0.35 was used. The exact value of P_p is not easy to evaluate. Without any corrections, P_p is given by beta decay theory as the average value of $\langle v/c \rangle$, which for Na^{22} is 0.67. If all the forward electrons are focused onto the target $P_p = \frac{1}{2} \langle v/c \rangle$. Backscattering and possible slight depolarization[22] in the target will reduce this value, absorption in the source and the stainless steel window will increase it. The shape of $P(\theta)$ is unaffected by P_p. The sharp change in $P(\theta)$ for model *B* is due to the Wigner-Seitz approximation used. More mixing between the *s* and *d* bands will have the effect of smoothing the curve in the neighborhood of θ_f.

The predicted change in the three photon yield with magnetic field direction depends on the models used: $P^{3\gamma} = (N_\uparrow - N_\downarrow)/(N_\uparrow + N_\downarrow) = -0.035$ for model *A*, $P^{3\gamma} = -0.0013$ for model *B*, and $P^{3\gamma} = -0.06$ for model *C*. The very small effect predicted when negative conduction band polarization is used is due to the almost zero value of P_{eff} for such a model.

We have preliminary data on a new experiment designed to check these predictions.[23] The three-photon yield has been measured in a triple coincidence setup for positrons annihilating in magnetized iron. The change in the three-photon yield when reversing the saturating magnetic field is measured. Preliminary results yield $P^{3\gamma} = -0.002 \pm 0.005$, thus favoring model B, which includes a negative electron polarization. Another, independent test is the lifetime measurement. In view of the small P value, we predict a rather small difference between λ_+ and λ_-. Such lifetime experiments are presently being undertaken in our laboratory.

In the above discussion we have seen how experiments, designed to study the two-photon angular distribution from polarized positrons annihilating in magnetized media, can be analyzed in terms of the electron-band structure of the solid; the experiments can shed light on the momentum distribution of the spin-aligned electrons in the ferromagnets studied. Much needs to be done, both in experiment and theory. The use of stronger sources with multiple counter setups should allow an improved measurement of $P(\theta)$ for more ferromagnets; large computer programs are needed to perform the computations outlined above in more detail, without averaging over various crystalline directions; and finally, a more thorough many-body theory is needed to properly account for the positron–electron correlation, and its influence on the angular correlations.

ACKNOWLEDGMENTS

The author wishes to thank A. P. Mills, H. Weisberg, J. H. Terrell, and H. N. Pendleton for many illuminating discussions regarding various aspects of the positron annihilation problem.

REFERENCES

1. Hanna, S. S., and R. S. Preston, *Phys. Rev.* **106**, 1363 (1957).
2. Lee, T. D., and C. N. Yang, *Phys. Rev.* **105**, 1671 (1957);
   J. D. Jackson, S. B. Treiman and H. W. Wyld, *Phys. Rev.* **106**,
   517 (1957); for other references regarding parity nonconservation
   and beta decay see, for example, the review article by O. M. Kofoed-
   Hansen and C. J. Christensen, *Handbuch der Physik*, XLI/2; Springer-
   Verlag, 1962.
3. Ferrell, R. A., *Rev. Modern Phys.* **28**, 308 (1956).
4. Berko, S., and F. L. Hereford, *Rev. Modern Phys.* **28**, 299 (1956).
5. Berko, S., and J. S. Plaskett, *Phys. Rev.* **112**, 1877 (1958).
6. Hanna, S. S., and R. S. Preston, *Phys. Rev.* **109**, 716 (1958).
7. Page, L. A., and M. Heinberg, Phys. Rev. **106**, 1220 (1957).
8. Page, L. A., *Rev. Modern Phys.* **31**, 759 (1959).
9. Bisi, A., A. Fiorentini, E. Gatti, and L. Zappa, *Phys. Rev.* **128**, 2195
   (1962); L. Dick, L. Feuvrais, L. Madanski, and V. L. Telegdi, *Phys.
   Letters* **3**, 326 (1963).
10. Lovas, I., *Nucl. Phys.* **17**, 279 (1960).
11. McGlinn, W. D., *Nuovo Cimento* **22**, 225 (1961).
12. Weiss, R. J., and J. J. DeMarco, *Rev. Modern Phys.* **30**, 59 (1958);
    see, however, B. W. Batterman et al., *Phys. Rev.* **122**, 68 (1961).
13. Berko, S., and J. Zuckerman, *Bull. Am. Phys. Soc.* **9**, 211 (1964).
14. Berko, S., and J. Zuckerman, *Phys. Rev. Letters* **13**, 339a (1964);
    see also *Phys. Rev. Letters* **14**, 89 (1965).
15. Mijnarends, P. E., and L. Hambro, *Phys. Letters* **10**, 272 (1964).
16. Løvseth, J., *Phys. Norvegica*, **1**, 145 (1963); G. Trumpy, *Phys. Rev.* **118**
    668 (1960).
17. Shull, C. G., and Y. Yamada, *J. Phys. Soc. Japan* **17**, Suppl. B-III, i
    (1962).
18. Mijnarends, P. E., "Proceedings of the International Conference on
    Magnetism," p. 230. Nottingham, 1964 (Published in association with
    Proc. Phys. Soc. London).
19. For a review of annihilation cross sections and positronium physics,
    see, for example, M. Deutsch and S. Berko, "Alpha, Beta, and Gamma
    Ray Spectroscopy," p. 1583. North Holland Publishing Company,
    Amsterdam, 1965.

20. Berko, S., and J. Terrell, Optical Properties and Electronic Structure of Metals and Alloys, p. 210. North Holland Publishing Company, Amsterdam, 1966.
21. Wood, J. H., *Phys. Rev.* **126**, 517 (1962).
22. Braicovich, L., B. DeMichelis, and A. Fasana, *Nucl. Phys.* **63**, 548 (1965); C. Bouchiat and J. M. Levy-Leblond, *Nuovo Cimento* **33**, 193 (1964); A. Bisi et al., *Nucl. Phys.* **66**, 332 (1965).
23. Mills, A. P., and S. Berko, Brandeis University, to be published.

Positron Annihilation in Ionic Crystals and Alkali Halides

Antonio Fiorentini

Gruppo Nazionale Struttura della Materia del CNR, Istituto di Fisica
Politecnico di Milano, Milan, Italy

1. INTRODUCTION

The present lecture concerns the annihilation of positrons in ionic crystals and in particular in alkali halides. No reference will be made to the measuring techniques. Theoretical works will be mentioned only for their more significant conclusions, in order to frame and connect the experimental results. This lecture, then, will describe results known to all, and to these results it will add new ones not yet known; in any case it does not pretend to be an exhaustive review of the whole literature, but, rather, a starting point for future discussions.

To begin, I recall the ideas of Ferrell[1] on positron annihilation in ionic crystals: they are an attempt to analyze the positron behavior in ionic crystals, and were developed with semiquantitative intent on the basis of a very simple model. The essential points concern the nonformation of positronium, a mean life estimate and two-photon angular correlation. All positrons are assumed not to form positronium and to have the same fate. The basic argument for that, is simply the fact that there is no room in the ionic crystals for a positronium atom. On the other hand, the positron being repelled by the positive ions and attracted by the negative ones, the wavefunction will tend to be concentrated about the negative ions. By treating the periodic potential problem by the tight binding approximation, Ferrell finds the binding energy of a positron to a negative ion as a function of the hard-core radius. For the system $Cl^- e^+$, the resulting binding energy is equal to 2.37 eV, while an exact calculation made by Simons,[2] based on the Hartree-Fock self-consistent field, gives 3.74 eV. For such a system, the wavefunction is concentrated about the negative ion into a bound s wave with a maximum about the ion radius. Now, if one assumes that the eight electrons occupying the noble gas configuration, can be roughly thought of as uniformly spread out over the volume of the ion, the resultant mean life is inversely proportional to the cube of the ion radius. For the $Cl^- e^+$ case it predicts about 4×10^{-10} sec.

Ferrell has given an analysis of the two-photon angular correlation by adding, to the previous quoted assumption, that the electron and positron wavefunctions are separable. He finds that the curve has a shape more or less triangular with a width at half maximum inversely proportional to the Goldschmidt radius, as the result of a combination of contributions from electrons in s and p states with respect to the ion to which the positron is bound.

As a general comment to the ideas of Ferrell, it may be said that they yield an extremely schematic description of the positron behavior in ionic crystals, which can be made *a priori*. We mean that the annihilation phenomenon in its various aspects could be considered a plausible and direct consequence of the simplest properties of the ionic crystals. In effect, there were too few experimental data at disposal of Ferrell. Bell and Graham,[3] in their pioneer work on time annihilation spectra, had observed a single decay with a mean life of $(2.3 \pm 0.3) \times 10^{-10}$ sec in NaCl. Lang and DeBenedetti[4] had measured the angular correlation in LiF, NaCl, KCl, and KI. At present the situation is greatly changed; we have at our disposal, in fact, many quantitative results and qualitative information on hydrides, alkali halides, halides of Cu, Ag, and Au, and some oxides

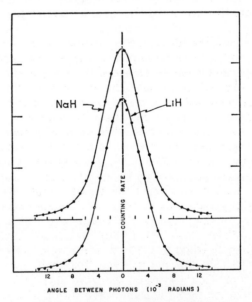

Fig. 1. Angular correlation of the two-photon annihilation radiation from positrons annihilating in LiH and NaH. The instrumental resolution function has a width of less than 1 mrad.[5]

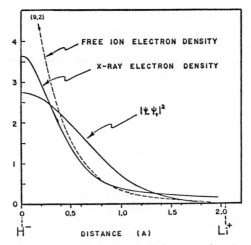

Fig. 2. Comparison of electron-density
distribution obtained from x-ray diffraction
and from free-ion calculations with "wavefunction product" squared obtained from
this experiment.[5]

with a high percentage of ionic binding. In particular, for the alkali halides, we know rather well the two-photon angular correlation, the time-annihilation spectra and the three-quantum decay.
Even the theoretical knowledge has been developed, so that the
situation should be mature for allowing the building up of a model
able to account for the acquired results, and to show the way to
future researches.

Now we shall examine the present disposable results, beginning
from the alkali hydrides.

2. ALKALI METAL HYDRIDES

a. Angular Correlation

Stewart and March[5] have investigated the angular correlation of
the two photons from positrons annihilating in polycrystalline specimens of LiH and NaH; they have found that the two correlations are
hardly distinguishable. This result suggests that the momentum
distribution depends mainly on the H^- ion so that the positrons
should annihilate only with the two electrons of the negative ion.
With the aim to interpret their experimental results, Stewart and
March deduce the electron–positron wavefunction product from the
momentum distribution. A comparison of the electron-density
distribution obtained from this wavefunction product with those

obtained from x-ray diffraction and from free-ion calculations, shows that the density curve from the wavefunction product, is much wider at the half maximum and falls much faster toward zero. This result is in contrast with the observation of Stewart and Pope[6] for some alkali halides for which these three distributions are much alike. In view of the fact that the angular correlation in alkali metal hydrides cannot receive a satisfactory explanation in this scheme, we suggest that a better agreement can perhaps be attained, with the use of an electron wavefunction perturbed by the positron, or even a correlation between the positron and the electrons.

A theoretical treatment of the annihilation of positrons which have formed a bound state with a negative hydrogen ion, has been given by Neamtan, Darewych, and Oczkowski.[7] They have obtained an estimate of the binding energy more accurate than that calculated previously by Ore,[8] who, for the first time, predicted the existence of such a system and even an improved wavefunction for the bound system in its ground state. The above wavefunction yields a mean life against two-photon annihilation of about four times that for singlet positronium, and this difference arises from spin considerations and not from average electron density (due to both electrons) which differs little from that found in the ground state of positronium. The theoretical angular correlation curve has only one quarter of the width of the experimental one, while that calculated with the aid of Ore's function is much wider. In spite of the disagreement between the experimental and calculated correlation curves, we think that the possibility remains that bound systems, type $H^- e^+$, might be formed in solids, and suggest that the discovery in the time annihilation spectra of a significant component, with an annihilation rate of approximately one fourth of that of singlet positronium, could be taken as partial evidence for the formation of bound $H^- e^+$ structures in the solids.

I wish to point out that Neamtan's calculations refer to the ground state of $H^- e^+$ so that the question remains whether the consideration of excited levels would allow agreement between theory and experiment.

b. Lifetimes

Bisi et al.,[9] in a set of measurements on positron annihilation in alkali chlorides and in lithium hydride, have shown that in these compounds positrons exhibit a complex time annihilation spectrum. In particular, in LiH, it is possible to distinguish a component having intensity $I_1 = 93\%$ and mean life $\tau_1 = (2.1 \pm 0.3) \times 10^{-10}$ sec and a second component having intensity $I_2 = 6.4\%$ and mean life $\tau_2 = (15.2 \pm 0.8) \times 10^{-10}$ sec.

The component τ_1 could be attributable, according to these authors, to the annihilation of free positrons if this circumstance occurs in LiH. In reference to the long-lived component, the authors, taking into account the difficulties faced by assuming positronium formation in ionic crystals, propose to ascribe it to the decay of a bound state of a positron with a negative hydrogen ion. This interpretation, however, leads to serious difficulties because the experimental value of the annihilation rate, disagrees with that evaluated by Neamtan by a factor of three.

In a following work, Neamtan and Verral[10] consider the possibility of the existence of a bound positronium-like system in an ionic crystal, with particular reference to LiH. The crystal field is described in an approximation which treats the potentials as being made up of a sum of spherically symmetrical potential centered on the ion sites. By treating the effect of the crystal field as a perturbation of the Hamiltonian for free positronium, they obtain an upper bound for the ground-state energy of a system of an electron and a positron in Coulomb interaction with each other, and moving in the crystal potential. Such a system deviates considerably from spherical symmetry and in its singlet ground state has a mean life 1.16 times that of singlet free positronium. On the basis of this result the authors indicate that positronium formation is probably an important part of the process of positron annihilation in LiH and perhaps in alkali halides. Furthermore, they suggest that, if positronium is formed in the triplet state, the subsequent two-photon annihilation of the positron with an electron through a "pickoff" process, would be expected to contribute to the I_2 component observed by Bisi et al.

Afterwards, Goldanskii et al.,[11] taking into account all previous results, both theoretical and experimental, have carried out a detailed theoretical investigation on positron annihilation in the field of negative hydrogen ions. Their starting point is the utilization of the Hartree-fock method. The results of the calculations lead to the following conclusions: the $H^- e^+$ system has a series of rather deep-bound levels, and the binding energy of the positron to the H^- is equal to 4.57, 2.72, 1.52 eV for the ground state, the first and the second excited level, respectively. The positron can be captured in these levels with probabilities which, according a preliminary estimate, are in the ratios $0.24 : 49.6 : 3.30$. The radiative transitions are characterized by much greater lifetimes than the corresponding annihilation lifetimes so that the annihilation time spectrum should reflect the decay of each level of the $H^- e^+$ system. The annihilation from the ground level should correspond to a component of low relative intensity having a mean life of 10^{-11} sec, very hard to be observed; the annihilation from the first two excited levels should give a more intense component having a mean life of 2.84×10^{-10} sec. The experimental value given by Bisi et al., is $(2.1 \pm 0.3) \times 10^{-10}$ sec. Moreover, if one considers that on going from the ground state to the excited levels the lifetime increases, the I_2 component should arise from the series of higher levels.

As far as the angular correlation is concerned, the calculated curves of the two-photon annihilation for the ground and first excited state of $H^- e^+$ are quite close to the experimental one. Consequently, the assumption of the Ore-system formation with the new interpretation of Goldanskii et al., seems to be able to explain the whole set of experimental data, presently available, in a satisfactory way.

We wish now to emphasize that Zappa et al.[12] had the opportunity to examine once more a few time spectra of annihilation in LiH. The lifetime of the I_1 component has been confirmed within experimental errors, while the I_2 component has been shown to exhibit an intensity and a mean life different from one specimen to another. In any case, the new values have been found lower than the previous ones. The specimens used were crystals with a grade of purity typical of custom laboratory uses. It is then necessary to proceed with great care in interpreting the origin of this component.

Quite recently Paulin and Ambrosino[13] have measured the time annihilation spectrum in LiH and found an I_2 component with a lifetime of 2.1×10^{-9} sec and an intensity of 1.25%.

c. Three-Quantum Decay

Bisi et al.[14] in a set of measurements on the three quantum decay of positrons in ionic crystals, have measured, for LiH, the decay probability P_3 relative to that in Al. As it will be shown afterwards, the measured three quantum decay probability in Al, was found to be in agreement with the value 1/372. By using a specimen in which the I_2 component was practically absent, it was found that

$$\frac{P_3(\text{LiH})}{P_3(\text{Al})} = 0.94 \pm 0.05$$

This result indicates that the spin state of the annihilating pair is singlet only one quarter of the time, and this conclusion does not conflict with the investigated properties of the $H^- e^+$ system.

3. ALKALI HALIDES

a. *Angular Correlation*

We know at present angular correlation curves for 11 salts. The first investigation was due to Lang and DeBenedetti[4] who obtained information on LiF, NaCl, KCl, and KI. The LiF sample was made of several large crystals, the others were polycrystalline specimens. The measured distributions are more or less triangular in shape so that the Ferrell's prediction seems to be verified. These authors, however, pointed out that if the NaCl lattice is expanded or contracted in such a way as to have the same lattice constant as the other ionic crystals investigated, the correspondingly contracted or expanded momentum distributions fit fairly well with those observed. Thus the possibility of interpreting the distributions in terms of characteristics of the whole crystal is not entirely ruled out.

Millet and Castillo-Behena[15] have analyzed the angular correlation in single crystals of LiF, NaCl, KCl, KBr, and KI. In order to account for the shape of the curves, these authors assume that the positron is bound to the halogen ion in an S state and that the annihilation takes place with one of the two S electrons or $6P$ electrons in the closed shell of the ion. With the choice of a product wavefunction which does not reflect electron positron correlation, but does take account of the repulsion by the core, about 30% of positrons annihilate with S electrons; it means that the positrons have a more or less equal probability of being annihilated by any of the eight electrons.

Stewart and Pope[6] have measured the angular correlation curves in all sodium halides and all alkali chlorides by using polycrystalline specimens. The obtained curves show that the negative ion determines the momentum distribution of the annihilation gamma rays, the effect of changing the positive ion being hardly observable. Indeed, the momentum distributions of NaCl, KCl and RbCl are displaced somewhat to lower momentum with respect to those for LiCl and CsCl. The authors, however, give a plausible explanation for this behavior. To account for the data Stewart and Pope take into consideration five models based on the free-ion wavefunction; the electron–positron wavefunction products, which yield fits to the experimental data, resemble Hartree-Fock free ion electron wavefunctions. A comparison for chlorides and fluorides of the electron density distribution obtained from this wavefunction product, and of that obtained with free-ion wavefunctions show that they are similar to the electron density obtained by x-ray measurements. In view of this fact, Stewart and Pope are of the opinion that a model of single

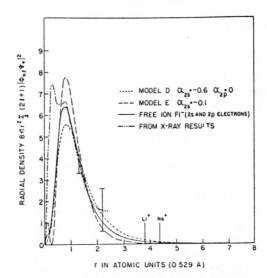

Fig. 3. Radial distributions from space
wavefunctions for models *D* and *E* fitted to
fluoride data. In model *E* it is arbitrarily
assumed that there are eight electrons in a
2s orbital. The electron radial distribution
from x-ray measurements and from Hartree-
Fock free ion wavefunctions are also shown.
The error bars refer to errors in the x-ray
measurements. The positions of the nearest
alkali ions are shown by vertical lines at the
appropriate radial distances.[6]

particle wavefunctions is improbable, which describes both the
electrons and the positron tightly bound to the negative ion.

It is worthwhile to note that all attempts made to interpret
the angular correlations have been made before any data on time annihilation spectra were available, so that they are based on the assumption that all the positrons have the same fate.

b. Lifetimes

The time annihilation spectrum of positrons in most alkali halides
was measured by Bisi et al.[16] In the spectra, at least two components are clearly distinguishable. The first, I_1, which as a matter
of fact, cannot be shown to be single, is that distorted by the resolution of the apparatus. Its lifetime, in chlorides, is about 2×10^{-10}
sec. The decay of free positrons should contribute to it, if this

process is to be taken into account. The second one, I_2, occurs
with an intensity between 25 and 85%, and is characterized by a
mean life, τ_2, whose value ranges between 4×10^{-10} and 8×10^{-10}
sec. In some cases, a third component, I_3, is present, whose intensity does not attain 1%, and whose lifetime is a few nanoseconds.
From the whole set of collected data, the following empirical
regularity can be extracted. Within each series of alkali halides,
the annihilation rate, λ_2, appears simply correlated with the molecular density n according to the relation:

$$\lambda_2 = \lambda_0 + \alpha n \tag{1}$$

λ_0 decreases, passing from fluorides to iodides, and α turns out to
be simply proportional to the square of the radius of the negative
ion. These results lead one to conclude that most positrons annihilate
through a process where the negative ion plays a prevailing role.
The relation (1), where the annihilation rate is expressed as a sum
of two terms, is certainly empirical in nature, and this fact must
be kept in mind when discussing it. In effect, if it is no more than
an interpolative formula which accounts quite well for the experimental results, there is no place for further comments on it. On the
contrary, if one attributes to it a precise physical significance, we
must conclude that the positrons responsible for the τ_2 component
annihilate through two competitive processes. The first is described
by a partial rate which is independent of the molecular density, and

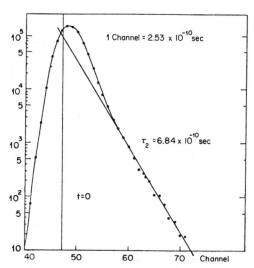

Fig. 4. Time spectrum of positrons
annihilating in CsBr.[16]

TABLE I

Long Lifetimes of Positrons in Alkali Halides; n Indicates the Molecular Density, τ_2, I_2, τ_3, I_3 Indicate Mean Lives and Intensities of the Long-Lived Components[a]

Halide	$n \times 10^{-22}$	$\tau_2 \times 10^{10}$ sec	I_2 (%)	$\tau_3 \times 10^9$ sec	I_3 (%)
LiF	6.04	4.02 ± 0.20	70 ± 15	2.7	0.8
NaF	4.00	5.05 ± 0.35	49 ± 5	2.5	1.4
KF	2.57	6.20 ± 0.40	33 ± 7	2.7	0.4
CsF	1.42	7.60 ± 0.21	46 ± 5		
LiCl	2.94	4.25 ± 0.25	30 ± 10		
NaCl	2.23	4.96 ± 0.24	52 ± 15	2.0	0.9
KCl	1.60	6.07 ± 0.12	50 ± 15		
RbCl	1.37	6.27 ± 0.19	31 ± 10		
CsCl	1.42	6.39 ± 0.18	25 ± 4		
LiBr	2.40	4.58 ± 0.20	85 ± 10	3.6	1.0
NaBr	1.87	5.56 ± 0.20	34 ± 7	3.6	0.9
KBr	1.39	6.73 ± 0.22	37 ± 7		
CsBr	1.26	6.84 ± 0.33	31 ± 4		
NaI	1.48	5.11 ± 0.18	61 ± 9	3.3	1.2
KI	11.13	6.40 ± 0.21	43 ± 7		
RbI	1.00	6.36 ± 0.18	56 ± 15	3.9	0.2
CsI	1.05	6.36 ± 0.29	25 ± 4	3.9	0.8

[a]See Bisi et al.[16]

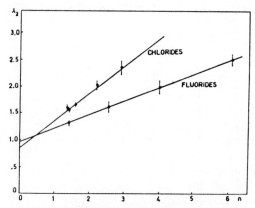

Fig. 5. Annihilation rate λ_2 (units: 10^9 sec^{-1}) of long-lived positrons in alkali chlorides and fluorides as a function of molecular density n.[16]

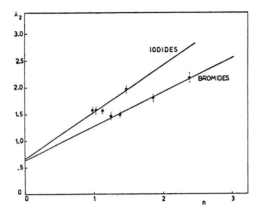

Fig. 6. Annihilation rate λ_2 (units: 10^9 sec^{-1}) of long-lived positrons in alkali iodides and bromides as a function of molecular density n.

the second by a partial rate simply proportional to n. The mechanism of these two processes is until now obscure.

The I_2 component appears to be sensitive to the application of a static magnetic field, but the observed magnetic quenching is much lower than can be predicted with the assumption of positronium formation. This fact emphasizes once more that a bound system having the same properties as the free positronium cannot be formed in alkali halides. If this quenching depends on the properties of the bound system once formed, and does not consist of a decrease of formation of the bound system, then we are led to the following conclusion. The bound system must be characterized by a set of levels whose spin properties play a fundamental role in determining the behavior of the system itself.

Recently, Goldanskii and Prokopo'ev[17] have made a theoretical investigation on positron annihilation in alkali halides, which follows and completes the one made by the same authors in LiH. In this work they discuss the new kinds of bound states in crystals: (a) polaron state of positron; and (b) positrons captured by negative impurity or "host" ions in interstices of the lattice or by negative cation vacancies. In the Pekar polaron state, it results that the annihilation from the first excited levels takes place with a mean life of about 5×10^{-10} sec for alkali chlorides. This value agrees favorably with the experimental data, but does not explain the empirical regularities and the magnetic quenching. In reference to the annihilation from the positron bound state by defects, it should be of interest in alkali halide crystals with a large concentration of point defects.

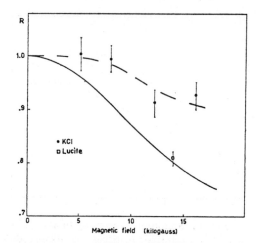

Fig. 7. Relative intensity of the τ_2 component in KCl with and without magnetic field. The full line gives the quenching for a free positronium atom.[16]

Finally, let us say a few words on the third component in the time spectrum. Kohonen[18] found in the time spectrum of positrons annihilating in NaCl polycrystalline, a faint component of 1.5×10^{-9} sec with an intensity of 1.4%, but this component disappeared by fusing the sample. Recently, Paulin[19] observed in NaCl a lifetime of 5×10^{-9} sec with an intensity of 0.3%. These observations indicate the possibility that the third component is sensitive to the sample preparation too.

c. *Three-Quantum Decay*

Gainotti et al.,[20] have investigated the three-quantum decay in a dozen alkali halides by measuring the small defect in the two-quantum annihilation rate as compared with that of a metal, in the annihilation energy spectrum. They conclude that the three-quantum production in most cases is much larger than would be expected by assuming that the I_2 component of Bisi et al., is due to positronium decay. The experimental method, however, is indirect and does not intrinsically appear able to yield accurate results.

Bisi et al.,[14] have recently investigated the three-quantum decay using a triple coincidence method similar to one used earlier by De Benedetti and Siegel.[21] The experimental apparatus has been previously checked in an investigation of positrons annihilating in metals and insulators and has given a very satisfactory performance.[22] As can be seen from Table II, in most alkali halides, the three quantum decay probability exceeds the value characteristic of aluminum by about 30%; and about a factor of 1.6 and 2 for LiF and NaF, respectively. This corresponds to a three-quantum production larger than that which would be expected by assuming that either the I_2 or I_3 components are due to positronium decay. The specimens used were multicrystalline analytical reagent grade. In one case, i.e., NaCl, a single crystal was employed: the same three-quantum yield was observed. Any attempt to correlate these results with those extracted from the time spectra, has been unsuccessful, due to the fact that the intensities of the various components are affected by too large errors to give significance to an analyses of this type. This fact emphasizes the opportunity to reexamine the time spectra by using a time-to-height converter of better characteristics than the one used by Bisi et al. That, in fact, is the future program of this group. In any case, the positron behavior with respect to the three-quantum decay is quite different from that in LiH: there, in fact, the spin state of the annihilating pair is triplet, more than three quarters of the time.

TABLE II

Experimental Data
on Three Quantum Relative Yield
in Alkali Halides with Respect to Al

Specimen	P/P_{Al}
LiF	1.64 ± 0.05
NaF	2.32 ± 0.04
KF	1.41 ± 0.04
CsF	1.32 ± 0.04
LiCl	1.38 ± 0.04
NaCl	1.27 ± 0.04
KCl	1.32 ± 0.03
RbCl	1.30 ± 0.04
CsCl	1.31 ± 0.04
LiBr	1.31 ± 0.04
NaBr	1.29 ± 0.04
KBr	1.42 ± 0.05
CsBr	1.34 ± 0.05
NaI	1.40 ± 0.04
KI	1.23 ± 0.04
RbI	1.22 ± 0.04
CsI	1.15 ± 0.03

ACKNOWLEDGMENTS

The author is especially indebted to Professors A. Bisi and L. Zappa, and to Dr. C. Bussolati for many suggestions and private communications of unpublished results.

REFERENCES

1. Ferrell, R. A., *Rev. Mod. Phys.* **28**, 308 (1956).
2. Simons, L., *Phys. Rev.* **90**, 165 (1953).
3. Bell, R. E., and R. L. Graham, *Phys. Rev.* **90**, 644 (1957).
4. Lang, G., and S. DeBenedetti, *Phys. Rev.* **108**, 257 (1957).
5. Stewart, A. T., and R. March, *Phys. Rev.* **122**, 75 (1961).
6. Stewart, A. T., and N. K. Pope, *Phys. Rev.* **120**, 2033 (1960).
7. Neamtan, S. M., G. Darewych, and G. Oczkowski, *Phys. Rev.* **126**, 193 (1962).
8. Ore, A., University of Bergen Yearbook No. 5, Bergen, Norway, 1952.
9. Bisi, A., A. Fiorentini, and L. Zappa, *Phys. Rev.* **131**, 1023 (1963).
10. Neamtan, S. M., and R. I. Verrall, *Phys. Rev.* **134**, A1254, (1964).
11. Goldanskii, V. I., A. V. Ivanova, and E. P. Prokop'ev, *Sov. Phys. JETP* **20**, 440 (1965).
12. L. Zappa (unpublished).
13. Paulin, R., and G. Ambrosino, private communication, to be published.
14. Bisi, A., C. Bussolati, S. Cova, and L. Zappa, to be published.
15. Millet, W. E., and R. Castillo-Bahena, *Phys. Rev.* **108**, 257 (1957).
16. Bisi, A., A. Fiorentini, and L. Zappa, *Phys. Rev.* **134**, A328 (1964).
17. Goldanskii, V. I., and E. P. Prokop'ev, *Sov. Phys. Solid State* **6**, 2641 (1964).
18. Kohonen, T., *Ann. Acad. Scientiarium Fennicae Series A, VI Physica*, No. 130 (1963).
19. Paulin, R., and G. Ambrosino (private communication).
20. Gainotti, A., E. Germagnoli, G. Schianchi, and L. Zecchina, *Phys. Letters* **13**, 9 (1964).
21. DeBenedetti, S., and R. Siegel, *Phys. Rev.* **85**, 371 (1952).
22. Bertolaccini, M., C. Bussolati, and L. Zappa, *Phys. Rev.* to be published.

Positronium Formation and Interaction in Gases

J. H. Green

University of New South Wales
Sydney, Australia

INTRODUCTION

In this paper I intend to discuss particularly the experimental results which have been published in the last few years. There has been a renewed interest in interactions in gases quite recently. This may be emphasized by pointing out that the "classical era" beginning in 1951 contributed 13 journal articles up to the end of 1962; the present era has provided 14 journal articles from the beginning of 1963 until now. The dividing line may be taken as the approximate mathematical analysis by Tao, Celitans, and Green[31] of the thermalization of positrons in argon.

POSITRONIUM FORMATION AND QUENCHING

Physical data on *positronium formation fractions* and electric and magnetic field effects are listed by Green and Lee[18] in their Table II. Since they were compiled, Falk and Jones[14] have contributed another value for argon, $f = 37 \pm 3\%$ and Page (private communication) confirms the value of σ_q for oxygen obtained by Celitans and Green[9,10] using different techniques ($1.2 \pm 0.2 \times 10^{-19}$ cm^2; but this gives a scattering cross section only about 5×10^{-19} cm^2).

Two points come to attention here: First, the data so far obtained have provided the most satisfying exercise in quantum electrodynamics of particles. Second, the Ore gap concept is not by any means adequate for quantitative prediction of positronium formation in gases. It is still convenient, to some extent, to use it to define the energy regions in which the interactions of positrons should be analyzed. The lack of correspondence of experiment with Ore gap limits for f, except for argon, which is itself a little unusual, is good enough support for this second point. It should also be realized that the recent experimental evidence for resonance annihilations of free positrons and annihilation from positron molecular ions needs a more detailed interpretation than is given by the simple Ore theory.

TABLE I*

Positronium Formation in Gases

(Numbers in parentheses refer to references at the end of the table)

Gas	Formation fraction (f, %)	Pressure (P, atm)	Ore limits f%	Magnetic field effect (5) $H_{1/2}$ at p^a (kG)	p^a (atm)	f (%) at saturating electric field (~500 volts/cm)	Remarks
Argon	27 ± 3 (2) 30 (5) 31 ± 3 (8) 36 ± 6 (6)	1 27 1 1.2	21-43	2.2	27	70 ± 8 (6) 75 (4) 87 (13)	^1S probably not thermalized 10^{-8} sec at 27 atm (5). Formation cross section, $\sigma_f \sim 10^{-16}$ cm^2 (4); Pressure quenching cross section $\sigma_p \sim 1.55 \times 10^{-21}$ cm^2 at $P > 15$ atm (12, 16).
Neon	55 ± 6 (6)	1.2	11-32			79 ± 9 (6)	$\sigma_p = 10^{-21}$ cm^2 at $P > 15$ atm (12).
Helium	32 ± 3 (8)	1	20-28			52 ± 6 (6)	$\sigma_p = 0.5 \times 10^{-21}$ cm^2 at $P > 15$ atm (12, 16).
Krypton	25 (3)		35-50				
Nitrogen^b	21 ± 1 (8) 34 (7)	1 15.5	0-44^c	4.5	28	51 (6) 86 (13)	$\sigma_q = 1.32 \times 10^{-21}$ cm^2 (15).
Hydrogen^b	38.4 (7) 35 ± 3 (8)	15.5 1	0-44			76 (6)	
Oxygen	50 (13, 5 cf. 7) 40 ± 4 (15)		0-54			80-90 (13)	Thermalization observed (27 atm) (5). An 80 nsec component annihilates with a line at 510 keV (10). $\sigma_q \cong 10^{-19}$ cm^2 (4). $\sigma_q = 1.2 \times 10^{-19}$ cm^2 (15).
Carbon dioxide	25 (9) 30 (2)	< 1	8-47			No increase at 2 atm (6)	$\sigma_p = 3.5 \times 10^{-21}$ cm^2 at $P > 15$ atm (12).
Methane						No increase at 2 atm (6)	

Ethane									No increase at 2 atm (6)
Ethylene	46	(2)	<1						
Propane	46	(2)							
Nitrous oxide				4.0		28			
Sulfur hexafluoride	32	(7)	4	3.2	3.8	3.2	26	18	4	Slight decrease (6)	Increase at low density and very high field, $f = 75\%$ (13).
Freon	40	(1)	<1						No increase (6)	$\pi_2 = 1.26 \times 10^{-7}$ sec at 1 atm, $\lambda_p^{-1} = 2.1 \times 10^{-8}$ sec at 1/3 atm (1) $\tau_2 = 1.25 \times 10^{-7}$ sec at 4.8 atm (10); no spin reorienting collisions (4); $\lambda = 6.8 \times 10^6 + 0.3 \times 10^6 P$ (11). $\lambda = 6.76 \times 10^4 + 0.56 \times 10^4 P$ (17).

Miscellaneous (9, 14): CO, SO_2, H_2O, CH_3OH, CH_3I, $CHCl_3$, and CCl_4 all have $\sigma_q < 10^{-19}$ cm²; Cl_2 and Br_2 have $\sigma_p \sim 10^{-16}$ cm².

[a] Magnetic field enhances the narrow component of the two-photon angular distribution and $H_{1/2}$ is the field required for half-saturation of this effect. Theoretically this should be about 2.2 kG (Karplus and Klein, 1952).

[b] High pressure quenching in the experiments of Benedetti and Siegel, 1954 decreases o-Ps formation, and values of f are therefore not directly comparable with those of Pond, 1952.

[c] For these diatomic molecules, the first excitation level used to calculate the Ore gap was assumed to be the energy of dissociation of the molecule; when this fell below the bottom of the gap, the minimum formation probability was assumed to be zero.

1. Gittelman and Deutsch, 1958.
2. Gittelman and Deutsch, 1956.
3. Gittelman, 1958.
4. Dulit, 1956.
5. Heinberg and Page, 1957.
6. Marder et al., 1956.
7. Benedetti and Siegel, 1954.
8. Pond, 1952.
9. Deutsch, 1953.
10. Lewis and Ferguson, 1953.
11. Deutsch, 1951, a, b.
12. Heymann et al., 1961
13. Obenshain and Page, 1962.
14. Obenshain, 1960.
15. Celitans and Green, 1964 a.
16. Duff and Heymann, 1962.
17. Green and Tao, 1963.

*Taken from "Positronium Chemistry," James Green and John Lee, Academic Press, New York, 1964.

TABLE II

Quenching Cross Sections of Oxygen in Argon

σ_q ($\times 10^9$ cm^2)	Method	Ref.
1	2γ rate and annihilation spectra	13
1.3	Annihilation spectra	21
1.2 ± 0.2	Lifetime	10
1.2	Electric field	26

In this field we have been plagued by an unsatisfactory degree of agreement between the results obtained in different laboratories. In this context, the agreement in *quenching cross sections* for oxygen in argon is gratifying (Table I). So is the agreement in quenching rates for O_2-Ar and N_2-Ar mixtures determined by 3γ coincidence and lifetime measurements, as shown in Tables II and III. However, there are several unsolved puzzles arising from the oxygen quenching results. In conversion quenching the cross section should be about one-quarter of the scattering cross section, since only one collision in every four should lead to a change in configuration of Ps. For oxygen, this means that the scattering cross section is at least two orders of magnitude less than the molecular cross section. In addition, although the quenching rate in oxygen is so high that no o-Ps triple coincidences can be observed, the quenching cross section is two orders of magnitude less than for nitric oxide. (These estimates require the introduction of the mean thermal velocity of o-Ps, 6.6×10^6 cm sec^{-1}, on the evidence from the angular

TABLE III

Quenching Rate Coefficients for Oxygen-Argon Mixtures

Oxygen fraction	Lifetime results	Three-photon coincidence results
1×10^{-6}	$(2.1 \pm 0.3) \times 10^{-3} \lambda_0$ atm^{-2}	$(1.8 \pm 0.2) \times 10^{-3} \lambda_0$ atm^{-2}
2×10^{-6}	—	$(1.7 \pm 0.2) \times 10^{-3} \lambda_0$ atm^{-2}
5×10^{-6}	$(3.7 \pm 0.2) \times 10^{-2} \lambda_0$ atm^{-1}	$(3.8 \pm 0.3) \times 10^{-2} \lambda_0$ atm^{-1}
7×10^{-6}	—	$(3.8 \pm 0.3) \times 10^{-2} \lambda_0$ atm^{-1}
1×10^{-5}	—	$(3.4 \pm 0.4) \times 10^{-2} \lambda_0$ atm^{-1}
2.5×10^{-5}	—	$(3.2 \pm 0.4) \times 10^{-2} \lambda_0$ atm^{-1}
5×10^{-5}	—	$(3.6 \pm 0.4) \times 10^{-2} \lambda_0$ atm^{-1}
1×10^{-4}	$(4.0 \pm 0.3) \times 10^{-2} \lambda_0$ atm^{-1}	—
2×10^{-4}	$(3.5 \pm 0.2) \times 10^{-2} \lambda_0$ atm^{-1}	$(3.4 \pm 0.4) \times 10^{-2} \lambda_0$ atm^{-1}
5×10^{-4}	$(3.9 \pm 0.3) \times 10^{-2} \lambda_0$ atm^{-1}	$(3.2 \pm 0.4) \times 10^{-2} \lambda_0$ atm^{-1}

distribution work of Heinberg and Page[20] that p-Ps is nearly ther-malized in oxygen before annihilation, and that the narrow distribu-tion precludes pickoff quenching or virtual compound formation. This also has precluded a determination of the dependence of the quenching rate on Ps velocity.) Again, perhaps due to the difficulty of obtaining and analyzing argon with traces of oxygen less than about 5 ppm, the variation in quenching rate with oxygen concentra-tion requires closer examination. This is shown in Fig. 1 from the results of Celitans et al.[10] Values of the quenching cross section quoted earlier apply to the almost linear region between 1 and 100% oxygen. However, below 1% and down to about 0.0005% (5 ppm), there is a yet unconfirmed very marked change. This may be due to factors determined by resonance annihilations of free positrons with such traces of oxygen.

The results of recent quenching rate studies, conducted by 3γ coincidence and lifetime measurements on the same gas systems,

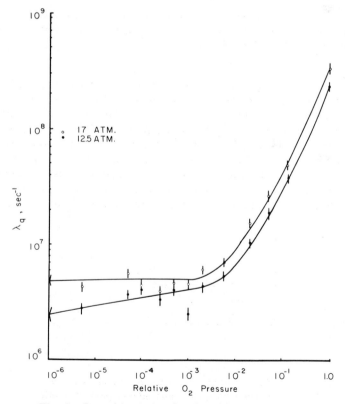

Fig. 1. Quenching rate of orthopositronium in oxygen argon mixtures.[10]

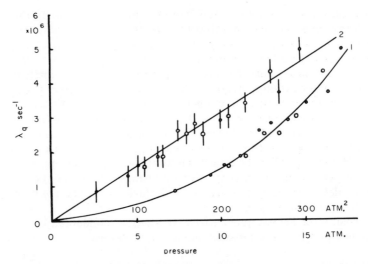

Fig. 2. Quenching rate of orthopositronium in commercial grade argon (1.0 ± 0.5 parts per million of oxygen). 1, pressure in atmospheres; 2, p^2 in atmospheres squared.[10]

leave several more puzzles to be answered. For example, although we have seen good agreement in the results of the two methods and with those obtained in other laboratories (Table I) the pressure dependence of the quenching rate in argon (1.0 ± 0.5 ppm of O_2) is clearly not linear. To get a value of λ_q (av.) a p^2 plot was required (Fig. 2). In nitrogen, also the quenching rate of o-Ps is not proportional to pressure (Fig. 3). In this case, since λ_q must be zero at $p = 0$, the quenching rate depends on some function of pressure other than on p or p^2, at least for nitrogen pressures between 7 and 17

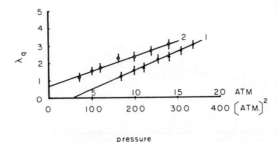

Fig. 3. Quenching rate of orthopositronium in commercial grade nitrogen (2 parts per million of oxygen). 1, pressure in atmospheres; 2, p^2 in atmospheres squared.[10]

atm.[10] Further information on these "anomalies" is given in the work of Abid and Paul[1] dealing with the nonlinear increase of the annihilation rate as the pressure of nitric oxide is increased. This is ascribed to a "second-order effect" which might arise from two-stage collision processes leading to the formation of e^+ NO or to collisions with dimers, such as $(NO)_2$, whose concentration depend on p^2.

It has become apparent in these and other researches that the high degree of gas purity required for positron studies cannot be overstated.

RAPID ANNIHILATION LIFETIMES

The next phase in gas studies developed from the time *analysis of free positron lifetimes in argon* (Tao et al., Ref. 31), and the development of *lifetime equipment* of better resolution and longer range (see Bell et al., Refs. 4-7). The first fruits from this sort of equipment to be plucked were presented by Green and Tao,[19] and a little later by Paul and Saint-Pierre.[28] The former reexamined the positron lifetime dependence on gas pressure in Freon-12. The results given in Table IV showed that the disappearance of the short component at higher pressures is probably due to attachment of low energy positrons to form the "collision complex" $e^+ CCl_2 F_2$. The annihilation rate, $\lambda_1 = 1.8 \times 10^8 \ p$ sec^{-1}, is much greater than the Dirac free rate, $2.5 \times 10^7 \ p$ sec^{-1}. (Deutsch, Ref. 11, referred to the large "positron attachment coefficient," and Duff and Heyman, Ref. 12, noted that Freon "quenches" free positrons). At the same time, the annihilation rate of positronium was found to be

$$\lambda_2 = [(6.76 \pm 0.56 \, p) \pm 0.38)] \times 10^6 \ \text{sec}^{-1}$$

The pressure coefficient is more accurate than Deutsch's[11] value

TABLE IV
Quenching Rate Coefficients for Nitrogen-Argon Mixtures

Nitrogen fraction	Lifetime results	Three-photon results
10^{-5}	$(2.1 \pm 0.3) \times 10^{-3} \ \lambda_0$ atm^{-2}	$(1.8 \pm 0.2) \times 10^{-3} \ \lambda_0$ atm^{-2}
10^{-4}	$(3.4 \pm 0.2) \times 10^{-2} \ \lambda_0$ atm^{-1}	$(3.4 \pm 0.3) \times 10^{-2} \ \lambda_0$ atm^{-1}
10^{-3}	$(3.8 \pm 0.3) \times 10^{-2} \ \lambda_0$ atm^{-1}	$(3.6 \pm 0.3) \times 10^{-2} \ \lambda_0$ atm^{-1}
10^{-2}	$(3.1 \pm 0.3) \times 10^{-2} \ \lambda_0$ atm^{-1}	$(3.2 \pm 0.3) \times 10^{-2} \ \lambda_0$ atm^{-1}
10^{-1}	$(3.5 \pm 0.2) \times 10^{-2} \ \lambda_0$ atm^{-1}	$(3.4 \pm 0.3) \times 10^{-2} \ \lambda_0$ atm^{-1}
1.0	$(3.1 \pm 0.2) \times 10^{-2} \ \lambda_0$ atm^{-1}	$(2.9 \pm 0.2) \times 10^{-2} \ \lambda_0$ atm^{-1}

TABLE V

The Lifetimes of Positrons in Freon-12 at Various Gas Pressures

Pressure at 20° C (atm)	τ_1 (10^{-9} sec)	τ_2 (10^{-9} sec)
5.3[a]	nd[b]	100
4.2	nd[b]	114
3.1	nd[b]	117
2.0	2.8 ± 0.3	124
1.2	4.5 ± 0.5	135

[a]Density of Freon at 5.3 atm is 0.026 g/cm^3.
[b]nd: not detectable.

but the zero pressure, free positronium, annihilation rate confirms his result, 6.8 ± 0.7 × 10^6 sec^{-1}.

Paul and Saint-Pierre[28] studied rapid annihilations in pure gases and argon to which varying amounts of NO (to quench τ_2) and polyatomic gases were added. The results are listed in Table V. It is clear, as the authors stated, that the enormous annihilation rates of the heavier molecules must either be due to elastic scattering, improbably pictured as involving several circuits of a slow positron round a molecule or positron capture into a bound state of positron molecular ions, or some other form of molecular excitation. These suggestions of the existence of positron-molecule ions at low positron energies were supported by the calculations of Khare et al.[22] showing that the species e^+ He would have a binding energy of about 0.55 eV, but it would lead to an annihilation lifetime in helium shorter than the experimental value. (This suggests that capture into the bound state e^+ He is fairly slow).

Positron attachment has, of course, been considered theoretically by various authors recently, and the experimental data are tending to confirm the conclusions reached by Spruch and Rosenberg,[29] Bransden,[8] and Goldanskii.[17] These matters will be discussed by Massey in the next paper.

DELAYED ANNIHILATION LIFETIMES

The study of positrons which fail to form Ps and fall below the Ore gap in the noble gases, particularly in Ar, has now developed in a most exciting and rewarding fashion. Measurements of *positron lifetimes* with more sophisticated equipment and more detailed data processing were stimulated by the reappraisal of Tao et al.[31] in Sydney of the slowing down times of positrons in selected energy ranges in argon. In the most interesting range, $E_{exc} > E > E_{thermal'}$ the analysis depended on neutron diffusion theory [see Amaldi, Ref. 3] assuming isotopic scattering with a constant scattering cross section. Ignoring the Doppler effect except at energies below about 1 eV, and ignoring any variations in the annihilation rate which affect the velocity distribution, the slowing down time from E_0 to E_1 is

$$ t = \frac{(2m)^{1/2}}{\zeta N \sigma_s} \left[\left(\frac{1}{E_1} \right)^{1/2} - \left(\frac{1}{E_0} \right)^{1/2} \right] \tag{1} $$

where ζ = logarithmic energy decrement = $2m/M$ above 1 eV; σ_s = elastic scattering cross section; and N = number of Ar atoms per unit volume. The value of σ_s to be used was reassessed from the electric field and theoretical studies of Teutsch and Hughes,[33]

TABLE VI

Annihilation Rates for the Nonpositronium Component in Gases, Divided by Molecular and Valence-Electron Densities

Component[a]	λ/n_m (10^{-12} cm^3/sec)	λ/n (10^{-13} cm^3/sec)	$(\lambda/n)/(\lambda/n)_{Dirac}$
Argon I	0.192 ± 0.003	0.240 ± 0.003	3.21
II	0.19	0.24	3.2
Methane	1.21 ± 0.03	1.52 ± 0.05	20.3
Ethane	5.22 ± 0.24	3.73 ± 0.18	49.9
Propane	28.8 ± 2.1	14.4 ± 1.0	192.7
n-Butane I	126.0 ± 5.6	48.5 ± 2.2	
II	120.7 ± 10.6	46.4 ± 4.1	623
III	118.3 ± 4.2	45.5 ± 1.6	
Isobutane I	107.5 ± 5.8	41.4 ± 2.3	555
II	108.0 ± 2.3	41.6 ± 2.3	
Carbon tetrachloride	168.1 ± 9.9	52.5 ± 3.1	702

[a]Roman numerals indicate the following grouping of runs: Argon I, all argon-nitric oxide mixtures. Argon II, pure argon; this result is from an analysis of a complex exponential decay. n-Butane I, 127 mm NO, 4060 mm Ar. n-Butane II, 254 mm NO, 4060 mm Ar. n-Butane III, 128 mm NO, 2040 mm Ar. Isobutane I, 128 mm NO, 2040 mm Ar. Isobutane II, 128 mm NO, 3160 mm Ar. The indicated pressures are approximate values in mm Hg after reduction to 0° C.

TABLE VII
Elastic Scattering Cross Sections of He, Ne, and Ar
for Positrons, Obtained by Different Authors (in πa_0^2 units)

1^a	2^b	3^c	4^d	5^e	6^f
He	0.023	0.07	0.71	0.10	0.014
Ne	0.12	0.4	3.0	—	0.11
A	1.5	2	7.0	—	1.4

[a] Element.   [d] Massey et al.
[b] Marder et al.   [e] Allison et al. (theor.).
[c] Teutsch and Hughes (theor.).   [f] Present authors.

and Marder, Hughes, Wu, and Bennett.[23] (The discussion of the proper cross sections to be used is only beginning, and perhaps will be settled by experiment rather than theory). A comparison of these cross sections is shown in Table VI, and the calculated slowing down times for $E < E_{exc}$ are given in Table VII. To emphasize the point, the time required for a positron in argon gas at 10 atm. pressure to slow down from 11.6 to 0.1 eV should be at least 100 nsec, whereas (assuming effective number of electrons per atom is 18) the free annihilation lifetime is only 27.6 nsec. The complete history of these positrons is summarized in Table VIII.

TABLE VIII
The Slowing-Down Time in Argon for a Positron
with Initial Energy 11.6 eV to a Final Energy E^a

E (eV)	pt (sec atm)	E (eV)	pt (sec atm)
11.6	0	0.25	6.12×10^{-7}
9.0	1.21×10^{-8}	0.16	8.19×10^{-7}
4.0	7.56×10^{-8}	0.09	1.22×10^{-6}
1.0	2.42×10^{-7}	0.04	2.71×10^{-6}
0.64	3.32×10^{-7}		

[a] The free annihilation lifetime τ of a positron in argon calculated from Dirac's formula assuming $Z = 18$ is $p\tau = 2.76 \times 10^{-7}$ sec atm. We can see that the thermalization time is considerably longer than the free annihilation lifetime. The time required for a positron with $E = 11.6$ eV to slow down to $E = 0.9$ eV is just equal to the free annihilation lifetime. In this energy range, 63% of the positrons will be lost owing to annihilation.

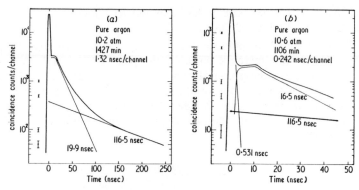

Fig. 4. Positron lifetimes in argon.[31]

Experimental studies of this aspect of the noble gases especially Ar, were carried out independently by Tao, Bell, and Green[30] in Sydney, by Paul[27] in Toronto, and by Falk and Jones[14] in Vancouver, and the results were sent out in the order given. All three groups have confirmed the appearance of a "shoulder" in the lifetime diagrams which is due to the time dependence of the annihilation rate of positrons with energies below the Ore gap. Examples of this behavior are shown in Fig. 4. It is to be noted that diagrams of this sort can only show fine details if the equipment used has a high time resolution ($fwhm \sim 0.5$ nsec), a small logarithmic slope on the prompt peak (~ 0.1 nsec), and wide range (~ 400 nsec). Two equipments were used in Sydney, one with $fwhm = 0.70$ nsec and range 30 nsec, the other with $fwhm = 1.2$ nsec and range 360 nsec. These diagrams are shown, partly as the first evidence of the experimental shoulder due to delayed annihilation, but mainly to show that the graphical determination of the onset of the shoulder is very subjective and open to error, and that very fine details are observed. It has been verified that the product of shoulder-width × pressure is nearly constant. However, due to the presence of contaminating oxygen, this product was found in Sydney to be only about 95 nsec atm, considerably less than the 190-300 nsec atm found by Paul[27] and the 270 nsec atm of Falk and Jones.[14] This means that before the annihilation rate begins to increase along the exponential tail of the resolved lifetime distribution, the positron will have dropped to about 1 eV or less.

Osmon[25] does not see any evidence in his results for the conclusions reached above, except the confirmation of the shoulder. This is probably due to poor equipment ($fwhm \sim 3$ nsec; unspecified range—probably very short). In fact, he finds an annihilation rate continuously increasing as the energy decreases (i.e., proportional to pressure) and no trace of the o-Ps component. These are contrary to the three sets of independent results described.

NUMERICAL ANALYSIS, RESONANCE ANNIHILATION, AND COMPOUND FORMATION

Paul[27] was the first to publish a numerical analysis of life-time data. First, he subtracts the long component (and background), and then unfolds the experimental resolution ("prompt peak") from the remainder. This takes out annihilations in flight, wall annihilations, singlet positronium, any $2p$ states and high energy positron-argon ions, leaving only the free positron delayed annihilations. These are represented by

$$H(t) = \lambda(t)N(t) \tag{2}$$

where $N(t)$ = number of positrons which remain after a lifetime t and $\lambda(t)$ = a velocity-averaged annihilation rate at time t

$$\lambda(t)dt = \frac{H(t)}{N(t)} \cdot dt \tag{3}$$

The result of the numerical computation (3) is shown in Fig. 5 for Ar at 2.19 atm.

Paul then attempted to convert the experimental results $\lambda_{(t)}$ to a function of positron energy λ. Two factors prevent an accurate conversion: the initial energy distribution of positrons just below the cut-off at 9 eV must be assumed, and the choice of the correct scattering cross sections is difficult.

Goldanskii and Sayasov[17] have made a brief theoretical examination of the resonance annihilation probabilities of positrons with particular reference to the formation of positron–molecule bound states with binding energies ~0.1 eV. This was stimulated by the determination of very fast annihilation rates in a number of gases reported by Paul and Saint-Pierre,[28] but they were apparently unaware of similar results and studies of pressure effects in Freon-12 reported about the same time by Green and Tao.[19] Goldanskii, assuming the existence of a positron-molecule ion, described the interaction by a centrosymmetrical potential, and proceeded to evaluate the level depth of the bound state and to define the conditions for the existence of such a level. This condition is

$$p\, a_0 /R^2 > 3/2$$

where p = polarizability, a_0 = Bohr radius, and R = radius of the potential well, taken to be approximately equal to the gas kinetic radius of the particle.

On the basis of this analysis, it was decided that a bound state Are^+ should not be formed in Ar for which Paul and Saint-Pierre[28] (1963) found σ_a/σ_{Dirac} = 3. (Whether this applies or not to N_2,

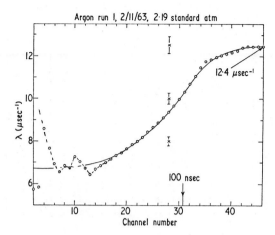

Fig. 5. Annihilation rate as a function of
time in pure argon.[27]

O_2 and Freon-12, for which Celitans et al. and Green and Tao found
the ratios to be 1.86, 1.37, and 7.2, remains to be seen. In the case
of $CCl_2 F_2$, the effect to be expected from the formation of $e^+ CCl_2 F_2$
certainly disappears as the gas pressure increases.)

Falk et al.[15] have reported some very interesting results of the
application of electric fields up to 1350 V/cm to free positrons annihilating in argon and helium (see Fig. 6). Argon (but not helium)
showed a clearly increasing delayed positron lifetime as the field
increased. (17.9 ± 0.7, 26.9 ± 1.0, and 34.8 ± 1.5 nsec at 0,329,
and 682 V cm^{-1}). A fit to the experimental results in terms of the
elastic-scattering (σ_s) and annihilation (σ_a) cross sections was made.

If the velocity dependent direct annihilation rate $r_a(v) = Nv\sigma_a$,
then the spectrum (neglecting Ps formation) is given by

$$\frac{dN(t)}{dt} = 4\pi \int_0^\infty r_a(v) \cdot v^2 \cdot f(v,t)\, dv$$

$f(v,t)$ is obtained by solving the diffusion equation (Frost and Phelps,
Ref.16; Zivanovic and Sodha, Ref. 34).

$$\frac{\delta f}{\delta t} = \frac{1}{v^2} \cdot \frac{\delta}{\delta v} \left\{ \left[\frac{a^2 v^2}{3r_c(v)} \right. \right.$$

$$\left. + \frac{m}{M} v^3 r_c(v) \frac{kT}{mv} \right] \frac{\delta f}{\delta v} + \frac{m}{M} v^3 r_c(v) f \right\}$$

$$- \left[r_a(v) + r_f(v) \right] f$$

TABLE IX

Fate of Positrons in Argon

Stage	Energy (eV)	Slowing-down mechanism	Slowing-down time	Fate of Positrons
I (a)	500	Inelastic collision dominates	$0.025\ \tau_f{}^a$	1. Slowing down 2. Loss to other processes negligible
I (b)	$E_{ion} = 15.8$	Inelastic collision comparable with elastic collision	$< 0.32\ \tau_f$	1. Slowing down 2. Loss to annihilation small
II	$E_{exc} = 11.6$	Elastic collision only	$0.044\ \tau_f$	1. Positronium formation 2. Free annihilation 3. Slowing down
III	$E_{thr} = 9.0$	Elastic collision only	$1.0\ \tau_f$	1. Positronium formation 2. Free annihilation small 3. Slowing down
IV (a)	0.9	Elastic collision only	Long	1. Slowing down 2. Compound formation Ae^+ (?) 3. Free annihilation eventually
IV (b)				1. Slowing down 2. Compound formation Ae^+ (?) 3. Free annihilation eventually

$^a\ \tau_f$ = Dirac free annihilation lifetime.

$f(v,t)$ is determined by this equation, provided that the functions $r_c(v)$, $r_a(v)$, $r_f(v)$, and $f(v,0)$ are defined. $r_f(v)$ may be neglected at low electric fields, and this simplifies the problem, but it is not yet possible to find the velocity dependence of even one of the remaining functions. This would be needed before the experimental results could be used to enable a unique description of the remaining functions. An attempt to define these functions in an exploratory way led to the fit shown by the heavy lines in Fig. 6. This approach is clearly most useful but the data to which it was applied were not as informative as that obtainable from equipment with better time resolution.

Tao[32] has reported briefly a numerical analysis of lifetime data obtained in Sydney for Cl_2, $Ar-Cl_2$ mixtures and N_2-Cl_2 mixtures. Two equipments were used, one with $fwhm$ 0.5 nsec and range 25 nsec, the other with $fwhm$ 1.2 nsec and range 360 nsec (Bell et al., Refs. 5 and 6). The λ_t vs t curves for the second (delayed positron component) show two definite resonances in Ar, and two more in Ar containing small amounts of Cl_2. The latter only appear as a "shoulder" on top of a "shoulder" when the third component (o-Ps)

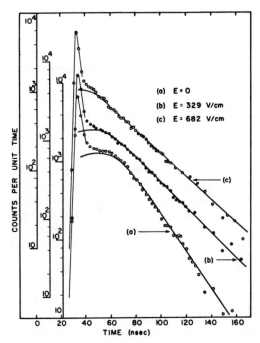

Fig. 6. Direct positron-annihilation spectra in argon for several values of applied electric field.[15]

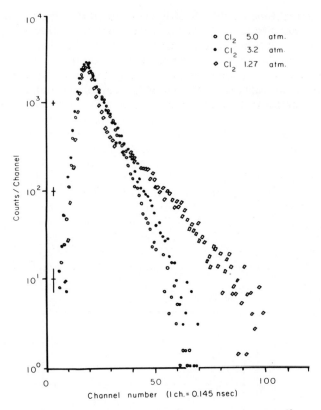

Fig. 7. Positron lifetime spectra in chlorine.[32]

begins to appear. This can almost be seen in the raw data of Fig. 7 for the case of pure chlorine. With large fractions of chlorine or in pure chlorine this component is completely quenched. Also, the sum of the intensities of the new shoulder and the third component remain constant although I_3 changes considerably. Hence, the new shoulder must arise from o-Ps, and a strong resonance perhaps associated with the reaction

$$Ps + Cl_2 \rightarrow PsCl + Cl$$

which has been shown to be possible at energies above 0.5 eV. The four resonances appear at roughly estimated energies of 0.9 and 0.7 eV for Ar and 0.5 and 0.3 eV for Cl_2, assuming the constant scattering cross sections of Teutsch and Hughes[33] below the Ore gap threshold for argon.

It is clear that the recent studies of positrons and positronium in gases, in addition to the beautiful experimental evidence for physical theory given by the classical era, have opened up new opportunities for the study of low energy positron interactions, cross sections, chemical reactions, excited states of molecules, and even perhaps for an effective reappraisal of positron and negatron low-energy interactions, both theoretical and experimental.

REFERENCES

1. Abid, I., and Paul, D. A. L., *Proc. Phys. Soc. (London)* **85**, 1038 (1965).
2. Allison, D. C. S., McIntyre, H. A. F., and Moiseiwitsch, B. L., *Proc. Phys. Soc. (London)* **78**, 1169 (1961).
3. Amaldi, E., *Handb. Phys.* **XXXVIII/2** (1959).
4. Bell, J., Tao, S. J., and Green J. H., *Nucl. Instr. Meth.* **35**, 213 (1965).
5. Bell, J., Celitans, G. J., Green, J. H., and Tao, S. J., *Nucl. Instr. Meth.* **37**, 51 (1965).
6. Bell, J., Green, J. H., and Tao, S. J., *Nucl. Instr. Meth.* **35**, 320 (1965).
7. Bell, J., Tao, S. J., and Green, J. H., *Nucl. Instr. Meth.* **35**, 222 (1965).
8. Bransden, B. H., *Proc. Phys. Soc. (London)* **79**, 190 (1962).
9. Celitans, G. J., and Green, J. H., *Proc. Phys. Soc. (London)* **83**, 823 (1964 a).
10. Celitans, G. J., Tao, S. J., and Green, J. H., *Proc. Phys. Soc. (London)* **83**, 833 (1964 b).
11. Deutsch, M., *Phys. Rev.* **83**, 866 (1951).
12. Duff, B. G., and Heymann, F. F., *Proc. Phys. Soc. (London)* **A270**, 517 (1962).
13. Dulit, E. P., Ph.D. Thesis, Massachusetts Institute of Technology, Physics Department, 1956.
14. Falk, W. R., and Jones, G., *Canad. J. Phys.* **42**, 1751 (1964).
15. Falk, W. R., Orth, P. H. R., and Jones, G., *Phys. Rev. Letters* **14**, 447 (1965).
16. Frost, L. S., and Phelps, A. V., *Phys. Rev.* **127**, 1621 (1962).
17. Goldanskii, V. I., and Sayasov, Yu. S., *Phys. Rev. Letters* **13**, 300 (1964).
18. Green, J., and Lee, J., "Positronium Chemistry." Academic Press, New York, 1964.
19. Green, J. H., and Tao, S. J., *J. Chem. Phys.* **39**, 3160 (1963).
20. Heinberg, M., and Page, L. A., *Phys. Rev.* **107**, 1589 (1957).
21. Heymann, F. F., Osmon, P. E., Veit, L. J., and Williams, W. F., *Proc. Phys. Soc. (London)* **78**, 1038 (1961).
22. Khare, H. C., Wallace, P. R., Bach, G. G., and Chodos, A., *Canad. J. Phys.* **42**, 1522 (1964).
23. Marder, S., Hughes, V. W., Wu, C. S., and Bennett, W., *Phys. Rev.* **103**, 1258 (1956).
24. Massey, H. S. W., and Moussa, A. H. A., *Proc. Phys. Soc. (London)* **71**, 38 (1958).

25. Osmon, P. E., *Phys. Rev.* **138**, B216 (1965).
26. Page, L. A., private communication.
27. Paul, D. A. L., *Proc. Phys. Soc. (London)* **84**, 563 (1964).
28. Paul, D. A. L., and Saint-Pierre, L., *Phys. Rev. Letters* **11**, 493 (1963).
29. Spruch, L., and Rosenberg, L., *Phys. Rev.* **117**, 143 (1960).
30. Tao, S. J., Bell, J., and Green, J. H., *Proc. Phys. Soc. (London)* **83**, 453 (1964).
31. Tao, S. J., Green, J. H., and Celitans, G. J., *Proc. Phys. Soc. (London)* **81**, 1091 (1963).
32. Tao, S. J., *Phys. Rev. Letters* **14**, 935 (1965).
33. Teutsch, W. B., and Hughes, V. W., *Phys. Rev.* **103**, 1266 (1956).
34. Zivanovic, S., and Sodha, M. S., *Progr. Theoret. Phys. (Kyoto)* **27**, 1128 (1962).

Gaseous Positronics

H. S. W. Massey

University College, London, England

1. INTRODUCTION

Considerable interest attaches to the study of reactions involving slow positrons in gases because the behavior of the positron in collisions with atoms and molecules introduces features different from those in the corresponding collisions with electrons. Thus, the three main factors that influence the scattering of slow electrons by atoms are the average interaction with the undisturbed atom (the static atomic field), electron exchange, which introduces a nonlocal interaction, and polarization of the atom by the electron. For the electron, the static and polarization fields are both attractive but for the positron, while the latter is unchanged, the static field is now repulsive—the two effects, while adding in the electron case, tend to cancel for positrons. Nonlocal interaction due to exchange in the electron case is replaced for positrons by one due to virtual or real positronium formation, depending on whether the energy of impact is below or above the threshold for such formation. We can therefore hope to gain new information about the effectiveness of atomic collision theory by applying it to positrons, provided there is the possibility of reliable experimental check.

In addition, there is the opportunity to study the collision of positronium duplexes with atoms and molecules. These introduce further novel features. The mean static interaction with an atom or molecule vanishes because of the coincidence of the center of mass and of charge in ground state positronium. No polarization effect arises in first order because neither the positronium nor the atom or molecule is electrically charged. This leaves as the dominant interaction the non-local one due to electron exchange. Once again there is a considerable challenge here to atomic collision theory provided reliable experimental information is available.

2. EXPERIMENTAL SOURCES OF INFORMATION

What are the most fruitful sources of experimental information from these points of view? Apart from the possibility, now no longer so remote, of carrying out scattering experiments with positrons of well-defined energy, there are four main types of experiments which bear on these matters.

2.1 Positron Annihilation Rate

The first is the measurement[1-4] of the rate of annihilation of positrons as a function of mean positron energy. Because of the uncertainty introduced by lack of knowledge of the velocity distribution as a function of time since emission, it is best to use only data obtained when a known equilibrium distribution has been reached. Thus the mean annihilation rate for thermal positrons can be observed from which we may derive the mean annihilation cross section $\overline{Q}_a{}^+$ under these conditions. This is given, for temperature T, by

$$\overline{Q}_a{}^+ = \int_0^\infty Q_a{}^+(v)f(v)\ dv \tag{1}$$

where $f(v)$ is the Maxwellian velocity distribution function

$$f(v) = 4(m^3/2\pi\kappa^3 T^3)^{1/2} v^2 \exp\left(-\tfrac{1}{2}\frac{mv^2}{\kappa T}\right) \tag{2}$$

m being the mass of the positron and κ Boltzmann's constant. $Q_a{}^+(v)$, according to Dirac's theory of positron annihilation, is given by[5]

$$Q_a{}^+(v) = \pi(e^2/mc^2)^2\ \xi c/v \tag{3}$$

where ξ is the effective number of annihilating electrons per atom. ξ depends on the wavefunction of relative motion of the positron with respect to the atomic system. In the simple case in which this can be written

$$\Psi = \psi_0(\mathbf{r}_a) F_0(\mathbf{r}_p) \tag{4}$$

where $\mathbf{r}_a$ denotes the atomic electron coördinates and $\mathbf{r}_p$ those of the positron relative to the nucleus, and

$$F_0 \sim \exp(i\mathbf{k}_p \cdot \mathbf{r}_p) + r_p^{-1} \exp(ik_p r_p) f(\theta_p, \phi_p) \tag{5}$$

then

$$\xi = Z \int |\psi_0(\mathbf{r}_p)|^2 |F_0(\mathbf{r}_p)|^2\ d\mathbf{r}_p \tag{6}$$

where Z is the number of atomic electrons. The corresponding formulas for more elaborate approximations to Ψ can be readily derived.

Measurement of $\overline{Q}_a{}^+$ thus provides a check on any calculated wavefunction Ψ but, as pointed out by Garth Jones and his collaborators,[6] it is possible to go much further by observing positron annihilation rates in the presence of electric fields. When such a field is present, the equilibrium velocity distribution $f(v)$ of the positron is changed from the Maxwellian form to a different form with a higher mean energy. For annihilation in atomic gases the magnitude of the mean energy is determined by the momentum loss cross section Q_m^+ for positron–atom collisions, while the shape of the distribution depends on the form of the variation of Q_m^+ with positron velocity. Hence, from measurements of the mean annihilation rate when the positrons have reached equilibrium in different applied electric fields, the scope is extended, not only by making available mean annihilation rates at different mean energies, but also by providing an additional check through the dependence on the momentum-loss cross section. This cross section is also determined by the wavefunction of the positron with respect to the atomic system. Thus in terms of the wavefunction (4)

$$Q_m^+(v) = \int_0^\pi \int_0^{2\pi} (1 - \cos\theta) |f(\theta, \phi)|^2 \sin\theta \, d\theta \, d\phi \qquad (7)$$

When annihilation occurs in an electric field with a molecular gas present the equilibrium velocity distribution will be strongly influenced by energy loss through excitation of molecular vibration and rotation by positron impact. It would be of great interest to be able to derive information about rates of vibrational excitation in nitrogen and hydrogen because, with electron impact, this occurs mainly through a resonance process[7] involving formation of an intermediate negative ion. A different process will certainly be involved with positrons, but it may still occur through formation of a complex.

The sorting out of the contributions from different processes would certainly be more complicated for even diatomic molecules than for atoms but is quite possible. Rotational excitation should occur mainly through interaction with the permanent molecular quadrupole moment as for electrons,[8] and the cross section should be readily predictable. The estimation of the momentum-loss cross section for positron-molecule collisions will be difficult but, by working with mixtures of molecule with atomic gases (already studied) in different proportions, it should be possible to sort out the contribution to energy loss from elastic collisions. This would leave the rate of vibrational excitation as the unknown to be determined.

Account must certainly be taken of the possibility of formation by the positron of a complex with a polyatomic molecule. Even if the lifetime of this complex is quite short, of the order 10^{-9} sec, the possibility of its formation will increase the positron annihilation rate. The chance of forming complexes of this sort increases with the number of degrees of freedom of the molecule. Even with atoms, however, there is the chance that a stable state of low binding energy is available for the positron in the atomic field, into which it may be captured with emission of radiation or in a three-body collision. The cross section for radiative capture, if a stable state exists, will be between 10^{-19} and 10^{-21} cm^2, somewhat greater than, or at least comparable with, the annihilation cross section for thermal positrons. At pressures much higher than atmospheric, capture in a three-body reaction

$$e^+ + X + Y \rightarrow e^+X + Y \tag{8}$$

will be of comparable or greater probability than radiative capture.

Considerable importance therefore attaches to a detailed theoretical search for bound states for positrons in the fields of such atoms as helium. Some calculations have been carried out for this case,[9] but are inconclusive in that the total energy of the positron + helium atom determined by a variational method, while less than that for the ground state of helium determined from a similar trial function, is still larger than the observed total energy of the ground state.

2.2 Positronium Formation

The proportion of positrons which end their lives through annihilation when bound in positronium may be measured for different gases as a function of gas pressure, temperature and applied electric field.[10–17] For most gases, the effect of an electric field[15–17] is to increase the positronium production because it increases the mean energy of the positrons so that a bigger fraction possess energies above the threshold for positronium formation.

Detailed experiments on the effect of electric fields on ortho-positronium formation in the rare gases and in hydrogen have been carried out by Marder, Hughes, Wu and Bennett.[15] The analysis of their data involves not only the momentum loss and annihilation cross sections but also the cross section Q_f^+ for positronium formation by positrons with energies close to the threshold. Strictly speaking, a great number of other cross sections are really required[30] as it is necessary to introduce a velocity distribution function for the positrons at the time they have been slowed down to an energy close to the positronium formation threshold energy, E_f. This initial distribution depends on the mechanism of slowing down of energetic positrons to which many inelastic processes contribute. However, if reasonable assumptions are made about this initial distribution, useful information about the cross sections Q_f^+, Q_m^+, and Q_a^+ can be obtained at positron energies close to E_f, at least for the atomic gases.[18] For molecular gases, serious extra complications arise from energy loss due to excitation of vibration and rotation.

2.3 Quenching of Orthopositronium

We turn now to experiments which give information about collisions of orthopositronium with gas atoms and molecules. The quenching of orthopositronium can arise from the following types of processes:

(a) Electron exchange involving spin reversal. This is possible in collisions with atoms and molecules whose ground states possess finite spin. The classic examples are nitric oxide with a doublet, and oxygen with a triplet, ground state. The simplest theoretical case occurs in collisions with atomic hydrogen.

(b) Pickoff annihilation. In a collision between an orthopositronium duplex and an atom or molecule the positron may annihilate with one of the atomic or molecular electrons. This is essentially similar to the annihilation of a free positron on collision, but the presence of the electron in positronium modifies the motion of the positron relative to the atom or molecule, so the chance of annihilation on collision is changed.

The simplest theoretical case in which this occurs is in helium in which exchange quenching is not possible.

(c) Quenching due to chemical reactions. On collision with a gas molecule a reaction of the form

$$e^+ e^- + XY \rightarrow Xe^+ e^- + Y, \tag{9}$$

may occur. Since such a reaction will bring the positron into the close proximity of several electrons, it will increase the annihilation probability of the positron, an effect which will be observed as orthopositronium quenching. No cases of this type are sufficiently simple for any quantitative theoretical treatment.

(d) Quenching due to radiative or three-body capture. If the energy of the complex $Xe^+ e^-$ is less than that of the ground state of X, then a positronium duplex may be captured by an atom or molecule X with emission of radiation. The capture cross section will be greater than or comparable with pickoff annihilation cross sections. As for free positrons, capture of orthopositronium in three-body collisions will be even more important at pressures much greater than atmospheric.

3. THEORETICAL CALCULATION OF POSITRON–ATOM COLLISION CROSS SECTIONS

3.1 Collisions with Atomic Hydrogen

Although there is little practical possibility of obtaining experimental information about collisions of positrons with hydrogen atoms until adequate sources of positrons of well-defined energy and direction of motion are available, the case is relatively so susceptible of detailed theoretical analysis that it is worthwhile investigating thoroughly in order to obtain some feeling for the important factors.

Consider the collision of positrons of wave number k with hydrogen atoms. We would expect, by analogy with the corresponding electron collision problem, that the simplest trial wavefunction that may be used in a variational treatment of the problem must include the effect of the undisturbed mean static field of the atom, the polarization of the atom, and the formation of positronium. Such a function is

$$\Psi_t(\mathbf{r}, \mathbf{r}_p) = [\psi_0(r) + \phi_0(\mathbf{r}, \mathbf{r}_p)] F_0(\mathbf{r}_p)$$
$$+ \chi_0(|\mathbf{r} - \mathbf{r}_p|) G_0\{\tfrac{1}{2}(\mathbf{r} + \mathbf{r}_p)\} \tag{10}$$

in which the symbols have the following significance. $\mathbf{r}$ and $\mathbf{r}_p$ are the respective coordinates of the electron and positron relative to the proton, $\psi_0(r)$ is the ground state wavefunction of the hydrogen atom, and $\chi_0(|\mathbf{r} - \mathbf{r}_p|)$ of positronium. $\phi_0(\mathbf{r}, \mathbf{r}_p)$ represents the disturbance of ψ_0 due to the positron, and is obtained by supposing the positron to be moving so slowly that the atomic electron moves under the combined influence of the proton and the positron, fixed at position $\mathbf{r}_p$. The perturbation is then expanded in a multipole series, for $r_p > r$, and the dipole term alone included.[19] It is then found that, for hydrogen, in atomic units,

$$\phi_0(\mathbf{r}, \mathbf{r}_p) = -\pi^{1/2} \, r^{-1/2} e^{-r_p} \, r^{-2} (r_p + \tfrac{1}{2} r_p^2) \cos \theta_{ap} \tag{11}$$

where θ_{ap} is the angle between r and r_p. For $r_p < r$ it is assumed that $\phi = 0$. Writing the wave equation as

$$L\Psi = 0 \tag{12}$$

where, in atomic units,

$$L = \nabla^2 + \nabla_p^2 + k^2 - 1 + \frac{2}{r} - \frac{2}{r_p} + \frac{2}{|\mathbf{r} - \mathbf{r}_p|} \tag{13}$$

we obtain equations for F_0 and G_0 by requiring, as for the corresponding electron collision problem, that

$$\int \psi_0(r) L\Psi_t \, d\mathbf{r} = 0, \tag{14}$$

$$\int \chi_0(|\mathbf{r} - \mathbf{r}_p|) L\Psi_t \, d(|\mathbf{r} - \mathbf{r}_p|) = 0 \tag{15}$$

At the low energies of impact with which we are concerned, both F_0 and G_0 may be taken as spherically symmetrical, and written in the form

$$F_0(r_p) = r_p^{-1}(r_p), \qquad G_0(\rho) = e^{-1} g(\rho) \tag{16}$$

where $\rho = \frac{1}{2} | \mathbf{r} + \mathbf{r}_p |$. Equations (14) and (15) then lead to the coupled equations

$$\left[\frac{d^2}{dr_p{}^2} + k^2 - U_{00}(r_p) - U_p(r_p) \right] f(r_p) = \int_0^\infty K(r_p, \rho) g(\rho) \, d\rho \quad (17)$$

$$\left[\frac{d^2}{d\rho^2} - \lambda^2 \right] g(\rho) = 2 \int_0^\infty K(r_p, \rho) f(r_p) \, dr_p \quad (18)$$

where $\lambda^2 = 1 - 2k^2$. U_{00} is the mean interaction $2(1 + r_p{}^{-1})$ $\exp(-2 r_p)$ with the undisturbed field of the atom, while U_p is a term which allows for polarization of the atom during the impact. It is given by

$$U_p = -\alpha |(r_p) / r_p{}^4 \quad (19)$$

where

$$\alpha(r_p) = \frac{9}{2} - \exp(-2r_p) \{ \frac{2}{3} r_p{}^5 + 3r_p{}^4 + 6r_p{}^3 + 9r_p{}^2 + 9r_p + \frac{9}{2} \} \quad (20)$$

$\alpha(\infty) = \frac{9}{2}$, being the polarizability of the hydrogen atom in atomic units. The kernel $K(r_p, \rho)$ represents the nonlocal interaction due to positronium formation, real or virtual. Below the threshold for positronium formation $(k_1{}^2 < \frac{1}{2})$, the boundary conditions for $f(r_p)$ and $g(\rho)$ are that

$$f(r_p) \sim k^{-1} \sin kr_p + \alpha \, \exp(ikr_p), \quad f(0) = g(0) = 0$$

$$g(\rho) \sim c \, \exp(-\lambda \rho) \quad (21)$$

The momentum loss cross section is then given by

$$Q_m{}^+ = 4\pi | \alpha |^2 / k^2 \quad (22)$$

Above the threshold, the boundary conditions for $f(r_p)$ remain unchanged but now

$$g(\rho) \sim \beta e^{i\kappa\rho} \quad (23)$$

where $\kappa^2 = -\lambda^2 = 2k^2 - 1$. The cross section for positronium formation is now given by

$$Q_f{}^+ = 4\pi(\kappa/k^3) | \beta |^2 \quad (24)$$

Numerical calculations have been carried out[20] using the Eqs. (17) and (18) for energies below the threshold for positronium formation. As an indication of the relative importance of the different contributory interactions, we give in Table I, the values of the scattering length a (such that the zero energy limit of the momentum loss cross section is $4\pi a^2$), calculated including different sets of interactions. Positive values of the scattering length correspond to

TABLE I

Scattering Lengths Calculated for Positron-Hydrogen Atom Collisions,
with Different Approximations

	Approximation	Scattering length (a.u.)
Eqs. (17) and (18)	Static, $U_p = K = 0$	0.582
	Static + virtual positronium, $U_p = 0$	0.17
	Static + polarization, $K = 0$	-1.27
	Static + polarization + virtual positronium, U_{00}, U_p, $K \neq 0$	-3.06
	Variational (Schwartz[21])	-2.10

net repulsion, negative to net attraction. The importance of polarization and virtual positronium formation in converting the net interaction to an attraction, is clear.

If Eqs. (17) and (18) had been derived strictly from the Kohn variational method, the scattering lengths of Table I derived from these equations would be upper bounds. An elaborate variational treatment of positron–hydrogen atom collisions has been carried out by Schwartz[21] on similar lines to his successful calculations for the electron case. This gives a value -2.10 a.u. for the scattering length, which is a true upper bound. It is considerably larger than the value -3.06 a.u., obtained from the full Eqs. (17) and (18). This may mean that the latter overestimate the polarization effect, and are less satisfactory than for the electron case. On the other hand, the trial function used by Schwartz made no explicit allowance for virtual positronium production, and may not give such accurate results as for the electron case. There is clearly room for further investigation here to bring out more clearly if, and where, a different approach is called for in the positron, as compared with the electron problem.

The calculations have not yet been extended beyond the threshold to obtain cross sections for positronium formation. It appears likely that, when such cross sections are obtained, they will differ very considerably from those derived using Born's approximation.[22] The magnitudes of the latter are so large as to indicate that the kernel K, which is treated as small in Born's approximation, actually represents a strong interaction out to energies well beyond the threshold.

3.2 Collisions with Helium Atoms

This problem may be formulated[23] in a similar way to the preceding problem but there is the further complication that the wavefunction for the ground state of helium is not known exactly. Calculations are now in progress using for this wavefunction the Hartree-Fock approximation, which gives good results for electron scattering. These calculations include the possibility of positronium production just as for hydrogen. As for the latter atom, calculations, carried out for the positronium production cross section by Born's approximation indicate that the results which it gives are unreliable. It is therefore desirable to extend the more elaborate calculations to positron energies beyond the positronium production threshold.

Once numerical results are available, they may be applied immediately to calculate the equilibrium positron-annihilation rate in helium as a function of applied electric field strength. Comparison may then be made directly with observation.

It is also possible to apply the calculated cross sections, including that for positronium production, to predict the results of experiments of the type carried out by Hughes and his collaborators.[15] Comparison with observation will provide a further important check on the approximations involved in the theory.

3.3 Collisions with Neon and Argon Atoms

It is considerably more difficult to allow for positronium production in calculating cross sections for positron collisions with these more complex atoms. However, some calculations have been carried out for argon, where polarization has been allowed for semi-empirically.

Holtsmark[24] was able to reproduce the observed cross sections for collisions of slow electrons with argon atoms, including the Ramsauer-Townsend effect, by adding an empirical polarization term to the Hartree field. Thompson[25] has calculated equivalent positron cross sections by taking as interaction the Hartree field with sign reversed, plus the same empirical polarization term as for electrons. The results are interesting in that they show a shallow minimum of the cross section at low energies of impact which is a "washed out," but still detectable, effect of Ramsauer-Townsend type. While the true positron cross section almost certainly behaves somewhat differently, it is nevertheless of interest that polarization effects can so dominate that the sign of the static background field is relatively unimportant.

Garth Jones and Orth[26] have carried out an empirical analysis of their data on the annihilation spectra of positrons in argon in different applied electric fields, using a similar model where the empirical polarization potential involves variable parameters, adjusted to give the best agreement with observation.

Considerable further theoretical work is possible for these atoms, even allowing for positronium production, and it is hoped that observations will be extended to neon.

4. THEORETICAL CALCULATION OF POSITRONIUM–ATOM COLLISION CROSS SECTIONS

As pointed out earlier, two of the three main contributory inter-actions in the case of positron scattering by atoms disappear when the positron is bound to an electron in the ground state of positron-ium. Thus there is no mean static interaction and no polarization. On the other hand, electron exchange between the positronium duplex and the atom leads to a nonlocal interaction of such strength that its scattering effects cannot be calculated by the Born-Oppenheimer ap-proximation.[22] Because three light particles at least are involved, the calculations that must be carried out are on a considerably greater scale than for collisions with free positrons. Considerable progress has nevertheless been made for the analysis of impacts with hydro-gen[27] and helium atoms.[28] Extension to heavier atoms would be very difficult and expensive in computer time.

4.1 Collisions with Hydrogen Atoms—Exchange Quenching

We must begin by distinguishing two cases, depending on whether the spins of the two electrons involved are parallel or antiparallel. We then have corresponding to the single space wavefunction $\Psi(\mathbf{r}, \mathbf{r}_p)$ in the positron case, two wavefunctions $\Psi^{\pm}(\mathbf{r}_1, \mathbf{r}_2, \mathbf{r}_p)$, where $\mathbf{r}_1$, $\mathbf{r}_2$, $\mathbf{r}_p$ are the respective coordinates of the two elec-trons, and of the positron relative to the proton. The approximate trial forms assumed for these functions are

$$\Psi_t^{\pm}(\mathbf{r}_1, \mathbf{r}_2, \mathbf{r}_p) = \psi_0(r_1)\chi_0(\rho_2)\sigma_2^{-1} f^{\pm}(\sigma_2) \pm \psi_0(r_2)\chi_0(\rho_1)\sigma_1^{-1}f^{\pm}(\sigma_1)$$

$$(25)$$

where

$$\rho_{1,2} = \mathbf{r}_{1,2} - \mathbf{r}_p, \qquad \sigma_{1,2} = \tfrac{1}{2}(\mathbf{r}_{1,2} + \mathbf{r}_p) \qquad (26)$$

The $\pm$ signs refer, respectively, to the cases where the electron spins are antiparallel and parallel. With the signs as indicated the overall wavefunctions satisfy Pauli's Principle. Using these trial functions in the Kohn variational principle, we obtain equations for $f^{\pm}(\sigma_1)$ of the form

$$\left(\frac{d^2}{d\sigma^2} + k^2\right) f^{\pm}(\sigma_1) = \pm \int N(\sigma_1, \sigma_2) f^{\pm}(\sigma_2) d\sigma_2 \qquad (27)$$

where k is the wave number of relative motion of the positronium duplex and the atom. As for the positron case, we have assumed that the collisions are so slow that the wavefunctions for the relative motion are spherically symmetrical.

Although we have here a single integrodifferential equation, as compared with the coupled ones (17) and (18), the kernel N of (27) is much more difficult to tabulate than the kernel K of (17), (18).

Having obtained solutions (27) which satisfy

$$f^{\pm}(\sigma) \sim k^{-1} \sin k\sigma + \alpha^{\pm} \exp(ik\sigma), \qquad f^{\pm}(0) = 0 \qquad (28)$$

the momentum loss cross section is given by

$$Q_m^{\pm} = \frac{4\pi}{k^2} \left\{ \frac{1}{4} |\alpha^+|^2 + \frac{3}{4} |\alpha^-|^2 \right\} \qquad (29)$$

A further cross section of special interest for our purposes is that which refers to a collision where electron exchange occurs so that an incident orthopositronium duplex is converted to parapositronium, e.g., an electron exchange quenching collision. This is given by

$$Q_{ex}^{\pm} = \frac{\pi}{k^2} |\alpha^+ - \alpha^-|^2 \qquad (30)$$

Fraser[27] has carried out detailed numerical calculations using this formulation. He finds that in the low energy limit, $Q_m^{\pm} = 603$ a.u. (1.70×10^{-14} cm^2) and $Q_{ex}^{\pm} = 106$ a.u. (0.30×10^{-14} cm^2). These cross sections fall rapidly as the energy increases so that for positronium energies of $\frac{1}{2}$ eV $Q_m^{\pm} = 109$ a.u. (0.31×10^{-14} cm^2), $Q_{ex}^{\pm} = 16.1$ a.u. (0.045×10^{-14} cm^2).

No elaborate variational calculations corresponding to those of Schwartz[21] for positron collisions have yet been carried out. There is scope for increased accuracy attainable in this way or by allowing for other groupings in the trial wavefunction (25).

The quenching cross section due to electron exchange is quite large, considerably higher than that observed for NO and particularly O_2. As the nonlocal interactions are effectively attractive over considerable ranges of the variables it is to be expected that the cross section for any particular case will be very sensitive to the details of the interactions, and could give rise to cross sections in the low energy limit having any value between 0 and ∞.

4.2 Collisions with Helium Atoms—Pickoff Quenching

The formulation in Section 4.1 can be readily extended to collisions with helium. In this case there is no possibility of quenching through electron exchange, as this would involve large energy changes — the helium atom would need to be left in the lowest triplet state requiring 19.77 eV excitation energy. In place of the two functions $f^{\pm}$ of (a) there is only a single function which satisfies an equation of the form (27), but with an even more complicated kernel. Special interest attaches to the calculation because, from it, the cross section for pickoff quenching in helium can be obtained and compared with quite accurate observations.

Fraser[28] has carried through the numerical calculations using the corresponding formulation to that in Section 4.1. To avoid too much initial complexity he used the simple Hylleraas approximation for the helium ground state wavefunction rather than the more accurate Hartree-Fock function (see Section 3.2).

The momentum loss cross section behaves in a very different way to that for hydrogen. In the low velocity limit it is 18.1 a.u. (5.1 × 10^{-16} cm²) and falls very slowly at first with increasing energy being 17.9 a.u. (5.05 × 10^{-16} cm²) at $\frac{1}{2}$ eV.

The pickoff cross section has not been calculated accurately from Fraser's wavefunctions, but an approximate estimate gives a value within a factor of two of that observed by Duff and Heymann.[29] This is estimated to be correct to about 10%, and corresponds to an effective number ξ of annihilating electrons in helium of 0.44.

There is obvious interest here in improving the theory, using better helium wavefunctions, and allowing for other groups in the trial wavefunction on the one hand, and employing a fully variational procedure on the other.

5. CONCLUSION

It is clear that there are many directions where the theoretical and experimental research can jointly lead to clearer understanding of the dynamics of interactions of slow positrons and positronium with atoms and molecules in gases, expanding along lines indicated above, and gradually extending into new directions.

REFERENCES

1. Tao, S. J., J. Bell, and J. H. Green, *Proc. Phys. Soc.* **83**, 453 (1964).
2. Falk, W. R., and G. Jones, *Canad. J. Phys.* **42**, 1751 (1964).
3. Paul, D. A. L., *Proc. Phys. Soc.* **84**, 563 (1964).
4. Osmon, P. E., *Phys. Rev.* **138B**, 216 (1965).
5. Ore, A., *Univ. i Bergen Naturvit, rekke* **9** (1949).
6. Falk, W. R., P. H. R. Orth, and G. Jones, *Phys. Rev. Letters* **14**, 447 (1965).
7. Schulz, G. J., *Phys. Rev.* **116**, 1141 (1959); **125**, 229 (1962).
8. Gerjuoy, E., and S. Stein, *Phys. Rev.* **97**, 1671 (1955); **98**, 1848 (1955).

9. Khare, H. C., P. R. Wallace, G. G. Bach, and A. Chodos, *Canad. J. Phys.* **42**, 1522 (1964).
10. Pond, T. A., *Phys. Rev.* **85**, 489 (1952).
11. DeBenedetti, S., and R. Siegel, *Phys. Rev.* **91**, 955 (1954).
12. Heinberg, M., and L. A. Page, *Phys. Rev.* **107**, 1589 (1957).
13. Celitans, G. J., and J. H. Green, *Proc. Phys. Soc.* **83**, 823 (1964).
14. Celitans, G. J., S. J. Tao, and J. H. Green, *Proc. Phys. Soc.* **83**, 833 (1964).
15. Marder, S., B. W. Hughes, C. S. Wu, and W. Bennett, *Phys. Rev.* **103**, 1258 (1956).
16. Hughes, V. W., *J. Appl. Phys.* **28**, 16 (1957).
17. Obenshain, F. E., and L. A. Page, *Phys. Rev.* **125**, 573 (1962).
18. Teutsch, W. B., and V. W. Hughes, *Phys. Rev.* **103**, 1266 (1956).
19. This is the method introduced by A. Temkin and J. C. Lamkin, *Phys. Rev.* **121**, 788 (1961), for treating electron collisions, and found to be very satisfactory for most cases to which it has been applied.
20. Cody, W. J., J. Lawson, H. S. W. Massey, and K. Smith, *Proc. Roy. Soc. (London)* **A278**, 479 (1964).
21. Schwartz, C., *Phys. Rev.* **124**, 1468 (1961).
22. Massey, H. S. W., and C. B. O. Mohr, *Proc. Phys. Soc.* **A67**, 695 (1954).
23. Massey, H. S. W., and A. H. A. Moussa, *Proc. Phys. Soc.* **77**, 811 (1960).
24. Holtsmark, J., *Z. phys.* **55**, 437 (1929).
25. Thompson, N; Unpublished.
26. Jones, G., and P. H. R. Orth, see paper in present Conference Proceedings.
27. Fraser, P. A., *Proc. Phys. Soc.* **78**, 329 (1961).
28. Fraser, P. A., *Proc. Phys. Soc.* **79**, 721 (1961).
29. Duff, B. G., and F. F. Heymann, *Proc. Roy. Soc. (London)* **A270**, 517 (1962).
30. Mohr, C. B. O., *Proc. Phys. Soc.* **A68**, 342 (1954).

Positron Annihilation in Liquids and Condensed Gases[*]

L. O. Roellig

Wayne State University
Detroit. Michigan

INTRODUCTION

A high-energy positron injected into a liquid loses its energy by
ionization and excitation of the atoms or molecules of the liquid.
When its energy becomes small, it either undergoes direct annihilation with an electron in the liquid, or it forms a bound state
with an electron, atom, or molecule. In general, two annihilation
lifetimes have been observed in ordinary liquids, and three lifetimes are observed in condensed gases. The shortest lifetime observed in ordinary liquids is -2×10^{-10} sec, and it is within the
experimental resolving time, of the time measuring equipment.
This lifetime component is attributed to the annihilation of parapositronium, positrons bound to an atom or molecule, and free
positrons. The second lifetime observed in ordinary liquids $(1 - 3)$
$\times 10^{-9}$ sec, is believed to be due to positrons in the bound state of
orthopositronium annihilating with an electron of the surrounding
liquid whose spin relative to it is singlet. This process is known
as pickoff annihilation. The three lifetimes observed in condensed
gases have been attributed to the annihilation of parapositronium,
free positrons, and pickoff annihilation of orthopositronium.

The intermediate lifetime which is found in the condensed gases,
but not in ordinary liquids, generally is attributed to free positron
annihilation.

The description just given is a simplified and naive description of
positron annihilation in liquids, for in the past few years a wealth of
data has accumulated which, in some instances, contradicts the above
generalizations. We shall next consider the annihilation process in
more detail. Since the condensed gases are simpler liquids than the
ordinary liquids, they will be considered first.

[*]Work supported in part by the National Science Foundation.

CONDENSED GASES

The intermediate and long lifetime components in the condensed gases are summarized in Table I.[1-7] It was found by Liu and Roberts that the variation in the intermediate lifetime of hydrogen and helium is simply related to the change in density with temperature (Fig. 1).[1] The value of the intermediate lifetime, however, is not completely understood. For example, the calculated mean life of plane wave positrons in liquid helium at $4.2\,^{\circ}K$ and atmospheric pressure is 3.55×10^{-9} sec. Ore considered the effect of an attractive polarization force between the positron and the electrons in helium, and found the mean life would be shortened only to about 2.53×10^{-9} sec.[8] The very long lifetime, τ_2, in liquid helium is also very difficult to understand. This lifetime component was considered to be the pickoff lifetime of orthopositronium. However, Ferrell has calculated that there is a factor of 17 between the theoretically expected pickoff rate and the experimentally determined rate.[9]

At this point it would be useful to consider the recent work of low temperature physicists on the behavior of ions in liquid helium. Experimental studies of the mobility of positive ions in liquid helium, presumably alpha particles, show that the ion behaves as if it had an effective mass for mobility studies of about 100 helium atoms.[10-17] To explain this anomalous effective mass, Atkins proposed that the electrostatic attraction between the positive ion and the surrounding helium atoms causes a compression of helium atoms around the ion.[16] By considering the liquid helium as an incompressible fluid, he found that the density, ρ, as a function of the distance, r, from

TABLE I

Intermediate, τ_1, and Long Lifetime, τ_2, Components
of Positron Annihilation in Condensed Gases

Substance	τ_1 (nsec) Liquid	τ_1 (nsec) Solid	τ_2 (nsec) Liquid	τ_2 (nsec) Solid	Ref.
Helium	1.90 ± 0.06		88.0 ± 7.5		1–5
Hydrogen	0.92 ± 0.04	0.80 ± 0.03	28.6 ± 2.3	14.6 ± 1.2	1
Deuterium	0.83 ± 0.03	0.74 ± 0.03			6
Neon		0.43 ± 0.03			6
Nitrogen	0.56 ± 0.02	0.48 ± 0.02	10.8 ± 0.9	4.2 ± 0.4	7, 6
Argon	0.50 ± 0.02	0.43 ± 0.03	6.9 ± 0.7		7, 6
Oxygen	0.45 ± 0.02	0.38 ± 0.02			6
Xenon		0.40 ± 0.03			6

the ion is

$$\rho(r) - \rho_0 = \frac{\gamma N\alpha e^2}{2V_0 u^2 r^4 E_0}$$

where $N\alpha$ = molar polarizability; γ = ratio of specific heats; u = velocity of first sound; V_0 = the initial volume per mole; and ρ_0 = ambient liquid helium density. A plot of the density as a function of r is given in Fig. 2. It should be noted that for small values of r, the electrostrictive pressure is great enough to form solid helium around the ion. One can show the same situation would be true for low temperature gaseous helium, for Atkins' calculations

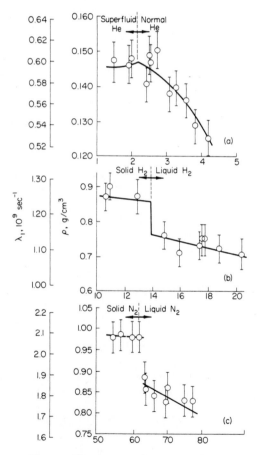

Fig. 1. The intermediate annihilation rate, λ_1, and the density, ρ, as a function of temperature for (a) He, (b) H_2, and (c) N_2.[1]

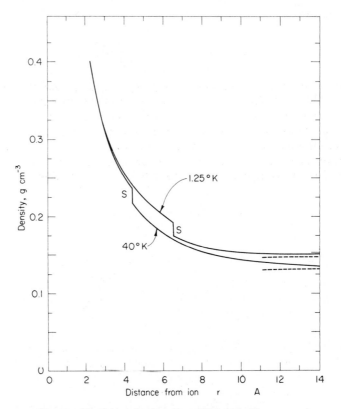

Fig. 2. Variation in density of liquid helium as a function of distance from a localized point charge.

can be modified by considering an ideal gas rather than an incompressible fluid. The chemical potential for the system can be
written as

$$\mu = u - Ts + pv - EP'$$

where P' is the polarization per mole due to the electric field E_0
($P' = N\alpha E_0$). From the first and second law of thermodynamics

$$T\ ds = du + p\ dv - E\ dP'$$

we have

$$d\mu = -s\ dT + v\ dp - P'\ dE$$

At equilibrium $d\mu = 0$ and $dT = 0$

$$v \; dp = P' \; dE$$

$$\int_{p_0}^{p} v \; dp = \int_{0}^{E} P' \; dE = \tfrac{1}{2} N\alpha E^2$$

Assuming the perfect gas law

$$pv = RT$$

we find

$$p = p_0 \; \exp\left[\frac{1}{2} \frac{N\alpha E^2}{RT}\right]$$

In cgs units and at $T = 4.2°K$

$$p = p_0 \; \exp[4.1 \times 10^3/r^4]$$

where r is in angstrom units.

This calculation shows that even in the gaseous phase at $4.2°K$, the positive ion is surrounded by solid helium to a radius 4.5 Å and by liquid helium from 4.5 Å to, depending upon the gaseous pressure, approximately 10 Å. In Table II, the radius of the liquid shell is tabulated as a function of pressure.

If the positron is not bound, its velocity, even at thermal energies, will be too great to cause a cluster of helium atoms to form around it. However, if it is bound to helium, then even in the low temperature gas phase we have to consider that the positron is surrounded by condensed helium atoms. A calculation by Wallace and co-workers has shown that the positron–helium atom system will have a binding energy of 0.55 eV, and they estimate the lifetime of the bound state to be 6.7×10^{-10} sec.[18] If a bound state exists in helium, one would

TABLE II

Radius of Liquid Shell Surrounding a Positive Ion in Gaseous Helium at $T = 4.2° K$ as a Function of Gaseous Pressure

P_0 (atm)	Radius (Å)
15/16	15.9
14/16	13.3
13/16	11.9
12/16	10.9
11/16	10.2
10/16	9.7
9/16	9.2
8/16	8.8

expect bound states to exist for all other atoms or molecules, for a
bound state would least likely occur in helium. There is some indication that a bound state has been observed in helium gas at 4.2°K
and atmospheric pressure, for it has been found that the annihilation
rate of positrons undergoes an abrupt change when the positron's
energy is about an electron volt.[19,20] The de Broglie wavelength of
the positron at this energy is equal to the average interatomic distance between helium atoms, in gaseous helium at 4.2°K and slightly
below atmospheric pressure, which suggests that an exchange
resonance may occur in low temperature helium gas.

As mentioned earlier, the situation is entirely different for
orthopositronium in helium, for not only is the system electrically
neutral, but also its mass is much lighter than the mass of a helium
atom-positron complex. The first attempt to explain the long lifetime
of the τ_2 component in liquid helium was made by Ferrell in 1959.[9]
He showed that there was a strong repulsive exchange force between
the orthopositronium and helium, which results in the orthopositronium residing in a cavity, commonly known as a zero point
energy bubble, in the liquid helium. The bubble is stabilized by the
zero-point kinetic pressure of the orthopositronium balancing the
usual contractual pressures on the bubble. Ferrell considered that
the total energy of a zero point bubble caused by the orthopositronium
was

$$E = \frac{\pi^2 \hbar^2}{4mb^2} + 4\pi b^2 \sigma$$

where b is the bubble radius, m the mass of the electron, and σ the
surface tension. The first term represents the zero point energy of
the positronium atom and the second term the surface energy of the
bubble. If the total energy is minimized with respect to the bubble
radius, one finds that the equilibrium bubble radius is 22.1 Å. By
assuming the interior of the bubble is filled with helium gas at its
saturated vapor pressure, Ferrell found the calculated pickoff rate
in the vapor was in satisfactory agreement with the experimental
value of τ_2. (The ambient density of helium atoms near the orthopositronium atom in the bubble is now that of the vapor rather than
the liquid which results in the lower annihilation rate found by experiment.) He suggested that a test of the bubble theory could be
made by varying the temperature, for at 5.2°K the saturated vapor
pressure is 2.3 atm, which would yield a mean life of 3.2×10^{-8} sec.
Stump performed this experiment and his results are shown in Fig. 3.[4]
The τ_2 component is not only not affected by the temperature, it also
is found to have approximately the same value in gaseous helium
above 5.2°K as was found in liquid helium.

Again it is useful to consider recent work of low temperature
physicists on the behavior of negative ions in liquid helium. The
mobility of positive and negative ions in liquid helium was found to

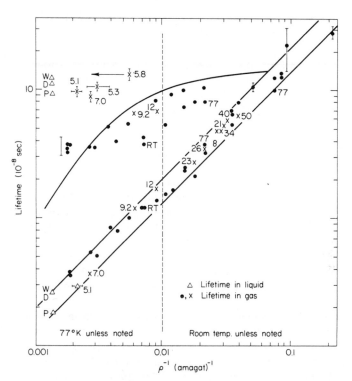

Fig. 3. Positron lifetimes in helium as a function of density^{-1}. Heavy curve indicates Ferrell's calculated values for pickoff orthopositronium.[4]

be approximately the same (i.e., both are anomalously low). Atkins' model, previously described, satisfactorily explained the positive ion mobility, but it would not account for the negative ion's mobility, for neither He$^-$ or He$_2^-$ are stable systems, and it is not likely that He$_n^-$ would be stable. One is forced to conclude that the negative ion is the electron, which excludes the cluster model for the same reasons that a cluster of helium atoms will not form around a free positron.

A beautiful experiment by Sommer has shown that there is a potential barrier of 1.3 ± 0.2 eV to electrons injected into liquid helium.[21] Sommer applied his experimental results to three models which have been proposed to explain the properties of an excess electron in liquid helium: (1) helium atoms form a cluster about the electron due to electrostrictive forces (Atkins' model); (2) the electron is essentially free, with an effective mass on the order of the electronic mass; and (3) the electron forms a zero point energy

bubble in liquid helium. He showed that his data are only consistent with the last model, and that the electron's energy is substantially lowered if it creates a cavity within the liquid sufficiently
large to reduce its zero point energy. A calculation by Kuper showed
that an electron in liquid helium would produce a bubble of radius
12.1 Å.[17] It was also shown that there would be *no* helium vapor in
the bubble, for the energy necessary for a helium atom to enter the
bubble would be 3×10^{-14} erg, whereas the zero point kinetic energy
of helium is only 3×10^{-15} erg. Thus the wave packet of the electron
prevents helium atoms from entering into the bubble. Kuper also
showed that such a bubble would behave in a mobility experiment as
if it had an effective mass of 100 times the mass of the helium atom,
and that this could account for the low mobility of an electron in
liquid helium. Donnelly has studied the interaction between negative
ions and quantized vortices in rotating HeII.[22] He found his experimental results are consistent with a negative ion radius of 12 Å and
a mass of 100 times that of helium. Experiments performed by
Meyer on the deflection of negative ions by a magnetic field also
show the effective mass of the electron is large in superfluid
helium.[23]

   The mobility of electrons in low temperature helium gas has recently been measured by Levine and Sanders, and the results are
shown in Fig. 4.[24,25] The electron mobility in 4.2°K helium gas at
pressures less than two-thirds an atmosphere has the value one would
predict on the basis of a free electron. The enormous decrease in mobility at higher pressures as seen in Fig. 4 has been interpreted by
Levine and Sanders to be due to the formation of a zero point energy
bubble in helium gas. They show that below 0.7 atm, it is energetically
more favorable for an electron to remain free, and at pressures above
0.7 atm, it is energetically more favorable for the electron to produce a cavity in the helium gas.

   If one considers Kuper's calculation, which shows that there will
be no helium vapor inside the bubble, and Levine and Sanders' work,
which indicates these bubbles may also exist in the gaseous phase,
as well as the liquid phase, we see that Stumps' results, that the τ_2
component is essentially independent of the temperature even above
the critical point, can be explained by an orthopositronium atom residing in a zero point energy bubble, which is free of helium atoms,
both in the liquid and gaseous phase.

   A model of an orthopositronium atom residing in a cavity in
helium has provided a qualitative explanation of the experimental
data. We shall now address ourselves to the question of whether
this phenomological model can also be used to calculate the lifetime of orthopositronium in liquid helium. Let us consider the
positronium atom to be in a cavity of radius b and approximate
the cavity by a radial potential well of depth V and radius b. A recent paper by Coopersmith has shown that the free energy of an

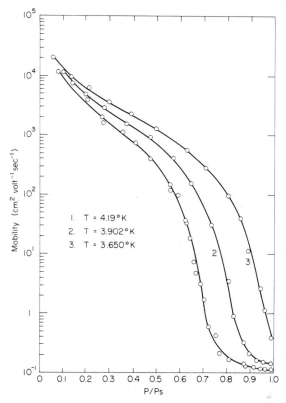

Fig. 4. Electron mobility in helium gas plotted against the ratio of gas pressure to the saturated vapor pressure at constant temperature.[25]

electron interacting with a system of helium scattering centers is given in the s-wave approximation (which is shown to be sufficient) by $2\pi\rho(\hbar^2/m)a$.[26] Here ρ is the average density of helium atoms, a is the electron–helium scattering length, and m is the electron mass. We shall assume that the positronium atom is trapped in a well of this depth where a now is the orthopositronium–helium scattering length ($a = +1.11 \times 10^{-8}$ cm), and m is the mass of orthopositronium.[31] The wavefunction inside the well, in the lowest state is $A(\sin kr)/r$, and outside it is $(Be^{-\alpha r})/r$ where

$$\alpha^2 = 2m(V - E)/\hbar^2, \qquad V = 2\pi\rho(\hbar^2/m)\,a$$

and

$$k^2 = 2mE/\hbar^2$$

The probability of finding the positronium outside of the well to the probability of finding it inside is given by

$$\frac{P_0}{P_i} = \frac{k^2/\alpha}{\alpha + (2mVb/\hbar^2)}$$

Here

$$E = \xi^2 \hbar^2 / 2mb^2$$

where ξ is obtained by the well-known graphical method for the finite potential well.[27] The equilibrium positronium bubble radius, b, has been determined by modifying Kuper's method of calculating the electron's bubble radius.[32] This modification results in a bubble radius of 9.2 or 10.2 Å for positronium atoms in liquid helium at 1.5°K, depending upon whether one uses the Margenau[28] interaction potential between helium atoms or the Slater-Kirkwood interaction potential.[29-30] Let us assume the annihilation rate inside the well is the vacuum annihilation rate (Kuper has shown the cavity will be free of helium atoms), whereas the annihilation rate outside the well is the vacuum annihilation rate plus the pickoff annihilation rate. Ferrell has calculated that the effect of the repulsive potential between orthopositronium and helium can be simulated by decreasing the number of electrons per helium atom from 2 to $0.0784 [1 - (1.872/r_s)]^{-3}$, where r_s is the radius of the sphere (in Bohr radii) whose volume is equal to the volume per helium atom.[9] The pickoff annihilation rate is then the Dirac annihilation rate modified by the above simulated number of electrons per helium atom, or

$$\lambda_{po} = \rho \pi r_0^2 c \left[0.0784 \left(1 - \frac{1.872}{r_s} \right)^{-3} \right]$$

where r_0 is the classical radius of the electron, ρ is the helium atom number density, and c is the velocity of light. The observed annihilation rate is

$$\lambda_{tot} = P_i \lambda_{vac} + P_0 (\lambda_{vac} + \lambda_{po})$$

A calculation of the theoretically predicted lifetime, τ_t ($\tau_t = 1/\lambda_{tot}$), for orthopositronium in liquid helium at 1.5°K at a pressure equal to its vapor pressure gives values of 7.8×10^{-8} sec and 8.9×10^{-8} sec, depending upon whether the equilibrium bubble radius is obtained from the Margenau or Slater-Kirkwood interaction potential between helium atoms.[32] The observed lifetime is $8.4 \pm 0.4 \times 10^{-8}$ sec.[7] The agreement between the calculated value and the experimental data is surprising, for the bubble may not possess a definite radius, and there very well may be a transition region between the cavity which has a helium atom density of zero and the bulk density of the liquid.

A theoretical study of the free and localized (bubble) states of an excess electron in liquid helium has recently been published by Jortner et al.[33] and Hiroike et al.[34] They found that by pressurizing the liquid helium, the bubble radius would decrease, but that a pressure-induced transition from the localized state to the delocalized state would not be possible, for the pressure necessary to induce the transition is always higher, in the temperature range of 4 to 40°K, then the melting pressure of helium. A localized state for the excess electron is not found for liquid Ar, Kr, and Xe due to the increased polarizibility of these atoms in comparison with He. This is apparent from the measured scattering lengths of electrons by rare gas atoms as shown in Table III.[35-37] Here the scattering length, a, is defined as

$$a = \lim_{k \to 0} \left(\frac{\tan \eta}{k} \right)$$

where η is the s wave phase shift and k is the magnitude of the momentum vector. The large negative scattering lengths of Ar, Kr, and Xe indicate that the polarization potential dominates the short range repulsion effects. It is seen that for neon, the two effects almost cancel.

TABLE III
Electron-Rare Gas Atom Scattering Lengths
(in Bohr Radii)[35-37]

Atom	a
He	1.19
Ne	0.24
Ar	−1.70
Kr	−3.7
Xe	−6.5

In conclusion, we have examined the environment of positrons in helium, the simplest of the condensed gases. We have noted that the shortest lifetime component can be assigned to parapositronium annihilation; the intermediate component can probably be assigned to a bound positron, and if the positron is bound, we have noted that due to electrostriction the environment may be drastically altered. (It is possible to have solid helium surround the ion, even in the gaseous phase at low temperatures.) The long-lived component, τ_2, may be attributed to the annihilation of orthopositronium which resides in a zero point energy bubble. A test of this model is presently being conducted in our laboratory, for as the density of helium gas is lowered, one would expect to find the positronium will no longer be localized in a bubble, and the density of helium atoms near the positronium atom may actually increase when the gaseous pressure is reduced to the point where it is energetically more favorable for the positronium to be free rather than localized. One would expect a decrease in lifetime if this occurred.

More theoretical work is needed to predict the intermediate and long lifetimes of the other condensed gases listed in Table I, for there is at present no quantitative explanation for these lifetimes. There is evidence that positronium is not formed in liquid oxygen.[38] Paul has suggested that the chemical compound $(e^+ e^-)O_2$ is formed, which would have too fast an annihilation rate to be measured by present experimental equipment.[39]

ORDINARY LIQUIDS

If we consider ordinary liquids, it was found that the long-lived component, the pickoff lifetime, increased with increasing temperature of the liquid. This variation was shown to be primarily a free volume effect.[40,41] As mentioned earlier, Wallace and Ferrell have shown that the positronium atom experiences a strong repulsive exchange force to other atoms.[42,43] Thus the positronium atom will tend to reside in local low density regions in a liquid, and it will be able to follow local density variations due to its low mass. Wilson et al.[41] showed this to be true by measuring the long-lived component as a function of pressure with the temperature held constant. They found a single lifetime for orthopositronium in all samples, and as the pressure on the liquid was increased, thus squeezing the holes in the liquid, the lifetime decreased. Their results are shown in Figs. 5 and 6. The abscissa in these figures is the volume of the liquid relative to its volume at 30°C and atmospheric pressure. The ordinate is the ratio of the intensity of the long-lived component, I, to the intensity of this component at 30°C and atmospheric pressure, I_0; and the mean life of the long-lived component is measured in nanoseconds. This work showed that a microcrystalline model of the liquid state discussed by Frenkel is in qualitative agreement with his experimental data.[44] The liquid is assumed to be made up of a number of microcrystallites and holes formed by noncompatible grain boundaries. The positronium is confined to the holes by exchange forces.

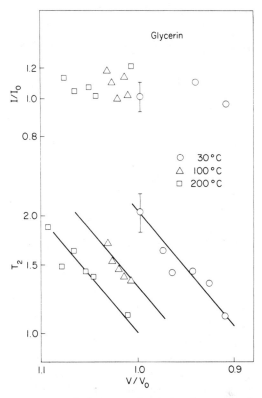

Fig. 5. Lifetime and relative intensity of orthopositronium in glycerin as a function of volume.[41]

This model predicts a lifetime $\tau = \mathrm{const} \times [(v - b)/T^3]^{0.87}$ where $(v - b)$ is the Van der Waal expression for the free volume and T is the temperature. The result of the Wilson et al. calculation is shown as the dashed curves in Fig. 6. The constant was chosen to give the correct lifetime at 30° C and 1 atm.

An attempt will not be made in this lecture to discuss the chemical effects of positron annihilation in ordinary liquids. Most of the experimental studies of positron annihilation in liquids not mentioned have been concerned with the chemistry of positronium reactions, which will be discussed by the succeeding lecturers of the Conference.

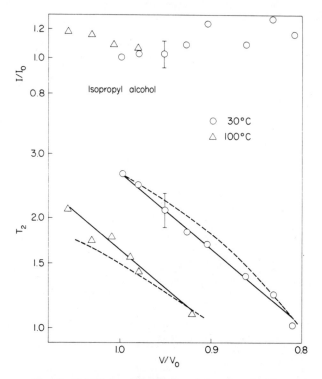

Fig. 6. Lifetime and relative intensity of orthopositronium in isopropyl alcohol as a function of volume.[41]

REFERENCES

1. Liu, D. C., and W. K. Roberts, *Phys. Rev.* **130**, 2322 (1963).
2. Paul, D. A. L., and R. L. Graham, *Phys. Rev.* **106**, 16 (1957).
3. Wackerle, J., and R. Stump, *Phys. Rev.* **106**, 18 (1957).
4. Daniel, T. B., and R. Stump, *Phys. Rev.* **115**, 1599 (1959).
5. Roellig, L. O., T. Kelly, H. H. Madden, and J. McNutt, "Proceedings of the IX International Conference on Low Temperature Physics" (J. G. Daunt, D. O. Edwards, F. J. Milford, and M. Yaqub, eds.), p. 195. Plenum Press, New York, 1965.
6. Liu, D. C., and W. K. Roberts, *Phys. Rev.* **132**, 1633 (1963).
7. Paul, D. A. L., *Canad. J. Phys.* **36**, 640 (1958).
8. Ore, A., Univ. i Bergen Arbok, Naturvitenskap. Rekke, No. 9 (1949).
9. Ferrell, R. A., *Phys. Rev.* **108**, 167 (1957).
10. Williams, R. L., *Canad. J. Phys.* **35**, 134 (1957).
11. Careri, G., J. Reuss, F. Scaramuzzi, and J. O. Thompson, "Proceedings of the Fifth International Conference on Low Temperature Physics and Chemistry (Madison, Wisconsin, 1957)" (J. R. Dillinger, ed.), p. 155. University of Wisconsin Press, Madison, Wisconsin, 1958.

12. Careri, G., F. Scaramuzzi, and J. O. Thompson, *Nuovo Cimento* **13**, 186 (1959).
13. Meyer, L., and F. Reif, *Phys. Rev.* **110**, 279 (1958).
14. Meyer, L., and F. Reif, *Phys. Rev. Letters* **5**, 1 (1960).
15. Meyer, L., and F. Reif, *Phys. Rev.* **119**, 1164 (1960).
16. Atkins, K. R., *Phys. Rev.* **116**, 1339 (1959).
17. Kuper, C. G., *Phys. Rev.* **122**, 1007 (1961).
18. Khare, H. C., P. R. Wallace, G.G. Bach, and A. Chodos, *Canad. J. Phys.* **42**, 1522 (1964).
19. Kelly, T. M., and L. O. Roellig, "Proceedings of Positron Annihilation Conference (Detroit, Michigan)" (A. T. Stewart and L. O. Roellig, eds.) Academic Press, New York, 1966.
20. Roellig, L. O., and T. M. Kelly, *Phys. Rev. Letters* **15**, 746 (1965).
21. Sommer, W. T., *Phys. Rev. Letters* **12**, 271 (1964).
22. Donnelly, R. J., *Phys. Rev. Letters* **14**, 39 (1965).
23. Meyer, L., "Proceedings of the IX International Conference on Low Temperature Physics (Columbus, Ohio)" (J. G. Daunt, D. O. Edwards, F. J. Milford, and M. Yaqub, eds.), p. 338. Plenum Press, New York, 1965.
24. Levine, J., and T. M. Sanders, *Phys. Rev. Letters* **8**, 159 (1962).
25. Levine, J., Ph.D. Thesis, University of Minnesota, 1963 (unpublished).
26. Coopersmith, M., *Phys. Rev.* **139**, A1359 (1965).
27. Schiff, I., "Quantum Mechanics," 2nd ed., Chapters 2 and 4. McGraw-Hill, New York, 1955.
28. Margenau, H., *Phys. Rev.* **56**, 1000 (1939).
29. Slater, J. C., and J. G. Kirkwood, *Phys. Rev.* **37**, 682 (1931).
30. Goldstein, L., *Phys. Rev.* **100**, 981 (1955).
31. Fraser, P. A., *Proc. Phys. Soc.* **79**, 721 (1961).
32. Roellig, L. O., (to be published).
33. Jortner, J., N. R. Kestner, S. A. Rice, and M. H. Cohen, *J. Chem. Phys.* **43**, 2614 (1965).
34. Hiroike, K., N. R. Kestner, S. A. Rice, and J. Jortner, *J. Chem. Phys.* **43**, 2625 (1965).
35. O'Malley, T. F., *Phys. Rev.* **130**, 1020 (1963).
36. Ramsauer, C., and R. Kollath, *Ann. Phys.* **3**, 536 (1929).
37. Ramsauer, C., and R. Kollath, *Ann. Phys.* **12**, 529, 837 (1932).
38. Briscoe, C. V., and A. T. Stewart, "Proceedings of Positron Annihilation Conference (Detroit, Michigan)" (A. T. Stewart and L. O. Roellig, eds.) Academic Press, New York, 1966.
39. Paul, D. A. L., *Canad. J. Phys.* **37**, 1059 (1959).
40. Brandt, W., S. Berko, and W. W. Walker, *Phys. Rev.* **120**, 1289 (1960).
41. Wilson, R. K., P. O. Johnson, and R. Stump, *Phys. Rev.* **129**, 2091 (1963).
42. Wallace, P. R., *Phys. Rev.* **100**, 738 (1955).
43. Ferrell, R. A., *Rev. Modern Phys.* **28**, 308 (1956).
44. Frenkel, J., "Kinetic Theory of Liquids." Clarendon Press, Oxford, 1946.

Positronium Reactions in Solutions

John D. McGervey

Western Reserve University, Cleveland, Ohio

INTRODUCTION

Injection of positrons into a liquid produces what has been called "the elementary free radical,"[1] positronium (Ps). A great many solutions have been studied in this way since the discovery in 1953 of Ps in water,[2] but the full possibilities of Ps studies have yet to be realized.

One difficulty with such research is that in such a complex medium as an aqueous solution many reactions can occur, yet only a few different effects can be observed in a positron experiment. As a result, a single effect (for example, a reduction in the intensity of the long-lived component in a positron lifetime measurement) may be attributed to any one of several possible reactions in the solution. However, a careful study of the dependence of such an effect on concentration or, possibly temperature, can often lead one to the correct explanation, or at least eliminate incorrect explanations.

A second difficulty is that the end products of a reaction involving positronium are often unstable intermediate states which are never encountered in ordinary chemistry. This might turn out to be an advantage, for some of these intermediate states could be of theoretical importance.

Effects of reactions in solutions are observed by means of the three "classical" measurements — of three-quantum annihilation rate, of the angular correlation of the annihilation quanta, and of the lifetime distribution of the positrons. Of the three, the measurement of the three quantum rate is perhaps the least informative, for it yields only a single number which cannot be measured with high accuracy, and which has a rather complicated dependence on the rates of various processes in solution. This measurement may be useful, however, if the results are carefully correlated with results of the other types of measurement. Measurements of the lifetime distribution are most popular, for they give a somewhat direct measure of the rates of various processes, but the angular correlation method has been very helpful in distinguishing between processes which have similar effects on the lifetime.

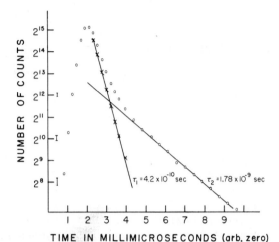

Fig. 1. Positron lifetime distribution in water.

To understand the interpretation of the various observations, let us review briefly the fate of a positron in a solution. A fast positron is slowed by inelastic collisions until its energy reaches a range of values corresponding to the "Ore gap"; in a solution this range is not so well defined as in a gas, because of possible effects of solvation on the excitation potentials. After passing through this range of energies, a positron in water approaches thermal energy, either bound in a Ps atom (about 30% of the time), or as a free positron which interacts further only by elastic collisions and eventual annihilation. In a solution there is also the possibility that the positron may emerge from this energy range as part of a molecule, which may have been produced either by direct interaction between the positron and a solute particle, or by formation of positronium followed by interaction with a solute particle. The time of decision probably occurs within about 10^{-11} sec of the birth of the positron. After a positronium atom reaches nearly thermal energy, it may interact with solute particles; such interaction may cause a conversion of ortho- to parapositronium (or vice versa), ionization (oxidation) of the Ps atom by transfer of its electron to a solute ion, or formation of a compound containing the positron. Eventually, the positron is annihilated, either with an electron to which it is bound (in parapositronium or in a molecule), or with an electron in the surrounding medium ("pickoff" annihilation).

The positron lifetime distribution in water is shown in Fig. 1.[3] The long-lived component consists of pickoff annihilations of ortho-positronium. The shorter-lived component contains annihilations of

free positrons. A third component, of still shorter lifetime, consisting of parapositronium annihilations, is not resolved, and appears as part of the "short-lived component." A repeated measurement, with presently attainable time resolution, should resolve this
component, whose mean life is expected to equal the mean life of
parapositronium in free space: 1.25×10^{-10} sec.

The angular distribution of the annihilation quanta has no such
easily identifiable features, but parapositronium annihilation does
contribute to the narrow part of the distribution, a fact which becomes clearer when solutes are added which either increase or decrease the number of parapositronium annihilations. It is significant that a very pronounced narrow peak appears in the distribution from annihilations in ice.[4] The area under the peak is consistent with the assumption that it is produced by annihilations of
parapositronium, and the width of the peak indicates that this parapositronium has thermal energy. By comparison of the angular distributions in ice and water, a narrow component was separated from
the water curve as well; the greater width of this component suggests that parapositronium in water has an energy several times
thermal when it annihilates. This energy is probably the quantum-
mechanical zero-point energy of a Ps atom trapped in a hole in the
water; the zero-point energy is smaller in ice because the holes
are larger.

RELATIONS BETWEEN REACTION RATES
AND OBSERVABLE QUANTITIES

Even though Ps may never reach thermal energy in a solution, it
is safe to assume that soon after the initial time of decision the Ps
energy becomes essentially constant, so that rates of all reactions
are time independent thereafter. This assumption is supported by the
observation of a single exponential decay of the annihilations occur-
ing at large times ($t > 1$ nsec) after the birth of the positron.

Let us now derive the dependence of the various observable decay
constants on the rates of reactions in which Ps takes part. We shall
follow and extend the notation of Dixon and Trainor,[5] who first treated
this problem for the case of a conversion process only. Three broad
categories of reaction are of interest; they are classified according to
the nature of the products of the reaction:

(1) Conversion of one Ps state to another. The probability per
unit time for conversion to any one of the four states—three triplet
(*ortho*) and one singlet (*para*)—is denoted by γ.

(2) Oxidation by electron transfer, leaving a bare positron. The
probability per unit time is denoted by λ_0. A typical reaction is

$$Ps + Cu^{2+} \rightarrow e^+ + Cu^+$$

(3) Formation of a positron compound. Mechanisms which have been proposed are Ps capture by a molecule or a reaction such as

$$Ps + MnO_4^- \rightarrow PsO + MnO_3^-$$

or

$$Ps + H_2O_2 \rightarrow PsOH + HO$$

Compound formation probability per unit time is denoted by λ_c.

The annihilation rates in the various states are λ_s for singlet Ps, λ_t for triplet Ps, λ_p for pickoff, λ_f for free positrons, and λ_m for a positron in a molecule. If a positron is born at time $t = 0$, the probabilities of observing it in the various states at time t are $P_s(t)$, $P_t(t)$, $P_f(t)$, and $P_m(t)$. These probabilities obey the following equations:

$$dP_s/dt = -(3\gamma + \lambda_s + \lambda_p + \lambda_0 + \lambda_c)P_s + \gamma P_t \tag{1}$$

$$dP_t/dt = -(\gamma + \lambda_t + \lambda_p + \lambda_0 + \lambda_c)P_t + 3\gamma P_s \tag{2}$$

$$dP_f/dt = -\lambda_f P_f + \lambda_0(P_s + P_t) \tag{3}$$

$$dP_m/dt = -\lambda_m P_m + \lambda_c(P_s + P_t) \tag{4}$$

Equations (1) and (2) are easily solved, yielding

$$P_s = Ae^{-\lambda_1 t} + Be^{-\lambda_2 t} \tag{5}$$

$$P_t = Ce^{-\lambda_1 t} + De^{-\lambda_2 t} \tag{6}$$

where

$$\lambda_{1,2} = 2\gamma + \lambda_s/2 + \lambda_t/2 + \lambda_p + \lambda_0 + \lambda_c$$
$$\pm (4\gamma^2 + \gamma\lambda_s + \lambda_s^2/4 + \lambda_t^2/4 - \lambda_s\lambda_t/4 - \gamma\lambda_t)^{1/2} \tag{7}$$

$$A = \frac{\lambda_s + \lambda_p + \lambda_0 + \lambda_c - \lambda_2}{\lambda_1 - \lambda_2} \cdot P_s(0) \tag{8}$$

$$B = \frac{\lambda_1 - (\lambda_s + \lambda_p + \lambda_0 + \lambda_c)}{\lambda_1 - \lambda_2} \cdot P_s(0) \tag{9}$$

$$C = \frac{\lambda_t + \lambda_p + \lambda_0 + \lambda_c - \lambda_2}{\lambda_1 - \lambda_2} P_t(0) \tag{10}$$

$$D = \frac{\lambda_1 - (\lambda_t + \lambda_p + \lambda_0 + \lambda_c)}{\lambda_1 - \lambda_2} P_t(0) \tag{11}$$

Substitution of (5) and (6) into (3) and (4) now yields

$$P_f = \frac{\lambda_0(B + D)}{\lambda_f - \lambda_2} (e^{-\lambda_2 t} - e^{-\lambda_f t}) + P_f(0)e^{-\lambda_f t} \tag{12}$$

$$P_m = \frac{\lambda_c(B + D)}{\lambda_m - \lambda_2} (e^{-\lambda_2 t} - e^{-\lambda_m t}) + P_m(0)e^{-\lambda_m t} \tag{13}$$

In order to relate these quantities to observation, we note that the observed "lifetime distribution" is the time distribution of the two quantum annihilations. If one ignores the possibility of three quantum annihilations of free positrons and positrons in molecules, one obtains the two quantum annihilation rate as

$$R(t) = \lambda_s P_s + \lambda_f P_f + \lambda_m P_m + \lambda_p (P_s + P_t) \tag{14}$$

Clearly, there exists the possibility of observing four distinct "mean lives," provided that λ_1, λ_2, λ_f, and λ_m are sufficiently different to be resolved by the apparatus. The intensity of each component is equal to the coefficient of the corresponding exponential in (14). However, in some cases a coefficient is negative, so that the idea of an "intensity" does not apply; the lifetime distribution would then appear, with sufficient resolution, to have a "shoulder," as observed in gases.[6] It is interesting to note that the intensity of the longest lived component is not, in general, equal to the fraction of positrons which initially form triplet Ps.

The total number of counts in the narrow component in the angular distribution is given by

$$I_N = \int_0^\infty \lambda_s P_s \, dt = \frac{\lambda_s}{\lambda_1 \lambda_2} (4\gamma + \lambda_p + \lambda_0 + \lambda_c) \tag{15}$$

This expression may be difficult to apply in cases where positronium compounds are formed, unless the angular distribution resulting from annihilation in the compound is known.

OBSERVED EFFECTS OF REACTIONS

A. Changes in λ_2

The equations of the preceding section can be simplified considerably for cases in which only one of the three possible types of reaction occur. The "conversion" curve of Fig. 2 shows the increase of λ_2 (over the rate from pickoff alone) as a function of the conversion rate γ, in the absence of other reactions. The "conversion limit" is the value of the increase in λ_2 at an infinite conversion rate; this limit is just one fourth of λ_s, because the Ps atom spends one fourth of its time in the singlet state. The "reaction" curve shows the increase of λ_2 with reaction rate in the absence of conversion. Here the limiting factor is the annihilation rate of free positrons; if $\lambda_2 > \lambda_f$, the long-lived component consists of free positron annihilations rather than Ps decays.

The points plotted in Fig. 2 were obtained from the data of Green and Bell,[7] who studied aqueous solutions of paramagnetic salts, in which the unpaired electrons of the positive ions would be expected

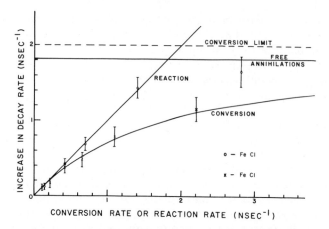

Fig. 2. Dependence of the decay rate of the long
component in aqueous solutions on the rate of processes
involving Ps in the solution. The ordinate shows the increase in rate over that observed in pure water. The
"conversion" curve gives this increase as a function
only of the rate of conversion between singlet and triplet Ps states. The "reaction" curve gives the increase
as a function of the rate of an oxidation or compound
formation reaction. At large reaction rates, the long-
lived component consists of annihilations of free positrons; the increase in decay rate then follows the "free
annihilation" line.

to cause conversion by exchange with the Ps electron. It is clear
from Fig. 2 that the data for $FeCl_2$ fit the conversion curve very
well; in order to fit the curve, the only adjustable parameter used
is a proportionality factor between concentration and reaction rate.

Data for many of the other paramagnetic salts fit equally well, but
for three of the salts studied — $FeCl_3$, $CuCl_2$, and $SbCl_3$ — the conversion curve cannot be made to fit at all well. These three solutions differ from the others in being good oxidizers. It is also significant that the cross sections found for "conversion" in $FeCl_3$
and $CuCl_2$ solutions are far larger than those found in the other solutions, and that $SbCl_3$, a nonparamagnetic salt, would not be expected
to produce a conversion effect at all. One might therefore suspect
that in the $FeCl_3$ and $CuCl_2$ solutions Ps is oxidized, in the reactions

$$Ps + Fe^{3+} \rightarrow e^+ + Fe^{2+}$$

$$Ps + Cu^{2+} \rightarrow e^+ + Cu^+$$

The effect in the $SbCl_3$ solution is probably not so simple as this;

the solution contains SbO$^+$ which does not oxidize by simple electron capture.

The good fit of the FeCl$_3$ data to the "reaction" curve in Fig. 2 strengthens this hypothesis. Additional evidence comes from the angular correlation results of Trumpy,[8] who found that I_N is decreased in solutions of SbCl$_3$, FeCl$_3$, and CuCl$_2$, as well as in solutions of NaNO$_3$, H$_2$O$_2$, and KMnO$_4$, also good oxidizers. The expected increase of I_N, due to the conversion effect, was observed in other paramagnetic salts. Since all of Trumpy's data were taken at the rather high concentration of 2 mole/liter, Eq. (15) cannot be applied in a very meaningful way.

Other observations of reactions involving good oxidizing agents have been observed,[3,9-11] and an attempt has been made to correlate the results with chemical oxidation potentials.[3,8,9] Although Ps in solution differs in many ways from the usual oxidation-reduction system, the oxidation potential should still be a rough guide to the power of an ion to oxidize Ps, especially in cases where the potential for transfer of a single electron is known. One should expect this guide to be useful only insofar as it indicates the electron affinity, in solution, of a single ion which could destroy Ps. For example, the overall chemical oxidation potential depends on the pH of a solution; but one should not expect pH to have much effect on Ps reactions, because no Ps reactions are observed in acids containing no dissolved salts. Goldanskii et al.,[12] have found experimentally that there is no pH influence on Ps behavior in KMnO$_4$ solutions.

It may be worthwhile here to give some elementary chemistry, from a physicist's point of view. The statement that the oxidation potential for

$$M^{m+} + e^- \rightarrow M^{(m-1)+} \tag{16}$$

is greater than that for

$$N^{n+} + e^- \rightarrow N^{(n-1)+} \tag{17}$$

is equivalent to the statement that in the reversible reaction

$$M^{m+} + N^{(n-1)+} \rightleftharpoons M^{(m-1)+} + N^{n+} \tag{18}$$

the rate constant for the forward reaction is greater than the rate constant for the reverse reaction, or that the electron affinity of an M^{m+} ion is greater than that of an N^{n+} ion. The reverse reaction in (18) therefore involves only those ion pairs with sufficient kinetic energy to overcome the difference in electron affinity. In a Ps reaction of this sort only the forward reaction rate is observed, so that the comparison of rates necessary to compare oxidation potentials is not possible. However, in a solution containing ions with a smaller electron affinity than that of a positron, one would expect the reaction rate to be quite small, even for a difference of 0.1 eV in affinity, while the reaction could proceed easily if the reverse were true.

The oxidation observed in $CuCl_2$ solutions, in which

$$Cu^{++} + e^- \rightarrow Cu^+ \qquad E_0 = +0.17 \text{ V}$$

combined with the fact that no change in λ_2 is seen even in very concentrated HCl solutions, has been used to suggest[9] that an "oxidation potential" for Ps could be defined in the following way: In aqueous solutions, Ps is oxidized at a measurable rate by oxidizers for which a similar single electron potential is +0.17 V or greater, while no effect on λ_2 occurs when the single electron potential is zero or negative. No exception to this rule has been found among the limited number of ions for which the single electron potential is known.

In the more numerous cases where the oxidation potential involves the transfer of two or three electrons, the potential quoted is proportional to the average energy released per electron in the electron transfer. In these cases, the potential applicable to Ps would presumably involve only the transfer of the first electron, so that one cannot predict with certainty which of these should oxidize Ps. Experiments have shown no oxidation in salts of Cd, Zn, Sn, and Ga, for which the standard E_0 lies between 0 and -1. This would indicate, if the reasoning above is correct, that $E_0 < 0$ for the reactions

$$Cd^{2+} + e^- \rightarrow Cd^+$$

$$Zn^{2+} + e^- \rightarrow Zn^+$$

$$Sn^{2+} + e^- \rightarrow Sn^+$$

$$Ga^{3+} + e^- \rightarrow Ga^{2+}$$

Information of this sort may or may not be useful to somebody someday.

Reactions apparently involving formation of a Ps compound have also been observed to have an effect on λ_2. Berko and Zuchelli[13] observed an increase in λ_2 on addition of the free radical diphenyl-picryl-hydrazyl (DPH) to benzene. It is interesting that, as in the case of some of the oxidizing reactions, the effect was at first attributed to conversion caused by exchange of the unpaired electron. It was shown by Ferrell,[14] using a graph similar to Fig. 2, that the observed dependence of λ_2 on concentration fits a reaction mechanism better than the conversion mechanism, and the reaction was assumed to be capture of Ps by DPH. Angular correlation measurements subsequently reported by de Zafra[15] showed that I_N is decreased by addition of DPH to benzene, confirming that the effect is not primarily one of conversion. In the course of his investigation, de Zafra also found that chloroform seems even more effective than DPH in reducing I_N in benzene; this too may be a case of Ps capture.

B. Changes in I_2

One of the most quoted results in Ps chemistry has been the decrease in I_2 with no change in λ_2 observed by Green and Bell[16] in nitrate and nitrite solutions. The explanation given was that capture of positrons by the NO_3^- or NO_2^- ions competes with Ps formation. Although this mechanism is adequate to explain the effect, it was not clear why these ions should capture positrons when no other negative ion has been observed to do so. It was suggested by McGervey and DeBenedetti[17] that the oxidizing property of the NO_3^- ion has something to do with the effect, but the effect is clearly different from the oxidation previously discussed, in which λ_2 rather than I_2 is affected. However, if oxidation of Ps were energetically possible before Ps is thermalized but not afterwards, I_2 would change with no change in λ_2. This seems to occur in $Pb(ClO_4)_2$ solutions;[3] the reduction in I_2 is far greater than in other solutions containing ClO_4^- ions, so it appears to be caused by the Pb^{2+} ion. A similar but much smaller effect in HCl solutions has been reported by Tao and Green.[11] It was pointed out by Goldanskii et al.,[10] that the effect observed with nitrates might involve a simple Ore gap effect, if the nitrates provide additional excited states in the critical energy range. However, the *broad* component in the angular distribution from nitrate solutions is broader than that from water,[15] indicating, in support of the original explanation, that some other positron state is present.

Recently, Tao and Green[11] have reopened this problem by measuring lifetime distributions in solutions of HNO_3, H_2SO_4, $HClO_4$, and H_3PO_4. A variation in I_2 was found, and was explained on the basis of the possible reactions

$$Ps + H_2PO_4^- \;\rightarrow\; PsO + H_2PO_3^- \tag{19}$$

$$Ps + HSO_4^- \;\rightarrow\; PsO + HSO_3^- \tag{20}$$

$$Ps + ClO_4^- \;\rightarrow\; PsO + ClO_3^- \tag{21}$$

$$Ps + NO_3^- \;\rightarrow\; PsO + NO_2^- \tag{22}$$

Since no increase in λ_2 was seen, these reactions must occur only before Ps thermalization. A monotonic decrease in I_2 values from (19) thru (22) was attributed to the bond strengths of 6.8 eV for $(H_2PO_3-O)^-$, 5.0 eV for $(HSO_3-O)^-$ and 2.3 eV for $(NO_2-O)^-$; from this the strength of the unknown $(ClO_3 - O)^-$ bond was deduced to be between 3 and 4 eV. The PsO bond was then assumed to be only slightly weaker than the $(NO_2—O)^-$ bond, or about 2.2 eV, to explain the strong I_2 effect observed with NO_3^- ions. The previously observed effects in $KMnO_4$ and K_2Cr_2O, solutions[3,10] were also explained on the basis of PsO formation. Since here λ_2 is strongly affected, it is assumed that the $(MnO_3—O)^-$ and $(Cr_2O_6—O)^{2-}$ bonds are weaker than the PsO bond, so that PsO formation is energetically possible after Ps thermalization. In still another oxidizing agent, H_2O_2, in water the reaction

$$Ps + H_2O_2 \rightarrow PsOH + OH \tag{23}$$

was suggested by Tao and Green. They observed a linear increase in λ_2 with increasing H_2O_2 concentration in water, but the effect is about 100 times smaller than that seen in solutions of the oxidizers mentioned previously, and it was considered to be caused simply by an increase in λ_p. But a reduction in I_2 was seen which was almost equal at the observed concentrations (up to 0.2 m.f.) to that seen in nitrate solutions. It was this effect which was attributed to the occurrence of reaction (23) before thermalization. If this interpretation is correct, the Ps—OH bond is slightly weaker than the 1.5 eV H—OH bond.

These ideas are intriguing, but much more evidence is needed to support them. One wonders why the Ps—OH bond should be weaker than the Ps—O bond, when the H—OH bond (5.0 eV) is stronger than the H—O bond (4.5 eV). One also wonders where the effect seen in nitrites fits into this scheme. Finally, there is the question of the dependence of the effects on concentration.

For a reaction competing with Ps formation (such as the proposed $e^+NO_3^-$ formation), it was shown by Green and Bell that I_2 is proportional to $1/(1 + aM)$ where M is the concentration. But a reaction such as (22), which occurs after Ps is formed, I_2 should be proportional to $A + Be^{-cM}$, where A, B, and c are constants, since e^{-cM} is the probability that a Ps atom makes no collision with an NO_3^- ion before reaching thermal energy. The observed concentration dependence in nitrates seems to fit the first hypothesis better. As a check on these ideas, it would be interesting to measure I_2 vs concentration in Pb $(ClO_4)_2$ solutions; in those, since the effect is caused by the Pb^{2+} ion, the reaction must occur after Ps formation and the exponential concentration dependence should be seen.

It is possible that the weakness of the $(NO_2—O)^-$ bond is responsible in a different way for the reduction in I_2. Simple inelastic collisions with positrons in the right energy range could compete with Ps formation just as effectively as the proposed $e^+NO_3^-$ production, to give the observed dependence of I_2 on concentration. The difficulty with this idea is that it fails to explain

de Zafra's observation that nitrate ions broaden the broad component in the angular distribution. There simply seems to be no
entirely satisfying explanation of the observations in nitrate solutions; probably a combination of several causes is involved.

FUTURE POSSIBILITIES

There may never come a time when most chemistry laboratories
are equipped to use positrons as a tool in analysis. It is nevertheless possible that positrons may provide useful chemical data. The
investigation of positron compounds is a likely source of such data,
but more evidence is needed to show that such compounds are really
formed in solutions. Clues may come from studies of the temperature dependence of I_2 and λ_2. Horstman[18] has shown that λ_2 increases with temperature in oxidizing solutions, as one would expect for chemical reactions involving thermalized positronium. He
has also found evidence of compound formation in some solutions by
studying the temperature dependence of I_2, but much work remains
to be done to clarify the situation.

The best evidence for compound formation would be the detection
in the lifetime distribution of a separate component produced by annihilation of positrons in the compound. There have been no calculations of the positron mean life in large molecules, but Neamtan
et al.,[19] have found that the mean life in PsH is close to the spin-
averaged Ps mean life (5×10^{-10} sec). If this is true of the larger
molecules as well, it would be very difficult to separate this component from the free positron annihilations, because λ_m would be
almost equal to λ_f. (Inclusion of a small pickoff rate in λ_m would
not help matters any.) However, it might be possible to resolve
this component in other solvents in which λ_f has a value different
from its value in water. Of course, another solvent might introduce other complications. It would be reassuring if one could see
in other solvents the same effects now attributed to Ps compound
formation in water.

One hopes that as more chemists become interested in these
problems more meaningful experiments can be devised. Certainly,
the ability to measure reaction rates directly, by measurement of
the positron mean life, should provide many answers, if we only
ask the right questions.

REFERENCES

1. Brandt, W., S. Berko, and W. W. Walker, *Phys. Rev.* **120**, 1289 (1960).
2. Bell, R. E., and R. L. Graham, *Phys. Rev.* **90**, 644 (1953).
3. J. E. Jackson and J. D. McGervey, *J. Chem. Phys.* **38**, 300 (1963).
4. de Zafra, R. L., and W. T. Joyner, *Phys. Rev.* **112**, 19 (1958).

5. Dixon, W. R., and L. E. H. Trainor, *Phys. Rev.* **97**, 733 (1955).
6. The effect in gases, which is presumably of a different nature, is well covered in other papers presented at this conference.
7. Green, R. E., and R. E. Bell, *Canad. J. Phys.* **36**, 1684 (1958).
8. Trumpy, G., *Phys. Rev.* **118**, 668 (1960).
9. McGervey, J. D., H. Horstman, and S. DeBenedetti, *Phys. Rev.* **124**, 1113 (1961).
10. Goldanskii, V. I., T. A. Solonyenko, and V. P. Shantarovich, *Dokl. Akad. Nauk. S.S.S.R.* **151**, 608 (1963).
11. Tao, S. J., and J. H. Green, U. of New South Wales, Dept. of Nucl. and Rad. Chem. Report NRS21, 1964.
12. Goldanskii, V. I., O. A. Karpukhin, and G. G. Petrov, *Zh. Eksperim. i. Teoret. Fiz.* **39**, 1477; (English Transl.) *JETP* **12**, 1026 (1960).
13. Berko, S., and A. J. Zuchelli, *Phys. Rev.* **102**, 724 (1956).
14. Ferrell, R. A., *Phys. Rev.* **110**, 1355 (1958).
15. de Zafra, R. L., *Phys. Rev.* **113**, 1547 (1959).
16. Green, R. E., and R. E. Bell, *Canad. J. Phys.* **35**, 398 (1957).
17. McGervey, J. D. and S. DeBenedetti, *Phys. Rev.* **114**, 495 (1959).
18. Horstman, H., Thesis, Carnegie Institute of Technology, 1962.
19. Neamtan, S. M., G. Darewych, and G. Oczkowski, *Phys. Rev.* **126**, 193 (1962).

Positron Annihilation in Molecular Substances and Ionic Crystals

Werner Brandt

New York University, New York, New York

> 'Well! I've often seen a cat without a grin,' thought
> Alice; 'but a grin without a cat! It's the most
> curious thing I ever saw in all my life!'
>
> Lewis Carroll

Although a wide span of topics has been allotted to this chapter, the thorough reviews in these Proceedings by other authors permit us to limit the discussion to only a few of the most recent developments in the study of the positron annihilation characteristics of dielectrics. The conclusions we will draw are then necessarily tentative, but they may suggest ways for further clarification. In making this choice I am reminded of a conjecture by Freeman Dyson which states that if an author has to present a paper or plans to publish a book at time T, and brings it up-to-date to a time $(T - t)$, it is probably out of date at the time $(T + t)$.

The chapter falls into two parts. The first part concerns itself with positron annihilations in molecular substances. This topic is difficult, because the substances investigated in the greatest detail are polymers with complicated morphology, because their positron annihilation characteristics are complex, and because recent experimental data in part appear to run counter to what had been anticipated before they became available.

The second part concentrates on ionic crystals. Here, some discrepancies had been noted between the experimental annihilation characteristics and their interpretation in terms of other well understood properties of these solids. If the nature of these discrepancies can be uncovered, ionic crystals offer a test case for answering the question behind much of the work done in the field of solid state positron physics: Are there some basic elements missing in the theory of positron annihilations in solids, or can we

understand in fact all annihilation characteristics within the framework of conventional solid state theory? And alas, hope springs
eternal that this may not be possible.

I. POSITRON ANNIHILATION IN MOLECULAR SUBSTANCES

1. THE EXPERIMENTAL SITUATION

1.1 Intensities

Since the pioneering work by Bell and Graham, a fairly straightforward picture had emerged of the structure of the positron annihilation time spectrum of substances in which positronium, Ps,
can be formed. It has a long-lifetime component attributed to the
pickoff annihilations of positrons bound in orthopositronium (o-Ps),
with lifetimes typically ranging from 2 to 4 nsec, and intensities
comprising $0.1 - 0.3$ of all annihilations. All other annihilations appeared unresolved as a short-lifetime component. Long-lifetime
components are observed primarily in diamagnetic substances,
where ortho-para conversion cannot take place. The lifetime for
the self-annihilation of parapositronium (p-Ps) is 0.125 nsec, and
such annihilations stay submerged in the short-lifetime component.
One surmised that whenever an o-Ps pickoff component appears,
the p-Ps pendant must be part of the short-lifetime component,
ideally with an intensity one third as large as that of the long-lifetime component, and lifetimes close to 0.125 nsec. The remaining
annihilations, 0.6-0.8 of the total, could then be expected to come
from positrons not bound in Ps atoms, with lifetimes ~ 0.5 nsec.

One looked forward to what one might really find once the short
component could be resolved further. Only very recently, improvements in fast coincidence techniques and in photomultiplier design,
and refinements in the data analysis by computational means made
it possible to resolve the annihilation time spectra further. In particular, it became possible to decompose them consistently into
three components.[1-4] The study of positron annihilations in substances with long-lifetime components took a new turn then, because in some essential respects these data are at variance with the
simple arguments just presented.

The current experimental situation, as it is relevant for our discussion, can be summarized briefly as follows. The minimum number of exponential time decay functions fitting these spectra is
three, by an iterative least-square fit criterion. An example is
shown in Fig. 1. In the following, we shall call the components A,
B, C', in the order of decreasing lifetimes; the prime indicates
that at present the experiments or the method of decomposition

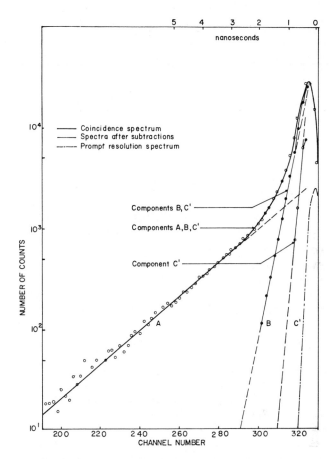

Fig. 1. Typical delayed coincidence time spectrum of
positrons annihilating in polyethylene at room temperature.
The spectrum can be fitted to three exponentially decaying
components, as indicated by the straight lines.[4]

employed here cannot decide whether C' is a single component, or
a composite. We shall denote the fractions of the annihilations in
these components and the corresponding lifetimes by i_A, τ_A, etc.,
respectively; annihilation rates are denoted by Γ or γ.

Figure 2 depicts the intensities of the resolved components of
annihilations in polyethylene, and their temperature dependence.
At low temperatures, the intensities stay essentially constant.
Above 200°K, the intensity of the short-lifetime component $i_{C'}$ begins to drop from its initial value of 0.6 to 0.3 at temperatures above
the crystalline melting point. Concurrently, i_A, the intensity of the
long-lifetime component, grows from 0.1 to become larger than $i_{C'}$

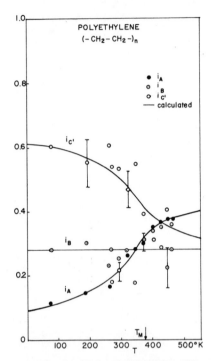

Fig. 2. The relative intensities
of the three resolved components in
polyethylene. The calculated curves
are discussed in Section 2.[4]

at the high temperatures. The intensity i_B of the component with
the intermediate lifetime remains constant over the entire temperature range. The few other molecular substances investigated so far
behave similarly. The recurrent features are

(1) $i_{C'}$ is always larger than $i_A/3$;

(2) i_A grows at the expense of $i_{C'}$;

(3) i_A increases with increasing temperature or, by the equation
     of state, with increasing volume.

Is (3) predominantly a thermal effect, or a volume effect? If the
temperature data are compared by volume ($\sim$reciprocal density),
with the isothermal pressure data of Stump and his co-workers[5] and
with the data of Tao and Green[3] on high vs low-density polymers, the
trends point to the volume as being the important variable determining the variations of i_A. Although this observation calls for more experimental confirmation, in the following we shall adopt the view that
the volume is the important variable. Also, we shall adhere to the

usual assignment that the A component stems from electron pickoff annihilations of positrons bound in o-Ps.

One might invoke changes in the positronium formation cross sections as the primary reason for the large variations of i_A and $i_{C'}$ with volume. However, the energies relevant for the Ore gap are so high that thermal variations should be without detectable effect in the molecular substances under discussion. Model calculations show a high stability of the Ps atom in such structures. In short, the assumption of large variations in the formation cross section would not be a palatable one. The constancy of i_B bears this out, if one assigns this component to the annihilation of positrons which have not formed positronium. One is led then to attribute the fraction $1 - i_B = i_A + i_{C'}$ to annihilations of positrons bound in Ps atoms. Because of (1), $i_{C'}$ must be the sum of at least three unresolved components. First, it must serve as a reservoir for o-Ps atoms to be able to feed i_A when the volume increases; we denote this part of the annihilations, coming from o-Ps atoms via fast electron pickoff, by i_{C_3}. Second, in competition with self-annihilation of the p-Ps pendant of the o-Ps component, a fraction i_{C_1} derives, as does i_{C_3}, from fast electron pickoff. Third, a fraction i_D comes from p-Ps atoms in the same habitat of low pickoff rates as the o-Ps atoms annihilating as i_A, which therefore decay merely by self-annihilation with a lifetime τ_D close to τ_{p}-Ps = 0.125 nsec.

In summary, the new experimental data suggest tentatively that, of all annihilations, the fraction

$$i_A + i_{C_3} = (\tfrac{3}{4})(i_A + i_{C'}) \tag{1}$$

is attributable to pickoff annihilations of positrons bound in o-Ps. The fraction $(\tfrac{1}{4})(i_A + i_{C'})$ comes from the corresponding p-Ps atoms, while i_B accounts for the positrons which have eluded positronium formation. In these terms, a change of volume affects a redistribution between i_{C_3} and i_A (and presumably between i_{C_1} and i_D). We shall discuss possible causes for these changes after reviewing the corresponding behavior of the lifetimes.

Where investigated, angular correlation data show a narrow component in substances with long-lifetime annihilations.[6,7] It varies primarily with volume, and can be identified with the self-annihilations of p-Ps atoms formed in these substances.[4,7] Following Fabri et al.,[8] Walters and McGervey[9] succeeded in giving experimental support to an important consequence of the interpretation of i_A as stemming from pickoff annihilations of positrons bound in o-Ps, namely, that the long lived component on the average must encompass more annihilations with high momenta than the spectrum as a whole. Bisi et al.[10] studied the quenching of o-Ps atoms by a magnetic field. Their experiment clearly identifies the

long-lifetime component with the decay of o-Ps atoms via pickoff.
It even permits the deduction of a lifetime for the self-annihilation
of p-Ps atoms in matter, which should be identified with the lifetime associated with i_D. The value is found to be very close to
0.125 nsec, the lifetime of p-Ps *in vacuo*. However, short of drastic
improvements in the time resolution, a direct experimental confirmation of Eq. (1) can be expected only from experiments as those
described by Dick et al.,[11] with high time resolution. Such experiments exploit the fact that, in effect, the relative population of
o-Ps and p-Ps, if formed by polarized positrons in a magnetic field,
differs depending on whether the magnetic field direction is parallel
or antiparallel with regard to the direction of positron polarization.

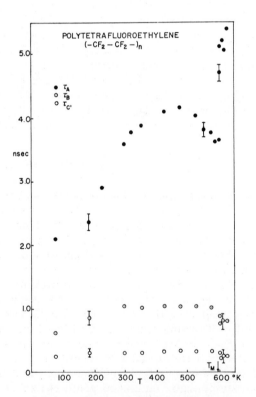

Fig. 3. The mean lifetimes of the three
components in the annihilation spectrum of
positrons in polytetrafluoroethylene (Teflon)
as a function of temperature.[4]

1.2 Lifetimes

Figure 3 displays the temperature dependence of the lifetimes associated with the three components A, B, C' in polytetrafluoro-ethylene. The intermediate lifetime, τ_B, and the shortest lifetime, τ_C, appear to be fairly constant on this scale. On occasion, these variations may be as large relatively speaking as those of τ_A, but they are not well established within the uncertainties of experiment and analysis. Condensed inert gases offer a better opportunity for a study of these trends.[12]

The long-lifetime τ_A is of order 2 nsec, and rises sharply with temperature. At high temperatures, τ_A tends to level off. Indeed, if melting does not interfere, a maximum can develop as shown in Fig. 3.[4] Phase transitions generally, as does melting, change τ_A smoothly if expressed in terms of the accompanying change in the volume.[13-17] In one revealing experiment, on H_2,[18] τ_A was found to be shorter in the gas phase than in the liquid phase of the same density. Qualitatively, this observation, namely, that heating at constant volume decreases τ_A, anticipated the thermal effects exhibited in Fig. 3, as discussed below.

Many studies have been published on other aspects of the positron annihilation characteristics of condensed molecular substances. They were reviewed by Wallace in 1960.[19] A recent summary emphasizes their chemical implications.[20] The conclusions drawn in most of these investigations presuppose a detailed understanding of the underlying primitive processes. As our views about these processes change in accommodating the new experimental developments, these conclusions need be reexamined.

2. DISCUSSION

For the reasons given in Section 1, we take i_B to account for the decay of positrons which have not formed positronium. This component appears to be insensitive to changes in temperatures or volume, as we would expect from such an assignment. After i_B has been subtracted out we attribute the remaining time spectrum to annihilations of positrons bound in Ps atoms. To trim matters further, we shall not deal with the fraction $(\frac{1}{4})(i_A + i_{C'})$ due to p-Ps atoms, since its annihilation rates are high, irrespective of the condition of the lattice; it acts merely as a constant unresolved part of $i_{C'}$. What remains is given by Eq. (1), the fraction comprising all o-Ps atoms decaying via electron pickoff. It is this component which most sensitively responds to changes in the properties of molecular substances.

Consider a simple van der Waals substance composed of closed-shell atoms or molecules, in which o-Ps atoms have been formed and are thermalized. Let $\psi_{+b}(\mathbf{x})$ be the wavefunction at the point $\mathbf{x}$ in a lattice of a positron bound in o-Ps, such that $\rho_{+b}(\mathbf{x}) = |\psi_{+b}(\mathbf{x})|^2$ is its density at $\mathbf{x}$. The spin averaged pickoff annihilation rate can be written as

$$\Gamma_p = \pi r_e^2 c \int_{\text{lattice}} \rho_{+b}(\mathbf{x})\rho_-(\mathbf{x}) \, d^3x \tag{2}$$

where r_e is the classical electron radius, and c the velocity of light. The electron density $\rho_-(\mathbf{x})$ as seen by the positron is some-what enhanced over the density in the absence of the positron, in domains where $\psi_{+b}(\mathbf{x})$ extends into the atoms making electron pickoff possible. Here the screening of the charge of the positron by the electron to which it is bound remains small by the exclusion principle (cf. Fig. 4). We shall assume that this effect has been incorporated in Eq. (2), correcting in an average manner for the errors introduced by factorizing the wavefunction of the annihilating positron-electron pair. Equation (2) permits us to study the dependence of Γ_p on lattice parameters. The assignment of i_A as the pickoff component of o-Ps decay in the free volume of the lattice implies that τ_A and Γ_p^{-1} should exhibit the same trends.

In van der Waals solids all electrons are tightly bound, and the potentials have only a short range. A change in volume changes the free volume between the molecules in which the Ps atoms move; it does not change the effective excluded volume occupied by the molecules. Of course, this is true only within certain limits; for example, the excluded volume can be compressed at high pressures, and thermal vibrations tend to swell the excluded volume on the average, thereby reducing the effective free volume. In any case, given the type of molecule and the lattice structure, the pickoff rate should be a function only of the effective free volume, v. This conclusion was corroborated by model calculations.[4,13]

When $v \rightarrow 0$, the Ps atoms are forced into close proximity with

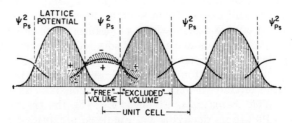

Fig. 4. Density of Ps atom in a lattice (solid line) and the densities of its positron (+) and electron (−) components as polarized by the lattice (dashed curves); schematic.[13]

the molecules M, and the pickoff annihilation rate $\Gamma_p(v)$ approaches some high but characteristic value $\Gamma_p(0)$, which must be comparable to that of the corresponding compound $(o\text{-PsM})$. As v increases, the Ps atoms recede from the lattice molecules. This reduces sharply the overlap between $\psi_{+b}(\mathbf{x})$ and the lattice wavefunction, and we observe a fast initial drop of $\Gamma_p(v)$. As the volume increases further, merely the tails of the wavefunctions overlap, and $\Gamma_p(v)$ decreases more slowly. In going from low to high temperatures, we expect the influence of lattice vibrations, or of density fluctuations generally, to become important. While the accompanying small fluctuations of the lattice potential probed by the positronium wavefunction affect $\psi_{+b}(\mathbf{x})$ only in second order, the tightly-bound electrons follow the thermal motion adiabatically, in effect raising the electron density in the free volume. The net result is that Γ_p is shortened, relative to its value in a cold lattice of the same density. Indeed, model calculations show that under favorable conditions, the opposing effects of volume and temperature can be expected to manifest themselves in the form of a minimum in the isobaric temperature dependence of Γ_p. The investigation leading to the data exhibited in Fig. 3 was motivated by this expectation.

We can estimate the magnitude of this effect by extending the cell model discussed earlier[13] to include thermal effects. Let the central molecule in a cell oscillate with amplitude $\mathbf{U}$. We treat the accompanying change of the potential experienced by the positron as a slowly varying perturbation. To first order, the positron wavefunction of the perturbed quasistationary state differs from the unperturbed wavefunction only by a phase factor, and $\rho_{+b}(\mathbf{x})$ remains unchanged. The tight binding in molecular substances forces the electrons to move adiabatically with the nuclei, contributing in turn to the change in the potential seen by the positron. Therefore to this order, we must identify $\rho_-(\mathbf{x})$ in Eq. (2) with the thermal average of the electron density. We overestimate the thermal effects somewhat in this approximation, because in second order, the correlation between the molecular motion and $\psi_{+b}(\mathbf{x})$ contributes. It is significant only near the nuclei, where $\psi_{+b}(\mathbf{x})$ is small, and consequently, does not affect the first-order results importantly. The effects of molecular oscillations of mean-square-amplitude $\langle U^2 \rangle$ have been worked out in this approximation for the hard-core cell model.[4] The result is given in Eq. (3).

$$\Gamma_p = \Gamma_{op} \frac{1 + G(S, V^*)\{\exp[2\xi^2(S, V^*)\langle U^2\rangle/R_0^2]-1\}}{1 + F(S, V^*)} \tag{3}$$

where S is a dimensionless parameter proportional to the potential set up by the molecule in the cell, and $V^* = V/V_0$ denotes the reduced cell volume. The mean-square amplitude is measured relative

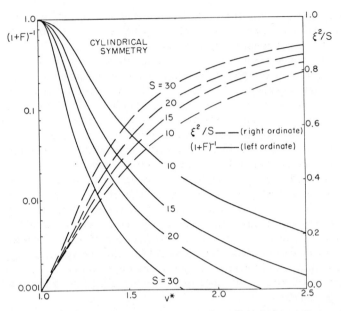

Fig. 5. The functions $F(V^*, S)$ and $\xi^2(V^*, S)$, calculated
for the cell model of lattices composed of chain molecules,
drawn for a range of values of the cell potential parameter S.

to R_0, the radius of the central molecule. $G(S, V^*)$ is a slowly varying function, which in the range of interest can be set equal to $1/2$.
The functions F and ζ were calculated for the axial symmetry of
polymeric chain lattices and for spherically symmetric lattice
cells.[21] Figures 5 and 6 summarize some of the results for typical
ranges of S. We note the large differences between the two types of
lattices in the sensitivity of the relevant functions to changes in S
and V^*. Little wonder that the pertinent experimental data derive
almost exclusively from substances composed of chain molecules!

In applying Eq. (3) to temperature data, we make the simplest
possible approximation to the temperature dependence of $\langle U^2 \rangle$. At
temperatures T less than T_M, the crystalline melting temperature,
we set $\langle U^2 \rangle / R^2 \sim T / T_M$, where R is the radius of the molecular
cell. Above the melting point, $\langle U^2 \rangle / R^2$ is taken to be constant.
This amounts to employing the Lindeman melting criterion.[4] In
Figs. 7 we compare the pickoff lifetime Γ_p^{-1} as calculated from
Eq. (3) for a chain lattice with $S = 25$, and the experimental data
on τ_A of polyethylene and Teflon. We see that polyethylene just
fails to develop a maximum before melting, but Teflon with its
high melting point shows the effect outside experimental error.

It would seem then that the salient features built into Eq. (3) can reproduce the important trends of the long lifetimes measured to date. Predictions for other types of Γ_p-dependence on lattice parameters follow directly from Eq. (3), and should be tested experimentally.

We may recall the main conclusion of Section 1.1, that the intensity distribution in the annihilation time spectra suggests two o-Ps pickoff components i_A and i_{C_3}, where i_A increases with the free volume at the expense of i_{C_3}. Let us consider in detail what happens when a lattice expands. If we start from a tight-packed configuration, the lattice expands initially by a uniform dilation of the lattice cells; but it will not do so indefinitely. Rather, beyond a certain critical cell size, the lattice becomes unstable with regard to a state in which the additional free volume is randomly distributed throughout the lattice. We elaborate on this process by following the argument of Turnbull and Cohen given in a different context.[22] Consider a molecule of volume V_0 held in a cell of volume V formed by the surrounding molecules, leaving the free volume

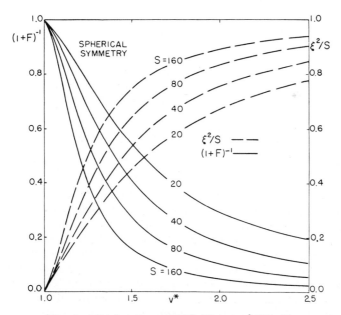

Fig. 6. The functions $F(V^*, S)$ and $\xi^2(V^*, S)$, calculated for the cell model of lattices composed of spherically symmetric molecules, drawn for a range of values of the cell potential parameter S.

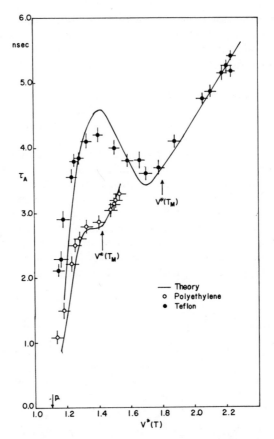

Fig. 7. Comparison of calculated pickoff
lifetimes Γ_p^{-1} with τ_A.[4]

$v = V - V_0$. The potential in the cell is determined by the intermolecular van der Waals interaction. For illustration, Fig. 8 shows
such a potential as it varies with the reduced cell volume $V^* = V/V_0$,
calculated for a face-centered cubic lattice.[23] When the volume is
small, the molecule executes oscillatory motions in a smooth potential well. As the volume increases, a dimple develops at the center
of the well, which however is of little consequence, as long as it
stays $<k_B T$. Turnbull and Cohen argue that when the dimple reaches
a certain height, i.e., when the cell volume exceeds a critical size
V_{cr}, no energy is required to redistribute the free volume added beyond V_{cr}, and the system will do so to lower its free energy by the
configurational entropy gained in the process. Loosely, when $v >$
$v_{cr} = V_{cr} - V_0$, the free volume increment $v - v_{cr}$ precipitates

out, and we are left with ordered domains comprising cells of size V_{cr}, and with voids built up of cellular increments of free volume. It follows from simple statistical arguments that for a mean-free volume v_f the size distribution of the voids is of the form $\exp(-v/v_f)$.

An o-Ps atom formed in such an environment must annihilate with high pickoff rate in the ordered domains where $v \lesssim v_{cr}$, and with low pickoff rate in the voids. Let P_{cr} be the probability that o-Ps atoms once formed with a relative yield η_{o-Ps} find themselves in the free volume, and $(1 - P_{cr})$ the probability that they are in ordered domains. The total o-Ps population decays with time as

$$n(t) = \eta_{o-Ps}\, P_{cr}\, \exp(-\Gamma_p(v > v_{cr})t)$$

$$+ \eta_{o-Ps}\, (1 - P_{cr})\, \exp(-\Gamma_p(v \lesssim v_{cr})t) \qquad (4)$$

If the distribution of void sizes is taken to be $\exp(-v/v_f)$, then $P_{cr} = \exp(-v_{cr}/v_f)$. We identify the measured quantities i_A, i_{C_3} with $\eta_{o-Ps} P_{cr}$, $\eta_{o-Ps} (1 - P_{cr})$, and γ_A, γ_C with $\Gamma_p(v > v_{cr})$, $\Gamma_p(v \lesssim v_{cr})$, respectively. For illustration, the curves in Fig. 2 were calculated in this way, using the appropriate density-tempera-ture relation of polyethylene. It appears that even in the cursory form presented here, our interpretation of Eq. (4) accounts in some detail for the experimental observations enumerated in Section 1.1.

Two important assumptions have been made in writing down Eq. (4). The first is that the presence of o-Ps atoms does not influence

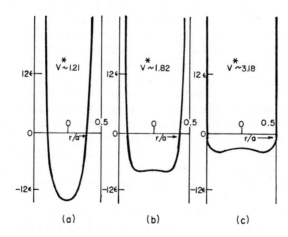

Fig. 8. The potential in a molecular cell at various cell volumes[23].

P_{cr} . While this is a realistic assumption for the substances considered here, it does not seem to hold, e.g., for condensed He, as
discussed elsewhere in these Proceedings. The second assumption
is that the o-Ps wavefunction in the free volume probes all void
sizes in times so short, compared to the lifetime τ_A, that

$$\gamma_A(v_f) = \int_{v > v_{cr}} p(v_f, v) \Gamma_p(v) \, dv$$

where for given v_f, $p(v_f, v) \, dv$ is the probability of finding the free
volume between v and $v + dv$. Actually, the lattice function $p(v_f, v)$
should be weighed somewhat proportional to v before applying it
here because the Ps atoms will tend to slide into the larger voids
where their energy is lowest.

In the other extreme, if o-Ps atoms were trapped with probability $p'(v_f, v)$ in a void of volume v, assumed to be stationary
over times of order $\Gamma_p^{-1}(v)$, then the first term of Eq. (4) would
take the form

$$i_A \int_{v > v_{cr}} p'(v_f, v) \exp[-\Gamma_p(v) t] \, dv$$

Such a component cannot be represented by a simple exponential decay law (except in the unlikely event that $p'(v_f, v)$ is a delta function); instead, the effective annihilation rate decreases with time in
such rigid media. If it is nevertheless analyzed in terms of sums of
exponential time decays, the change of γ_A with time simulates new
long-lifetime components.[23] They should fade when the rate of the
density fluctuations are made to rise, for example, by heating the
sample to temperatures above the glass transformation range. No
such situations appear to have been observed so far.

The evidence to date suggests, then, that two conditions for o-Ps
decay by electron pickoff exist in the substances investigated so far.
They differ in degree more than in kind. There are indications that
the shift of annihilations coming from one condition C to the other
A is associated with disorder in the lattice, and determined by a redistribution of the free volume. At ordinary temperatures and pressures, the respective pickoff rates are a factor ten or so apart. The
small values of τ_{C_3} are comparable to the lifetime of Ps$^-$, and reflect the high pickoff rates in the ordered domains of the lattice. The
values of τ_A, as plotted in Fig. 7, extrapolate to just such short lifetimes as $v^*(T) = 1 + v_f^*(T)$ approaches the tight packing (tp) condition $v^*(0) = 1 + v_{tp}^*$.

The free volume dependence implies a close kinship between the
microscopic conditions underlying the variations with density, temperature, and even molecular volume, of the transport properties
(such as fluidity and diffusion) and of the positron annihilation

characteristics of molecular substances. Correlations between the two classes of phenomena indeed are not uncommon. But clearly one can not invoke this fact *per se* as sufficient evidence for a direct causal connection between them.

II. POSITRON ANNIHILATION IN IONIC CRYSTALS

1. THE EXPERIMENTAL SITUATION

Until quite recently, the field of positron annihilation in ionic crystals was a comparatively tranquil one. No search for long-lifetime components had been made after the negative result of Bell and Graham, and on the strength of Ferrell's argument that in ionic crystals there is simply not room enough for positronium to be energetically stable.[25] The 2γ angular correlation data appeared to resemble the momentum distribution of the Wheeler compounds between a positron and a negative ion closely enough to lend support to the conjecture that the positrons are so tightly bound that the annihilation properties of a crystal are equal to those of the constituent isolated negative ions. Although of considerable theoretical interest, many studies of the annihilation characteristics of Wheeler compounds like Cl^-e^+ or $ClPs$, HPs and others were stimulated in part by the expectation of testing such calculations through measurements on the corresponding ionic crystals.

Some doubt was stirred up on this point when, in comparing their angular correlation data of all alkali chlorides and all sodium halides with extensive model calculations, Stewart and Pope[26] concluded that the positrons cannot be considered localized on a single negative ion. The best fits were obtained with positron-electron wavefunctions resembling closely the best wavefunctions of the electrons in the outer shells of the free negative ions and, therefore, the uncorrected angular correlation data appeared to be consistent also with the electron densities extracted from x-ray diffraction data. This is possible only if the positron wavefunctions behave as if they were nearly plane waves in the relevant domains of the atomic volume.

The field gained momentum with the advent of two new discoveries. The first was the observation by Stewart and March[27] that contrary to what one was led to expect from the experience with alkali halide crystals, a significant discrepancy exists between the momentum distribution of the annihilating positron-electron pairs in lithium hydride, LiH, and the one derived either from the wavefunction of the isolated H^- ion, or from the x-ray density distribution. More puzzling, the discrepancy did not seem to go in the right direction qualitatively to support the notion that although perhaps not in the alkali halides, at least in LiH the positrons are bound to the H^- ion. The second was the discovery of Bisi, Fiorentini, and Zappa[28] of long-lifetime components in the annihilation time spectra of ionic crystals, comprising 40% of all annihilations in the crystals investigated so far, save for LiH with only 6%.

The first observation poses the question whether any basic ingredient is missing in our understanding of the positron annihilation characteristics of solids, which makes itself felt importantly in diatomic crystals or, more generally, in crystal lattices with a basis. If so, LiH seemed to be the best suited example for uncovering such deficiencies. It is the simplest heteroatomic lattice, and has attracted theoretical interest for many years. In the following, we report on our search, under the guidance of Stig Lundqvist, for the source of the discrepancies noted for the LiH crystal.[29]

The second observation is still so young that little is known as yet about the variations of the characteristics of the long-lifetime components with changes in crystal properties. Still, we can bring the measurements into a reasonable order by linking the available long-lifetime data to the dielectric properties of the crystals. The result suggests trends open to experimental scrutiny.

2. POSITRONS IN A LATTICE WITH A BASIS

2.1 Annihilation Characteristics

Let the system of N electrons and a positron in a crystal be described by the wavefunction $\Psi(\mathbf{x}_n; \mathbf{x}_+) \equiv \Psi(\mathbf{x}_1, \ldots, \mathbf{x}_n, \ldots, \mathbf{x}_N; \mathbf{x}_+)$. The annihilation operator probes $\Psi(\mathbf{x}_n; \mathbf{x}_+)$ at some $\mathbf{x}_n = \mathbf{x}_+$, i.e., the momentum density of the annihilating positron-electron pair becomes

$$
\begin{aligned}
|\Phi(\mathbf{p})|^2 &= \sum_n |\int d^3x_n \, d^3x_+ \, \delta(\mathbf{x}_n - \mathbf{x}_+) \Psi(\mathbf{x}_n; \mathbf{x}_+) e^{-i\mathbf{p}\cdot\mathbf{x}_n}|^2 \\
&= \sum_n |\int d^3x \Psi_n(\mathbf{x}) e^{-i\mathbf{p}\cdot\mathbf{x}}|^2
\end{aligned}
\tag{5}
$$

We define an annihilation rate per unit volume in momentum space,

$$
\gamma(\mathbf{p}) = \pi\alpha^3 |\Phi(\mathbf{p})|^2
\tag{6}
$$

such that the spin averaged decay rate Γ is given by

$$
\Gamma = (2\pi)^{-3} \int \gamma(\mathbf{p}) \, d^3p
\tag{7}
$$

Γ is expressed in units of the time $\hbar^3/me^4 = 2.42 \times 10^{-17}$ sec, α being the fine structure constant. Most angular correlation data are recorded relative to a (xyz) coordinate system in the laboratory, in the form

$$I(p_z) = (2\pi)^{-3} \int_0^{2\pi} \int_{p_z}^\infty \gamma(\mathbf{p}) p \ dp \ d\varphi \tag{8}$$

such that $\int_{-\infty}^{+\infty} I(p_z) \ dp_z = \Gamma$, except for an unknown scaling factor for $I(p_z)$; in these experiments, $p_z = mc\vartheta$, where ϑ is the deviation from π of the angle between the two emerging photons, typically of order milliradians.

Our objective is to derive $|\Phi(\mathbf{p})|^2$ and from it to calculate $I(p_z)$ by Eq. (8). The p-dependence can then be compared with experiment on a relative scale in $I(p_z)$. The absolute magnitude can be compared separately with experiment in a global way by the annihilation rate as given in Eq. (7).

By invoking the periodicity of the crystal lattice, we can write

$$|\Phi(\mathbf{p})|^2 = \sum_{\mathbf{k}_+} g(\mathbf{k}_+) \sum_{\mathbf{K}} \delta_{\mathbf{p}, \kappa + \mathbf{K}} |\Phi_\kappa^c(\mathbf{p})|^2 \tag{9}$$

where $\kappa = \mathbf{k}_+ + \mathbf{k}_-$. $\mathbf{K}$ is a reciprocal lattice vector, $\mathbf{k}_+$ is the wave vector of the positron with distribution $g(\mathbf{k}_+)$, and $\mathbf{k}_-$ is the wave vector of the electrons ranging over all occupied electronic states in the crystal, up to some maximum value $(\mathbf{k}_-)_{max}$. $\Phi_\kappa^c(\mathbf{p})$ denotes the Fourier transform as in Eq. (5), the $\mathbf{x}$ integration now extending only over the unit cell. It follows from Eq. (9) that the photons created in the annihilation process carry away the momentum $\mathbf{p} = \kappa + \mathbf{K}$.

For a lattice with a basis, we decompose the unit cell into atomic cells, one centered about each atom in the unit cell. If $\mathbf{d}_j$ is the position of the jth atomic cell in the unit cell, $\Phi_\kappa^c(\mathbf{p})$ becomes

$$\Phi_\kappa^c(\mathbf{p}) = \sum_j e^{-i\mathbf{p}\cdot\mathbf{d}_j} \varphi_j(\mathbf{p}; \kappa) \tag{10}$$

where the atomic cell function

$$\varphi_j(\mathbf{p}; \kappa) = \int_{\text{cell } j} \psi_j(\mathbf{x}; \kappa) e^{-i\mathbf{p}\cdot\mathbf{x}} \ d^3x \tag{11}$$

is the Fourier transform of $\Psi_\kappa(\mathbf{x})$ in the jth atomic cell. The explicit form in which Eq. (10) is to be employed depends on the approximations for $\Psi_\kappa(\mathbf{x})$, chosen to describe a given physical situation. It is easiest to demonstrate this point for a lattice with atoms 1 and 2 in the unit cell.

(1) If we are concerned with free states of the annihilating positron-electron pair, $\varphi_j(\mathbf{p}; \kappa)$ is nonzero only if $\mathbf{p} = \kappa$, i.e., the photons carry away just the momenta of the annihilating particles.

The cell approximation implies that the wavefunction in the unit cell can be written as $\psi_C(\mathbf{x}; \kappa) = \psi_1(\mathbf{x}; \kappa) + \psi_2(\mathbf{x}; \kappa) \exp(i\kappa \cdot \mathbf{d}_{12})$, where $\psi_j(\mathbf{x}; \kappa) = u_j(\mathbf{x}; \kappa) \exp(i\kappa \cdot \mathbf{x})$. The original formulation of the cell method moreover approximates $u_j(\mathbf{x}; \kappa)$, the periodic part of the wavefunction in the jth atomic cell, by $u_j(\mathbf{x}; 0)$, and yields

$$|\Phi_\kappa^c(\mathbf{p})|^2_{\mathbf{p}-\kappa=\mathbf{K}} = |u_1(\mathbf{K})|^2 + |u_2(\mathbf{K})|^2$$
$$+ 2|u_1(\mathbf{K})| \, |u_2(\mathbf{K})| \cos(\mathbf{K} \cdot \mathbf{d}_{12})$$

The functions $u_j(\mathbf{K})$ are the Fourier transforms of $u_j(\mathbf{x}; 0)$ with regard to $\mathbf{p} - \kappa = \mathbf{K}$. If we express $\mathbf{K}$ in terms of unit reciprocal lattice vectors $\mathbf{b}$,

$$\mathbf{K} = 2\pi \{h\mathbf{b}_1 + k\mathbf{b}_2 + l\mathbf{b}_3\}; \quad h, k, l = 0, \pm 1, \pm 2, \ldots.$$

then in lattices with NaCl structure,

$$|\Phi_\kappa^c(\mathbf{p})|^2_{\mathbf{p}-\kappa=\mathbf{K}} = |u_1(\mathbf{K}) \pm u_2(\mathbf{K})|^2$$

the plus sign applies when $(h + k + l)$ = even integer, the minus sign otherwise. Similar results obtain when the κ-dependence of $u_j(\mathbf{x}; \kappa)$ is taken into account, but then $u_j(\mathbf{K})$ will not depend merely on the difference $(\mathbf{p} - \kappa)$ but on both arguments $(\mathbf{p}, \kappa)$ separately.

Approximation (1) should apply whenever an itinerant electron model offers an adequate description of the properties of the crystal (metals, intermetallic compounds, covalent and ionic crystals).

(2) If a tight binding approximation is appropriate for the atomic cells in the sense that the wavefunction in the unit cell can be represented by $\psi_C(\mathbf{x}; \kappa) = \psi_1(\mathbf{x}) + \psi_2(\mathbf{x}) \exp(i\kappa \cdot \mathbf{d}_{12})$, one finds

$$|\Phi_\kappa^c(\mathbf{p})|^2_{\mathbf{p}-\kappa=\mathbf{K}} = |\varphi_1(\mathbf{p})|^2 + |\varphi_2(\mathbf{p})|^2$$
$$+ 2|\varphi_1(\mathbf{p})| \, |\varphi_2(\mathbf{p})| \cos(\mathbf{K} \cdot \mathbf{d}_{12})$$

which simplifies to

$$|\Phi_\kappa^c(\mathbf{p})|^2_{\mathbf{p}-\kappa=\mathbf{K}} = |\varphi_1(\mathbf{p}) \pm \varphi_2(\mathbf{p})|^2$$

in NaCl structures. Here again, in case of a more general admixture of atomic states, the interference term does not depend only on the difference $(\mathbf{p} - \kappa)$, but on both $\mathbf{p}$ and κ separately. Approximation (2) should apply to crystals where the states in one atomic cell in the reference unit cell are nearly degenerate with the states of the atomic cells of the same kind in all other unit cells (semiconductors, insulators).

(3) Sometimes it suffices to choose a tight binding approximation for the entire unit cell of the form $\psi_C(\mathbf{x}; \kappa) = \psi_1(\mathbf{x}) + \psi_2(\mathbf{x})$, so that merely

$$|\Phi_\kappa^c(\mathbf{p})|^2_{\mathbf{p}-\kappa=\mathbf{K}} = |\varphi_1(\mathbf{p})|^2 + |\varphi_2(\mathbf{p})|^2 + 2|\varphi_1(\mathbf{p})| \, |\varphi_2(\mathbf{p})| \cos(\mathbf{p} \cdot \mathbf{d}_{12})$$

For example, states in van der Waals crystals consisting of condensed diatomic molecules fall into this category.

(4) In situations of extreme tight binding in each atomic cell, no phase relations remain within and between the unit cells, and

$$| \Phi_\kappa{}^c(\mathbf{p}) |^2_{\mathbf{p}-\kappa=\mathbf{K}} = | \varphi_1(\mathbf{p}) |^2 + | \varphi_2(\mathbf{p}) |^2$$

States in strongly ionic crystals, diatomic van der Waals crystals, and ion cores can justly be approximated in this way.

In most situations of interest, then, a cross term appears which depends on the structure of the unit cell. In previous work on ionic crystals, Approximation (4) had always been deemed adequate, accentuated by the assumption of an affinity between the positrons and negative ions so strong, that $| \varphi_{\text{positive ion}}(\mathbf{p}) |^2 \simeq 0$. The assumption of a locally bound positron-negative ion system gives rise to a significant distortion of the ion wavefunction, afflicting both the resulting angular correlation and the annihilation rate. As our example LiH demonstrates, when Bloch wavefunctions govern the annihilating positron-electron pairs, the cross term can play an important role in the angular correlation between the two gamma quanta created in the annihilation process in crystals.

2.2 Positron Momenta

As it stands, Eq. (9) applies to an adiabatically rigid lattice with an as yet unspecified distribution of positron momenta $g(\mathbf{k}_+)$. At any temperature T, the lattice points execute thermal vibrations about the equilibrium positrons, and in the expressions for $| \Phi_\kappa{}^c(\mathbf{p}) |^2_{\mathbf{p}-\kappa=\mathbf{K}}$, Debye-Waller factors of the argument $K^2 \langle U_{\mathbf{K}}{}^2(T) \rangle_j$ appear, where $\langle U_{\mathbf{K}}{}^2(T) \rangle_j$ denotes the mean square amplitude of the jth atom in the unit cell along the direction of $\mathbf{K}$. However, in contrast to x-ray diffraction data, the momenta $\mathbf{p}$ resolved by angular correlation measurements, do not extend far enough to probe the range where the contributions from $\mathbf{K} > 0$ become dominant, and therefore the effects of the Debye-Waller factors can be neglected in many instances.

We mention two important forms of $g(\mathbf{k}_+)$.

(1) If the positrons are in thermal equilibrium with the lattice of temperature T,

$$g(\mathbf{k}_+, T) = (\pi^{1/2} \zeta)^{-3} \exp(-k_+^2/\zeta^2)$$

where

$$\zeta(T) = (2m_+{}^* k_B T)^{1/2}$$

In a solid, the effective positron mass m_+^* governing the thermal distribution in general will differ from the electronic rest mass m_0.

We can exhibit the consequences of this temperature effect on the angular correlation by integrating Eq. (9) for a spherically symmetric $(\mathbf{k}_-)_{max}$. Abbreviating $\beta(T) \equiv \zeta(T)/|\mathbf{k}_-|_{max}$, one obtains

$$|\Phi(\mathbf{p}, T)|^2 = \sum_{\mathbf{K}} \mathcal{B}(|\mathbf{K} - \mathbf{p}|/|\mathbf{k}_-|_{max} ; \beta(T))|\Phi_c(\mathbf{K})|^2$$

where

$$\mathcal{B}(y, \beta(T)) = \tfrac{1}{2}\left\{1 + \mathrm{erf}[(1-y)/\beta] - \frac{\beta}{\pi^{1/2} y} \exp[-(1-y)^2/\beta^2]\right\}$$

in the experimentally important ranges of $y \sim 1$ and $\beta \sim 0.1$. Figure 9 shows $\mathcal{B}(y, \beta)$ for representative values of $\beta(T)$. The resulting change in the angular correlation can be used to extract information about m_+^* and $|\mathbf{k}_-|_{max}$, as demonstrated elsewhere.[29]

(2) If we apply an electric field E to the crystal so strong that $eEl_+ > k_B T$, where l_+ is the mean-free path, but not strong enough for the anisotropic part of $g(\mathbf{k}_+)$ to be significant, $g(\mathbf{k}_+, E)$ becomes a distribution of the form

$$g(\mathbf{k}_+, E) = [\Gamma(\tfrac{3}{4})\pi\eta^3]^{-1} \exp(-k_+^4/\eta^4)$$

where $\eta^4(E) = 2(eEl_+ m_+^*)^2$.

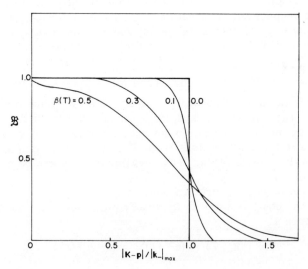

Fig. 9. The temperature function $\mathcal{B}$ for representative values of $\beta(T)$.[29]

We illustrate the effect of E on the angular correlation, by integrating, as in Example (1), over a spherically symmetric $(\mathbf{k}_-)_{max}$; with the abbreviations $y \equiv |\mathbf{K} - \mathbf{p}|/|\mathbf{k}_-|_{max}$, $\beta(E) \equiv \eta(E)/|\mathbf{k}_-|_{max}$ and $\Theta(x) = (\tfrac{1}{2})(1 - x/|x|)$, the function $\mathcal{B}$ takes the form

$$
\begin{aligned}
\mathcal{B}(y, \beta(E)) = {} & \Theta\left(\frac{y-1}{\beta}\right) \left\{ 1 - \exp\left[-\left(\frac{y-1}{\beta}\right)^4\right]\right\} \\
& + \frac{1}{2}\left\{ \frac{\beta}{2\Gamma(\tfrac{3}{4})y} \frac{y^2-1}{\beta^2} \pi^{1/2} \left(\mathrm{erf}\left[\left(\frac{y-1}{\beta}\right)^2\right] - \mathrm{erf}\left[\left(\frac{y+1}{\beta}\right)^2\right]\right) \right. \\
& \left. + \left(1 - \frac{\beta}{2\Gamma(\tfrac{3}{4})y}\right)\left(\exp\left[-\left(\frac{y-1}{\beta}\right)^4\right] - \exp\left[-\left(\frac{y+1}{\beta}\right)^4\right]\right)\right\}
\end{aligned}
$$

We see that the effect of the electric field on the isotropic distribution is similar to that of the temperature; it causes the largest change in $I(\mathbf{p})$ near $p = |\mathbf{k}_-|_{max}$. It should be possible to observe this effect in favorable cases and, from its magnitude, to deduce the mobility of the positrons.

2.3 Enhancement

Whenever Bloch wavefunctions govern the positrons in a crystal lattice, the term in the wave equation for the electrons in a unit cell accounting for the positron—electron Coulomb interaction is of order L^{-1}, where L is the number of unit cells in the crystal, i.e., the positron—electron interaction has no appreciable effect on the wavefunction of any particular electron nor, as a consequence, on the effective lattice potential in which the positrons move. Still, the cumulative effect of the polarization of all N electrons in the lattice can congest an appreciable enhancement of the electron density in the proximity of the positron. Manifestations of this disparity have been a puzzle for some time now. For example, on scaling, the measured angular distributions follow closely distributions calculated on the basis of unenhanced wavefunctions. However, if integrated over $\mathbf{p}$, one obtains unenhanced lifetimes often grossly at variance with experiment. But because of the small effects of positron—electron correlation on the momentum distribution of any annihilating positron—electron pair, as long as the positron is not localized, the functional $\mathbf{p}$-dependence of the angular correlation function indeed should be insensitive to the enhancement; it should show up sensitively only in the scaling of $I(\mathbf{p})$.

These implications are demonstrated most easily if the positron annihilation characteristics are formulated in the statistical approximation. Here, the electrons of local density $\rho_0(\mathbf{x})$ are treated as being free to form a local Fermi surface with a Fermi momentum $k_F(\mathbf{x})$. In this approximation,

$$|\Phi(\mathbf{p})|^2 = 2 \int d^3x \rho_+(\mathbf{x}) \, \Xi(\mathbf{x}) \, \Theta(p - k_F(\mathbf{x})) \qquad (12)$$

where $\Xi(\mathbf{x}) = \Xi(\rho_0(\mathbf{x}))$ is the density enhancement factor. The angular correlation function becomes

$$I(p) = \frac{\alpha^3}{4\pi} \int d^3x \rho_+(\mathbf{x}) \, \Xi(\mathbf{x}) \, \Theta(p - k_F(\mathbf{x})) (k_F^2(\mathbf{x}) - p^2) \qquad (13)$$

Noting that $k_F^3(\mathbf{x}) = 3\pi^2 \rho_0(\mathbf{x})$, we integrate over p and obtain the annihilation rate

$$\Gamma = \pi\alpha^3 \int d^3x \rho_+(\mathbf{x}) \, \Xi(\mathbf{x}) \, \rho_0(\mathbf{x}) \qquad (14)$$

The last two equations bear out the fact that the functional dependence of $I(\mathbf{p})$ on $\mathbf{p}$ is affected only weakly by the enhancement, while the annihilation rates can be affected strongly.

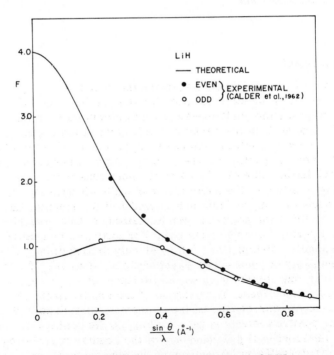

Fig. 10. Theoretical structure factors of LiH compared with the experimental points of Calder et al.,
[*J. Phys. Chem. Solids* **23**, 621 (1962)].[29]

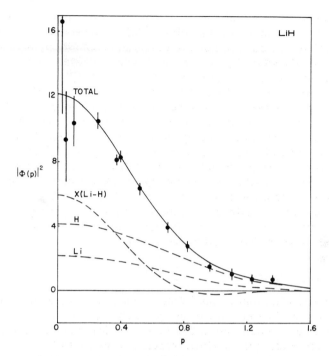

Fig. 11. Comparison of the theoretical momentum
density of annihilating positron–electron pairs in LiH
(solid curve) with the experimental points of Stewart
and March.[27] The broken curves Li and H indicate the
contributions from the separate atomic cells, and X
the contribution from the cross term.[29]

The density enhancement factor of the electron gas is discussed
in depth elsewhere in these Proceedings. Suffice it to say here that
the calculation of enhanced crystal wavefunctions is a very difficult
and subtle problem not yet tackled successfully. Fortunately, in
many instances of interest, such as the one in question here, one is
justified in applying the results of the statistical method for calculating approximate wavefunction enhancement factors.

2.4 Application To LiH

A detailed study of the LiH crystal was made to uncover the source
for the discrepancies noted by Stewart and March. Encouraged by the
work of Berko and Plaskett[30] on metals, we based our analysis, as
did they, on the cell method. Self-consistent electron wavefunctions

with exchange were calculated and, as a first test, applied to the co-
herent x-ray diffraction of the LiH crystal. The agreement between
the calculated structure factor for even and odd reflections, and experiment, as shown in Fig. 10, leaves the burden of the discrepancy
on the analysis of the annihilation data.

We argued in Section 2.1 that the momentum density of the annihilating electron-positron pairs can be expressed as the sum of three
terms, one for each of the two atoms in the unit cell and a third term,
an interference term, accounting for the phase relations between the
wavefunctions within the diatomic unit cell. Figure 11 shows how the
phase relations within the unit cell of the LiH crystal manifest themselves in a sharpening of the angular correlation function. On integration, we obtain a positron lifetime in LiH equal to 2.44×10^{-10}
sec; the measured dominant lifetime is $(2.1 \pm 0.3) \times 10^{-10}$ sec.[28]
These results resolve the apparent discrepancy within the framework of the Wigner-Seitz cell approximation.

3. LONG LIFETIMES

Bisi, Fiorentini, and Zappa[28] found a long-lifetime component in
the annihilation time spectra of many alkali halides. By graphical
decomposition, typically 30 to 50% of all annihilations are attributed
to this component, with lifetimes ranging from 0.4 to 0.7 nsec. Additional experimental evidence is cited against the notion that a
bound state with annihilation characteristics similar to those of Ps
atoms is the cause for this long-lifetime component. If this evidence
stands up in time, the observation of long lifetimes does not run
counter to Ferrell's argument that positronium is not stable in ionic
crystals, and one must search after other possible causes for these
components.[31]

We are lead to consider lattice defects as annihilation centers
(A centers) for bound positrons. Table I lists the simplest of such
possible A centers. In view of the evidence given by Bisi et al.,

TABLE I

The Simplest A Centers in Ionic Crystals

Designation[a]	Name	Lifetime	Angular correlation
[+ │ e⁺ │]	vacancy A center	~ Eq. (16)	as crystal
[+ │ e⁺e⁻ │]	vacancy A'_- center	~ Ps	narrow component
[− │ e⁻e⁺ │]	vacancy A_+' center	~ Ps	narrow component
[│ e⁺ │ −]	intersticial A center	~ Wheeler compound	

[a] Abbreviation for [missing ion │ trapped particles │ added ion] .

and in view of the fact that no narrow components have been observed in the angular correlation data, the second and third types of A centers do not appear to be of primary importance. Goldanskii and Prokopoev have considered the properties of interstitial A centers without electron-positron correlation, resulting in upper limits of the lifetimes.[32]

At this early stage of experimental development, it is instructive and helpful to study the consequences of the simplest model assumption, namely that the long-lifetime components are due to vacancy A-centers. For a first orientation, one can then resort to a continuum model of the vacancy A-center, and see whether it accounts for the dominant trends in the lifetimes. We describe the crystal surrounding the spherically symmetric vacancy of radius r_0 as a polarizable continuum characterized by the macroscopic static dielectric constant ϵ_0, the high-frequency dielectric constant ϵ, and some mean annihilation rate Γ_0. Then,

$$\Gamma = \Gamma_0 \int_{r > r_0} |\psi_+(\mathbf{r})|^2 \, d^3r \qquad (15)$$

Taking Simpson's variational self-consistent wavefunction[33] for $\psi_+(\mathbf{r})$, Γ/Γ_0 becomes a function only of the reduced variable $x = 2\mu r_0$, where $\mu = \epsilon_0^{-1} + (5/16)c$, with the abbreviation $c = (\epsilon^{-1} - \epsilon_0^{-1})$. Expressed analytically, $\Gamma(x)$ should decline with x in a manner indicated by

$$\Gamma(x) = \Gamma_0[1 + x + (1/2)x^2] \exp(-x) \qquad (16)$$

Setting $r_0 = (3/4\pi)^{1/3} d$, where d is the interionic distance in the crystal, we find that the experimental annihilation rates follow the general trend of Eq. (16) (cf. Fig. 12). The included data (the dielectric properties of all but the cesium halides were available to us from Ref. 34) fall into three groups clustered about $x = 1.15$, 1.75, and 2.25. Correlations among the Γ_0 of the same halides exceeding the stated experimental uncertainties are just barely discernable as deviations from the mean, viz. -10% for the fluorides and $+10\%$ for the chlorides. It would be interesting to search for long-lifetime components in crystals of LiI and RbF, not yet investigated, to see whether the associated annihilation rates fall into the first and second group, respectively, as one should expect from this model.

Turning now to the relative magnitude of the intensities, we can argue that if positrons annihilating in the perfect crystal with rate γ_c are captured at a rate $\nu\rho_a$ by the A centers present in the crystal with concentration ρ_a, on which they subsequently annihilate with rate γ_a, then the positrons disappear in time as given by

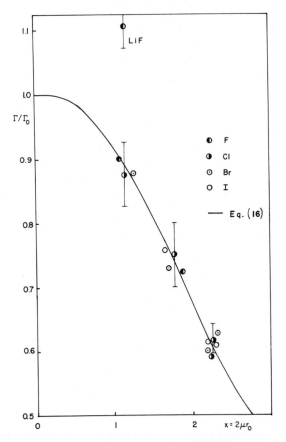

Fig. 12. The experimental annihilation rates of the long lifetime components of alkali-halide crystals[28] plotted as a function of the reduced variable x. Each point represents a different compound. The solid curve shows the x-dependence of Eq. (16).

$$\frac{n(t)}{n(0)} = \left(1 - \frac{\nu\rho_a}{\gamma_c - \gamma_a + \nu\rho_a}\right) \exp\left[-(\gamma_c + \nu\rho_a)t\right]$$

$$+ \frac{\nu\rho_a}{\gamma_c - \gamma_a + \nu\rho_a} \exp\left[-\gamma_a t\right] \qquad (17)$$

In this approximation the long lifetime γ_a^{-1} is independent of ρ_a; for example, on vacancy A centers, it would depend on the crystal proper-ties as sketched by Eq. (16). Since the ratio of the intensities in the two components, $i_a/(1 - i_a) = \nu\rho_a/(\gamma_c - \gamma_a)$, increases linearly with ρ_a, one might expect to uncover the relation between i_a and ρ_a merely from the dependence of the intensity of the long-lifetime component on the history of the crystal. In practice, however, great care is needed in producing changes in ρ_a, say, by exposing the crystal to radiation; γ_c may increase concurrently, e.g., because of F-centers created in the process acting as A' centers, leaving $i_a/(1 - i_a)$ nearly unaffected. In general, therefore, only measurements of the variation of the short lifetime, $\gamma_s^{-1} = (\gamma_c + \nu\rho_a)^{-1}$, in conjunction with determinations of i_a can give access to ρ_a or ν. For instance it follows from Eq. (17) that

$$\nu\rho_a = i_a(\gamma_s - \gamma_a) \tag{18}$$

In time, studies of this sort will point to the nature of the A centers responsible for the long-lifetime components. Should these centers prove to be linked to lattice defects as considered here in a preliminary manner, an attractive complement to the method of color centers may develop for the characterization of defects in ionic crystals.

ACKNOWLEDGMENTS

The author would like to acknowledge the hospitality of the Physics Division of the Aspen Institute for Humanistic Studies where these notes were prepared.

REFERENCES

1. Spirn, I., W. Brandt, G. Present, and A. Schwarzschild, *Bull. Am. Phys. Soc.* **9**, 394 (1964).
2. Sunyar, A. W., *Bull. Am. Phys. Soc.* **9**, 394 (1964).
3. Tao, S. J., and J. H. Green, *Proc. Phys. Soc.* **85**, 483 (1965).
4. Brandt, W., and I. Spirn, *Phys. Rev.* **142**, 231 (1966).
5. Stump, R., *Bull. Am. Phys. Soc.* **2**, 173 (1957); R. K. Wilson, P. O. Johnson, and R. Stump, *Phys. Rev.* **129**, 2091 (1963).
6. Stewart, A. T., *Phys. Rev.* **99**, 594 (1955).
7. de Zafra, R. L., and W. T. Joyner, *Phys. Rev.* **112**, 19 (1958).
8. Fabri, G., E. Germagnoli and G. Randone, *Phys. Letters* **3**, 6 (1962).
9. Walters, V. F., and J. D. McGervey, *Bull. Am. Phys. Soc.* **10**, 23 (1965); *Phys. Rev. Letters* **13**, 408 (1964).
10. Bisi, A., A. Fiorentini, E. Gatti, and L. Zappa, *Phys. Rev.* **128**, 2195 (1962).
11. Dick, L., L. Feuvrais, L. Madanski, and V. L. Telegdi, *Phys. Letters* **3**, 326 (1963).
12. Liu, D. C., and W. K. Roberts, *Phys. Rev.* **130**, 2322 (1963); ibid. **132**, 1633 (1963).

13. Brandt, W., S. Berko, and W. W. Walker, *Phys. Rev.* **120**, 1289 (1960).
14. Kohonen, T., *Ann. Acad. Sci. Fenn.* **A6**, No. **92** (1961).
15. Clarke, H. C., and B. G. Hogg, *J. Chem. Phys.* **37**, 1898 (1962).
16. Fabri, G., E. Germagnoli, and G. Randone, *Phys. Rev.* **130**, 204 (1965).
17. Groseclose, B. C., and G. D. Loper, *Phys. Rev.* **137**, A939 (1965).
18. Liu, D. C., and W. K. Roberts, *J. Phys. Chem. Solids* **23**, 1337 (1962).
19. Wallace, P. R., "Solid State Physics" (F. Seitz and D. Turnbull, eds.) Vol. 10, p. 1 ff., Academic Press, London and New York, 1960.
20. Green, J. H., and J. W. Lee, "Positronium Chemistry," Academic Press, London and New York, 1964.
21. We are grateful to Noelle A. Meyer for the numerical computation.
22. Turnbull, D., and M. H. Cohen, *J. Chem. Phys.* **31**, 1164 (1959); *ibid.* **34**, 120 (1961).
23. Lennard-Jones, J. E., and A. F. Devonshire, *Proc. Roy. Soc. (London)* **A163**, 53 (1937).
24. The author benefitted from discussions with Professor M. Deutsch and Dr. A. Schwarzschild on these points.
25. Ferrell, R. A., *Rev. Modern Phys.* **28**, 308 (1956).
26. Stewart, A. T., and N. K. Pope, *Phys. Rev.* **120**, 2033 (1960).
27. Stewart, A. T., and R. H. March, *Phys. Rev.* **122**, 75 (1961).
28. Bisi, A., A. Fiorentini, and L. Zappa, *Phys. Rev.* **131**, 1023 (1963); *ibid.* **134**, A328 (1964).
29. Brandt, W., L. Eder and S. Lundqvist, *Phys. Rev.* **142**, 165 (1966).
30. Berko, S., and J. S. Plaskett, *Phys. Rev.* **112**, 1877 (1958).
31. Neamtan, S. M., and R. I. Verrall [*Phys. Rev.* **134**, A1254 (1964)] concluded that the formation and persistence of Ps is energetically favorable in the LiH crystal, where only a 6% long-lifetime component has been observed, however.
32. Goldanskii, V. I., and E. P. Prokopoev, *Soviet Phys. Solid State* **6**, 2641 (1965).
33. Simpson, J. H., *Proc. Roy. Soc. (London)* **A197**, 269 (1949).
34. Gourary, B. S., and F. J. Adrian, "Solid State Physics" (F. Seitz and D. Turnbull, eds.), Vol. 10, p. 128 ff. Academic Press, London and New York, 1960.

The Quenching of Positronium and the Inhibition of Its Formation (Role of Phase Transitions, Magnetic and Chemical Factors)

V. I. Goldanskii

Chemical Physics Institute of the Academy of Science of the USSR
Moscow, USSR

INTRODUCTION

Research in positronium (Ps) formation and its various reactions is commanding increasing interest. Its significance lies not only in clearing up the properties of this uniquely light atom, but in solving a wide range of problems in current physical chemistry. Combining the results of the many experimental ways of observing positron annihilation makes it possible to follow up what happens to individual positrons, and to watch the reactions of positronium atoms in different environments.

The brief natural lifetime of positronium serves as a quite suitable time standard in investigating short-time processes characteristic of the condensed phase. Moreover, because of the unusually fast annihilation of free positrons and of singlet parapositronium ($^1S_0$), processes involving positronium are basically nonequilibrium processes, and the probability of their occurrence is determined by kinetic factors.

As an ultralight hydrogen-type atom—a "model" free radical— positronium represents as it were a "tagged atom," its properties depend primarily upon the properties of the surrounding medium.

Studies of positronium transformations can help reveal the mechanism of analogous processes involving hydrogen atoms. However, considerable differences appear between positronium and hydrogen that are caused by the negligible positronium mass. The study of such differences is interesting because it reveals the role of quantum effects in chemical kinetics. Positronium investigations offer additional possibilities, without analogous experiments with hydrogen atoms or with free radicals, related to the effects of phase transitions, radiation reactions, temperature, pressure, and other factors, on positronium formation and decay. Everything stated so far holds true, to a certain extent, also for the positive positronium ion, i.e., for the positron. Of course, the difference in behavior of the positron and the electron, in view of their opposite charges, is often much greater than that of positronium and hydrogen. However, a careful study of positron processes, as those of the "tagged electron," will no doubt yield data vital to understanding many important processes in chemistry—particularly in radiation chemistry—such as the attachment of electrons to molecules, the ionization and excitation of molecules via electron impact, etc. The study of such processes in condensed phase is now in its infancy.

Moreover, the study of positron annihilation *per se* presents numerous interesting possibilities, notably the studies of the momentum distribution of conduction electrons and the valence electrons which are obtained from the angular correlation of the annihilation quanta. Also of interest are the data on positron annihilation in crystals and multiatom gases, attesting to the formation of bound states of positrons with anions and neutral molecules. The "chemistry of positronium" receives further development in the "chemistry of the positron."

In recent years, many excellent surveys[1] have appeared dealing with this very question, among them the extremely useful book of Green and Lee. The plethora of results of theoretical and experimental studies of positron annihilation, and of the chemistry of positronium and the need for competent evaluation of further investigations, have made apparent the extreme urgency of calling the present conference. We must express our thanks to its organizers and approve of their initiative. They have given me the honor to present a survey lecture on positronium quenching by phase transitions and by magnetic and chemical reactions. After acquainting myself with the proposed program of the conference, and after having read through the titles of other survey lectures, I have judged it expedient to devote attention to the following four problems:

(1) Chemical inhibition of positronium formation.
(2) Role of phase transitions in positronium formation and decay.
(3) Magnetic quenching of positronium.
(4) Chemical quenching of positronium.

Most of the discussion concerns data for the condensed phases. It is possible that certain parts of my lecture will overlap lectures of other participants.

Also, in the few problems enumerated above, it is not my intention to present a full survey of the literature in the field. The task is rather that of somehow designating the problems themselves and

connecting them with new ones, pinpointing existing areas of uncertainty, and evaluating further areas of research. Evidently, the
number of problems cropping up before us exceeds the number of
answers that can be given to them at this time.

I. CHEMICAL INHIBITION OF THE FORMATION
OF POSITRONIUM

There exist two basic reactions characterizing the formation and
the annihilation of positronium in various media: (1) inhibition and
(2) quenching of positronium.

The inhibition of positronium we shall call, following the termi-
nology of Green and Bell,[2] the reduced probability of its formation.

Quenching of positronium will be taken to mean all possible
processes introduced to shorten the lifespan of the triplet state,
orthopositronium.

In experiments devoted to the direct observation of orthopositronium decay via recording of 3γ coincidence, or the determination of the three-photon portion of the energy spectrum of the annihilation gamma quanta, the effects of inhibition and quenching
appear in an identical way, i.e., both lead to the reduction of 3γ an-
hihilation of positrons.

Observations of the angular correlation of annihilation gamma-
quanta also presents difficulty of interpretation for both. The inhibition of positronium formation, as well as the intensification of
its chemical quenching, reduce the intensity of the narrow component, while *ortho-para* —conversion enhances it.

The most clearcut distinction between the effects of inhibition and
quenching of positronium is found in experiments that observe the
time spectrum of positron annihilation, permitting the determination
of both the intensity of each component (I_i) and the corresponding
mean life of its positrons (τ_i). This type of experiment permitted
Bell and Graham[3] in 1953 to demonstrate for the first time the
phenomenon of positronium formation in the condensed phase.

The advantage of such experiments is illustrated, for instance, by
the recent observations of Celitans, Tao, and Green[4,5] on the formation and extinction of positronium in gases. Data on positronium
formation in oxygen were obtained by them by observations of the
time spectra at a stage where the rate of 3γ coincidence in oxygen
from strong quenching did not exceed the background random coincidences.

One must, however, bear in mind the fact that even observations
of the annihilation time spectra still do not *per se* offer exhaustive
data as to the formation and extinction of positronium, The fact of
the matter is that the long-lived components in the time spectrum

of annihilation cannot always be identified with the destruction of orthopositronium. Thus, the presence of long-lived components of positron annihilation in a series of ionic crystals, recently discovered by Bisi, Fiorentini, and Zappa,[6] is connected apparently not with positronium formation, but with the emergence of various levels of the system $e^+ A^-$ (A^- anoin),[7,8] for instance, $e^+ H^-$ or of the spectra of the polaron states of positrons.[9] The complexity of the problem is high-lighted also by the presence in a number of systems of the third component of the time spectrum, originally detected in connection with liquid helium,[10,11] and lately found also for gaseous argon and mixtures of argon and nitrogen,[12] as well as for many polymers and for fused quartz.[13,14] Along with the decay of long-lived orthopositronium (accelerated by "pickoff" annihilation,[15] i.e., the annihilation of positrons in the bound state of orthopositronium with an electron of the surrounding media whose spin relative to it is singlet), the delay of annihilation of positrons in such systems is affected apparently by the relatively long time of thermalization.

The circumstances just indicated render extremely desirable the assembling of all the above-enumerated experimental methods for the study of the annihilation of positrons, and their supplementa-tion by the application of magnetic and electric fields.

Having stipulated all these features, we may now attempt to de-scribe the existing situation as regards the study of the inhibition of positronium formation. By way of an initial model, we shall ex-amine the picture of the "Ore model,"[16] which justifies itself by virtue of its qualitative interpretation of positronium formation.

Figure 1 will serve to illustrate the points to be discussed. According to the Ore model, positronium formation can occur at positron energies from E (energy of the first electronic level of the molecules of the medium) to $V - 6.8$ eV, where V is the ionization potential of the medium's molecules. The difference

$$\Delta = E_{max} - E_{min} = E - (V - 6.8) \text{ eV}$$

is the width of the Ore gap. The probability P of positronium formation with a flat spectrum of moderated positrons lies within the limits:

$$\frac{6.8}{V} > P > \frac{E - (V - 6.8)}{E} \tag{1}$$

We shall, for the time being, set aside the question of the modifi-cation of the Ore gap as regards solids, for which the parameters of the gap change due to the different affinities of positrons and of positronium for the crystal lattice, and as a result, the formation of positronium proves at times impossible.

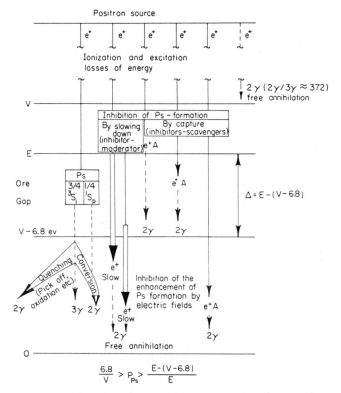

Fig. 1. Diagram of the formation and quenching of positronium, illustrating the Ore gap and possible deviation from it.

However, let the values of E and V be defined and fixed, i.e., let the position of the Ore gap be maintained. What, in this instance, can effectively bear upon the probability of positronium formation? First there can be free annihilation in the course of the positron's thermalization down to energy V, especially for energy losses due to ionization and excitation. However, such an additional removal of fast positrons is negligibly small, as is evident from the example shown in Table I of the comparison of ionization cross-sections σ_i of electrons with 20 eV energies and of free annihilation σ_a in several gases.

Disregarding also the positronium formation above the Ore gap, one may consider that the basic factors determining the deviations from the simple Ore model (regarding positronium yield) are:

(1) Inhibition of positronium formation via capture of positrons.

(2) Inhibition of positronium formation via slowing down of positrons to energies below the Ore gap.

TABLE I

Ionization Cross Sections[17] (σ_i)

and Cross Sections for Free Annihilation (σ_a)

for Electrons with Energies of 20 eV

Gas	H_2	O_2	N_2	CO	NO
$\sigma_i \times 10^{16}$ cm^2	0.23	0.41	0.20	0.41	0.84
$\sigma_a \times 10^{21}$ cm^2	0.057	0.34	0.28	0.28	0.31
$\sigma_a/\sigma_i \times 10^5$	0.25	0.83	1.4	0.68	0.37

One should also treat separately the various forms of self-inhibition, determining the probability of positronium formation in pure individual substances, and the inhibition caused by admixed materials.

Inhibition via positron capture (with consequent swift annihilation, mostly by 2_γ) may occur as in the Ore gap itself either above it (but chiefly at energies below ionization potential V) or below it. In the first instance, as a result of the inhibitions, there occurs a reduced probability of positronium formation. In the second instance, inhibition by capture should lead only to a drastic weakening of the electric-field induced enhancement of positronium yield, observed in a number of gases.

For a description of the various processes of the interaction of positrons and molecules, we shall use an analogy with corresponding electron processes. The data was adduced from the splendid survey of Craggs and Massey,[17] the collection of articles on atomic and molecular processes under the editorship of Bates,[18] and the review article by Buchelnikova.[19]

Experimental and theoretical data are available for electrons, but these are applicable exclusively to gases. We shall be forced to use such data for the qualitative description of the inhibition of positronium formation, principally in liquids. It is hard to say which seems more crude: the transfer of data on electrons to positrons, or data on gas systems to liquids. Clearly, multiplying minus by minus here does not yield a plus, but there is no other way out.

Two basic mechanisms for the capture of positrons evidently are the following:

(1) $e^+ + AB \rightarrow ABe^+ \rightarrow$ Annihilation
(capture with annihilation from the complex)

(2) $e^+ + AB \rightarrow A + Be^+ \rightarrow$ Annihilation
(capture with dissociation)

Capture with annihilation from the complex predominates in such cases where the mean life of the complex exceeds its characteristic annihilation time ($10^{-10} - 10^{-9}$ sec), or where the complex succeeds before annihilation in stabilizing itself in new collisions, e.g., for gases under pressures above several atmospheres and condensed phases.

The possibility of annihilation before the breakup of the complex increases the yield of the first of the above-mentioned processes of positron capture compared with the analogous capture of an electron without breakup.

By way of a rough estimate of the lifetime of a complex, we may assume

$$\tau = \frac{10^{-13} \text{ sec}}{\left(1 - \dfrac{E_{dis}}{E_{exc}}\right)^n}$$

where E_{dis} and E_{exc} are accordingly the energy of the dissociation of the complex and the energy of its excitation, while n represents the number of degrees of freedom molecules AB. With $n = 3$ already at the stage where $E_{exc} = 1.1 E_{dis}$, $\tau = 10^{-10}$ sec, which corresponds to the large fraction of annihilation of the complex before its decay.

Dissociative positron capture of type $e^+ + AB \rightarrow A + Be^+$ is illustrated in Fig. 2. The threshold of such a capture Q_c equals the

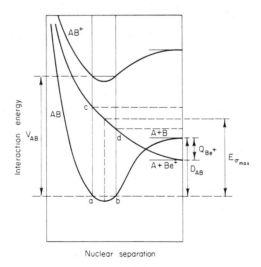

Fig. 2. Diagram of the dissociative capture of the positron type $e^+ + AB \rightarrow Be + A$.

difference between dissociation energy D_{AB} and affinity of B to the positron (Q_{Be_+}). The capture is most likely, i.e., the cross-section for capture shows a resonance maximum at positron energies, between ac and bd, in the vicinity of $E_{\sigma\,max}$. Like Q_c so also $E_{\sigma\,max}$ lies, as a rule, below both the ionization potential V_{AB} and the excitation energy of the first electron level AB, i.e., within the range of the Ore gap, and thus this capture process leads to the inhibition of positronium formation, provided the capture probability of the positron is commensurate with the probability of its passing through the resonance region by inelastic energy losses or elastic collisions.

The probability of the capture of positrons by molecules with energies ranging from zero to several electron volts can be judged by attachment of analogous data concerning cross sections of electrons as shown in Table II.

Although these cross sections reach geometric size only at zero energies, and within the range of the Ore gap are about 10^{-18} cm^2, inhibition via capture should prove quite effective in certain cases, because in the absence of energy losses from vibrational and rotational excitation of the molecules, the positrons must experience hundreds and thousands of elastic collisions in the region of the resonance capture. As will be mentioned further on, for multiatom molecules in the Ore gap, obviously, there predominate vibrational energy losses, the cross sections of which also reach $\sim 10^{-18}$ cm^2, thus reducing the probability of capture. The role of these losses, therefore, is analogous to the role of neutron collisions with nuclei of light moderators preventing their capture by U^{238} in the mixture of uranium isotopes. However, one must always bear in mind the fact that two competing processes both

TABLE II

Cross Sections of the Attachment of Electrons to Gas Molecules

Gas	E_{max_I} (eV)	σ_{max_I} (cm^2)	$E_{max_{II}}$ (eV)	$\sigma_{max_{II}}$ (cm^2)
SF_6	0.00	5.7 10^{-16}		
CCl_4	0.02	1.3 10^{-16}	0.6	1.0 10^{-16}
CF_3I	0.05	7.8 10^{-17}	0.9	3.2 10^{-17}
CCl_2F_2	0.15	5.4 10^{-17}		
BCl_3	0.4	2.8 10^{-17}		
HBr	0.5	5.8 10^{-17}		
HCl	0.6	3.9 10^{-18}		
H_2O	6.4	4.8 10^{-18}	8.6	1.3 10^{-18}
O_2	6.2	1.3 10^{-18}		
CO_2	7.8	5.1 10^{-19}		

lead to the reduction of positronium yield—vibrational energy losses, as well as dissociative resonance capture of the positron. Under inhibition by moderation of positrons, leading to their escape below the Ore gap, is implied first and foremost inelastic energy losses of positrons by excitation of vibrational and rotational molecular levels.

In the absence of such losses, for instance in inert gases, moderation of positrons is determined exclusively by means of elastic collisions. The average number of such collisions needed for the passage of positrons through the Ore gap equals

$$N = \frac{1}{\xi} \ln \frac{E_{max}}{E_{min}}$$

where $\xi = 2/1840\,M$ is the average logarithmic loss of energy for one elastic positron collision with a molecule of mass M. In such cases the minimum likelihood of positronium formation from a uniform distribution of moderating positrons would equal:

$$P = \frac{E - (V - 6.8)}{E} \left\{ 1 - \frac{\sigma_s}{N\sigma_{Ps}} \left[1 - e^{-\frac{\sigma_{Ps}}{\sigma_s}N} \right] \right\} \tag{2}$$

i.e., it would approximate $P = \Delta/E$ even with a very low ratio of the cross sections of positronium formation (σ_{Ps}) and the elastic scattering (σ_s). However, thanks to the excitation of the oscillatory and rotary levels, the average losses of positron energy upon one collision with a multiatom molecule will be apparently hundreds and thousands of times greater, so that the equation (2) in the general case cannot be applied to the finding σ_{Ps}, as was done by us.[20]

For the qualitative representation of the correlation of elastic and inelastic positron energy losses, it will be found useful to direct attention to experimental data regarding average energy losses of electrons (of energy below $V - 6.8$ eV) in several multiatom gases. Such data were presented in Reference 17, and are shown in Fig. 3.

Use of calculation (see Ref. 17) of the excitation of rotary levels of nitrogen and of oxygen, along with corresponding experimental data lead to the conclusion that energy losses due to rotary excitation predominate over elastic ones only at quite small electron energies, E_e (of the order of tens of units of eV), when the characteristic rotational energy B ($E_J = BJ(J + 1)$, for nitrogen, for instance, $B = 2.5 \times 10^{-4}$ eV) becomes larger than the energy transfer characteristic of elastic collisions, of the order of $10^{-3}\,E_e/M$.

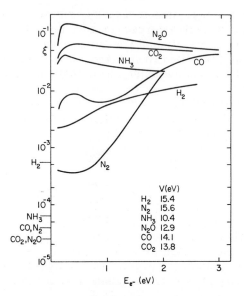

Fig. 3. Average energy losses of
electrons during collisions with molecules of multiatom gases.

Cross sections of elastic collisions and rotary excitations are similar. At higher electron energies (but still insufficient for excitation of electron levels and the knocking out of other electons), the
basic role is beginning to be played by the excitation of vitrational
levels. The cross sections for such processes are relatively small;
for instance, for excitation of the first vibrational level of H_2 with
energy 0.42 eV,

$$\sigma_{max} \approx 2.3 \times 10^{-2}\, \pi a_0^2 \approx 2 \times 10^{-18}\, cm^2$$

which, by way of example, is two orders below σ_s; however, here the
transfer of energy is high and is overcompensating the small cross
section. To sum up, rotary losses may turn out to be substantial
ones only during the thermalization of positrons. At higher energies,
energy losses of positrons by excitation of the vibrational levels of
the molecules, evidently predominate and can compete here with
the inhibition process by capture of positrons.

Let us now turn to the experimental data about the inhibition of
positronium formation.)

The possibility of positron attachment to Freon molecules was
presupposed already when positronium was originally discovered by
Deutsch,[21] to explain some increase in the rate of annihilation of

positrons in Freon at slight pressures. Positron attachment to molecules of multiatom gases of the type of CO_2, CH_4, C_2H_6, CCl_2F_2, SF_6, or the excitation of the oscillatory levels of these molecules, seems to be the cause of the absence of increased positronium yield in these gases upon application of an electric field. The same reason must account for the lack of an electric field effect in dilute mixtures of these gases in argon.[22,23] These then are the factors that prevent the attainment of 100% positronium yield in electric fields for diatomic gases of the type of H_2, D_2, and N_2, and even for single-atom inert gases.[22,23]

According to the data of Tao, Bell, and Green,[12] obtained from the analysis of the three component time spectrum of positron annihilation in argon (at 15 atm), approximately $18-23\%$ of all positrons form the complex Are^+, prior to positron thermalization to the Ore gap, and these positrons then annihilate very soon and show up in the "instantaneous" peak of the time-spectrum with the parapositronium annihilation events.

Insofar as in argon there are neither vibrational nor rotary losses of positron energy, therefore in the analysis of these data, it is permissible to derive the relationship used by us[20], of the capture cross section σ_c, leading to the formation of the stabilized complex Are^+ and of the elastic scattering, σ_s, of positrons by argon atoms:

$$\frac{\sigma_c}{\sigma_s} \approx 0.2 \, \frac{1}{N} \approx 8 \cdot 10^{-6}$$

Evidently, the formation of the complex Are^+ above the Ore gap is here excluded—it would require the condition

$$\sigma_c \approx 0.2 \, \sigma_{\text{excitation of Ar}}$$

but within the confines of the Ore gap such as high value for σ_c would cause the strongest self-inhibition of positronium formation in argon.

Quite a large body of data on the chemistry of positronium in pure gases and gas mixtures has been obtained by Deutsch, Dulit, and Gittelman. However, such data has remained unpublished, and is mentioned only briefly in the book by Green and Lee[1f] and in the review by Wallace.[1e] On the basis of the scanty available information, it is difficult to evaluate the part that was played in these studies by changes in the probability of formation of positronium and its quenching, all the more so as the evidence concerning the effect of small admixtures of multiatom gases, is contradictory.[1e,1f]

Finally, in connection with the attachment of slow positrons, one must bear in mind the data of Paul and St.-Pierre[24] on the

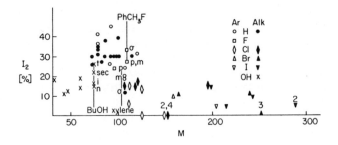

Fig. 4. Summary of data on the yield of long-lived components of the time spectrum of positron annihilation in several organic compounds. Ar, aryl; Alk, alkyl; numbers (2, 3, 4) show number of halide atoms in the molecule.

abnormally large positron annihilation cross section in a series of gases, which may be explained by the peculiar "resonance annihilation," described in the Ref. 25, and caused by the presence of polarisational virtual or weakly bound states positron-molecule.

In speaking of experiments with liquids, we note first the effect of self-inhibition, which leads to sharp differences in the positronium yield in various organic substances. Many such compounds have been systematically investigated by Hatcher and Millet,[26-29] Berko[30,31] Hogg,[32,33] and Goldanskii.[20]

A summary of the results is presented in Fig. 4, detailing data on aliphatic and aromatic hydrocarbons, their halogen and some other derivatives. Along the X-axis are given the molecular weights, and along the Y-axis, the yield of long-lifetime components I_2 (%), which hypothetically constitutes three quarters of the positronium yield.

Although at times there appears quite a great disparity in the data obtained from various laboratories, one may confidently note the following basic results: The probability of positronium formation in many hydrocarbons ($C_n H_{2n+2}$, where $n = 5-8$, benzene, toluene, propyl-benzene, cyclohexane) is about $40-50\%$ ($I_2 \approx 30-40\%$), and nearly what is expected from the Ore formula. Thus, for benzene, the first electronic excitation level $E = 4.72$ eV, while the ionization potential $V = 9.25$ eV, so that $\Delta/E = [E - (V-6.8)]/E = 48\%$. However, upon turning to alcohols, and particularly to halogen derivatives of various hydrocarbons, one observes a marked reduction in positronium yield, increasing from Cl to Br and I[26], and little dependence on the nature of the hydrocarbons.[33] For all benzene halogen-derivatives, the Ore formula yields $\Delta/E = 50-55\%$, while by actual experiment, $P \approx 20\%$ (PhCl), $10-12\%$ (PhBr), and 6% (PhI).*

Hatcher[29] has demonstrated that the value of P for halogen-derivatives is quite consistent with the Ore formula if one takes as the upper limit the energy of the weakest C-Hal bond: $E = D_{C-Hal}$ and the hypothesis based on this, viz, that positrons are moderated and escape below the Ore gap by bursting these bonds. However, a more probable explanation of this is self-inhibition by positron capture with dissociation of the type $PhCl + e^+ \rightarrow Ph + e^+Cl$. The affinity of positrons to halogen atoms Q_{e^+Hal} is considerably less than the analogous value for electrons and it is questionable whether it can substantially alter the reaction threshold compared with the energy of the C-Hal bond.

In favor of the positron capture mechanism (with the dissociation) is also the fact that the positronium formation probability decreases with the increasing dipole character of the molecules of the medium, i.e., with increased localization of the negative electric charge. This fact has been noted,[26] not only in examples of halogen-derivatives (or alcohols),[27] but also in comparison of positronium yield in ortho-, meta-, and paraxylene. Owing to the inductive action of electron-donor methyl groups on the benzene ring, an excessive negative charge is concentrated at that point, the extent of localization of which diminishes in the sequence ortho-, meta-, and paraxylenes.

The corresponding values are P_{ortho} (32%) $> P_{meta}$ (25%) $> P_{para}$ (16%). Drastic self-inhibition, complete quenching of the formation of positronium, is seen in compounds with two or more halogen atoms (dichlorobenzene, bromoform; CCl_4) or nitro groups (dinitrobenzene). Actually, in fact, the bond energy $C-Cl$ in CCl_4 equals ≈ 3 eV, and the ionization potential of CCl_4 is 11.1 eV, so that in determining the width of the Ore gap, according to Hatcher,[29] even without taking into account positron affinity, we obtain $\Delta = -1.3$ eV, i.e., the Ore gap in CCl_4 is completely shut off because of the possibility of positron capture accompanied by dissociation. However, the marked

---

*Interesting aspects of the application of positron annihilation in biological research projects are being opened up thanks to recent work of Zalukaev, Vikin and Perfilyev [Sov. "Biophysics" 11, No. 1 (1965)]. These authors have demonstrated that inhibition of positronium formation in compounds of the type:

is reinforced with increased anti-k-vitamin activity, and with lowered prothrombin index.

probability of positron attachment to CCl_4, most likely by the reaction

$$CCl_4 + e^+ \rightarrow CCl_3 + Cle^+$$

is obtained also with energies appreciably surpassing the stability of the CCl_3—Cl bond. Only in this way can be explained the extremely strong positronium formation inhibition in benzene (the upper boundary of the Ore gap E = 4.72 eV) with small admixtures of CCl_4, observed by Ormrod and Hogg,[32] (see Fig. 5). This case is evidently similar to the one also depicted in Fig. 5 of the first example of chemical quenching—the action in water of anion admixtures No_3^- and NO_2^-—according to Green and Bell,[2] who assumed in that case positron attachment with formation of $e^+ NO_3^-$ and $e^+ NO_2^-$.

The third example, studied in detail, of chemical inhibition—a marked drop in positronium formation in benzene with small admixtures of iodobenzene and chlorobenzene—was observed by us here (see particularly, Ref. 20 and Fig. 6). However, this example is a little different from the preceding ones. For pure CCl_4 and obviously for quite concentrated nitrate solutions, there is no adequate Ore gap, i.e., I_2 = 0, but in pure chlorobenzene and iodobenzene one does observe the formation of positronium. Therefore the quenching action of small concentrations of these admixtures, must not be explained as a binding of positrons—if such were the case, there would occur the supplementary self-inhibition of positronium formation in pure chlorobenzene and iodobenzene, and there would not result the equation noted by Hatcher.[29]

$$P \approx \frac{D_{\text{C-Hal}} - (V - 6.8)}{D_{\text{C-Hal}}}$$

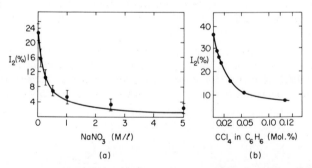

Fig. 5. Inhibition of positronium formation in solutions with small amounts of admixtures: (a) admixtures of $NaNO_3$ in water[2]; (b) admixtures of CCl_4 in benzene.[32]

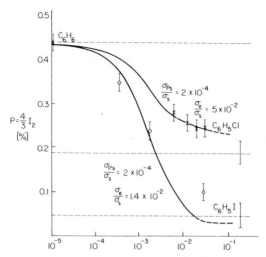

Fig. 6. Inhibition of positronium in benzene with small amounts of additives C_6H_5Cl and C_6H_5I. The abscissa is the molar fraction of the admixture.

For that very reason we assumed[20] that the quenching action of PhCl and PhI is connected basically, not with the capture, but with the fast slowdown of positrons below the Ore gap.

There remains the question as to the rates of the cross sections of σ_{inh} reactions with positron participation, leading to inhibition of positronium formation.

It is to be expected that for admixture concentration $n^*_{1/2}$ (cm^{-3}), representing a 50% reduction of positronium production probability, it is fair to assume that $n^*_{1/2} \bar{\sigma}_{inh} \bar{v} T = \ln 2$, where the cross section $\bar{\sigma}_{inh}$ and positron velocity $\bar{v}$ are averaged throughout the entire Ore gap of the basic substance, while T represents the passage-time of the positron across this gap. It is this very time factor that creates the principal vagueness of such a computation. With purely elastic moderation $T_{elast.} = N/(N_0 \sigma_s \bar{v})$, where N_0 is the molecular concentration of the basic substance. For benzene, $\sigma_s \approx 10^{-15}$ cm^2, $N \approx 5 \times 10^4$, $\bar{v} \approx 10^8$ cm/sec, so that $T_{elast} \approx 10^{-10}$ sec. Such a continued presence of the positron in the Ore gap would indicate quite a small quenching cross section—about 4×10^{-17} cm^2 for CCl$_4$ and about 6×10^{-18} cm^2 for PhI and PhCl. Along with elastic positron energy losses, however, preponderant losses occur from vibrational (and rotary) excitation, hence the actual passage time through the Ore gap $T \ll T_{elast}$, and consequently the actual inhibition cross section is considerably greater than those derived above. Assuming for water $T \approx 10^{-13}$ sec, Green and Bell cite for positron capture by anions NO_3^- the cross section: $\sigma_c \approx 1.7 \times 10^{-16} cm^2$, evidently over-estimated, for in this case, $n_{1/2} = 1.2 \times 10^{20} cm^{-3}$, against $1.8 \times 10^{18} cm^{-3}$ for CCl_4 and $1.2 \times 10^{19} cm^{-3}$ for PhI and PhCl.

In one of the later experiments on inhibition it will be possible, obviously, by using the maximum possible cross-section value, to obtain more precise moderation rates for positrons in the Ore gap, and in this way specify the character of the energy-loss mechanism in the gas and the liquid phase at certain energies. An interesting problem is posed also by comparison of the inhibition activity of a series of organic compounds with their stability against radiation-induced formation of radicals, since according to the view of Voje-vodskii and Molin,[34] radiation yields of radicals are determined by the energies of the first electronic excitation level and the weakest bond in the molecule, i.e., by the parameters playing an important part in inhibition of positronium formation.

As is evident from all that has been said, the problem of the chemical inhibition of positronium formation is most closely con-nected to the study of the elementary processes of electron-mole-cule interaction. Even in the cases of gases which at the present time have data relating to ionization cross sections, the cross sec-tions for electronic, vibrational, and rotary excitation by electronic impact and for different states of electronic excitation with energies up to ~10 eV are still quite scanty. As far as analogous data for li-quids are concerned, they simply do not exist. That is why the most important task for the future is the detailed study of positronium in-hibition in typical gas and liquid systems, of the role of external electric fields, of the effect of various admixtures, and the develop-ment of general calculation methods for the quantitative interpre-tation of data that has been obtained. The solution of this problem will transform the chemistry of positronium into an important sub-division of contemporary high-energy chemistry.

II. ROLE OF PHASE TRANSITIONS IN THE FORMATION AND THE ANNIHILATION OF POSITRONIUM

The effect of phase transitions on the fate of positronium was established in 1953 by Bell and Graham,[3] simultaneously with the first evidence of positronium formation in the condensed phase. This work demonstrated the presence (identified as positronium) of the long-lifetime component in the time spectrum of positron annihila-tion in plastic sulfur and fused quartz, while it was absent in mono-clinic sulfur and crystalline quartz. Moreover, with samples of ice, polystyrene, and Teflon, it was demonstrated that the lifetime of this component (τ_2 scale: $10^{-9} sec$), at lowered temperature, does not in-crease, as might have been expected, for gas-kinetic type of posi-tronium quenching in free collisions; on the contrary, it decreases.

A similar temperature dependence of τ_2 plays an important role in the interpretation of the behavior of positronium in the condensed phase. Confirming these results, Graham and Stewart[35] observed the nearly two-fold increase of probability of 3γ annihilation in switching from crystalline to fused quartz, while Page and Heinberg and their co-workers[36-38] established the relation of the narrow components in curves of angular correlation of annihilation γ quanta with the presence of long-lived components in the time spectrum of positron annihilation, finding that narrow component exists in fused quartz, but is absent in crystalline quartz.

Among various studies of positronium in the condensed phases, one must note the observation of the reduced probability of 3γ annihilation (basically in connection with reduced τ_2) due to the cooling of ice and frozen methyl alcohol and glycerine;[39] and also the work of Stewart[40] who demonstrated the increased narrow component in the angular correlation of annihilated γ quanta, i.e., intensified positronium formation, when Teflon is heated from 77 to 525°K. A series of studies indicated the important role of fusing in positronium formation and destruction.

For instance, in observing the time spectrum of positron annihilation in naphthalene, Landes, Berko and Zuchelli[30] found that the intensity of the long-lived components above the melting point (80.2°C) rises sharply from $I_2 = 9\%$ to $I_2 = 29\%$. Simultaneously, the lifetime of this component also increases from $\tau_2 = 1.3 \times 10^{-7}$ sec to 2.6×10^{-9} sec (see Fig. 7). The long-lived component is also present in solid anthracene where $I_2 = 40\%$, while $\tau_2 = 2.25 \times 10^{-9}$ sec[41-42].

De Zafra and Joyner[43] confirmed the data[30] by another method, showing that melting of naphthalene sharply increases the narrow component of the angular distribution. On the other hand, in the case of water, an unusual narrow peak resulting[43] from thermalized positronium, appears not upon melting, but upon solidifying: it is present in ice and absent in liquid water[43,44] (see Fig. 8).

Essential for understanding this entire group of problems is the work of Stump,[45] showing the marked decrease of τ_2 for lucite, Teflon, and polyethylene with the compression of these substances under about 10,000 atm.

The studies enumerated above describe the main part of the experimental material for the condensed phase, seen in surveys 1a to 1f. Before turning to newer experimental data, we pause to interpret the basic initial results.

Just as in the first part, we must accurately separate the questions of the probability of positronium formation and of its lifetime, in relation to the state of the substance.

First, one must stress the fact that positronium formation in the condensed (particularly the solid) phase is not a characteristic of all

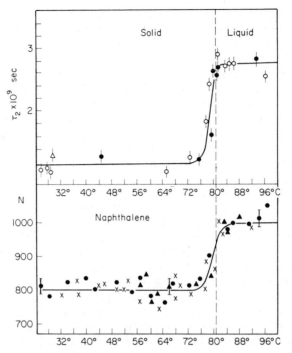

Fig. 7. Change of coincidence counting rate in
the angular correlation peak[43] and the lifetime, τ_2,
of the time spectrum of positron annihilation[30] during fusion of naphthalene (m.p. 80.2° C).

substances. According to the classification of Wallace[1e], positronium
is formed in crystalline or amorphous "molecular" substances
where electron interchange occurs only within individual molecules,
so that covalent forces between molecules, if such actually exist, are
repellant in character.

Ferrell[46] proposed the use of the Ore model to study the probability of positronium formation in the condensed phases, including
in the model the affinities of the positron (Q_{e_+}) and of positronium
(Q_{Ps}) to molecules in a given medium. Thus the upper boundary of
the Ore gap becomes $E_{max} = E - Q_{e_+}$, the width of the gap:

$$\Delta = (E - Q_{e_+}) - (V - 6.8 - Q_{Ps}) = \Delta_0 - (Q_{e_+} - Q_{Ps}) \qquad (3)$$

i.e., less than the width of the gap in gas (Δ_0) by the difference
($Q_{e_+} - Q_{Ps}$). According to this interpretation, in ionic crystals
(here E represents the band gap, and the difference $V - E = Q_{e-}$

represents the affinity of the electron) of the metal halogen type $Q_{e+} = 3 - 5$ eV, $Q_{Ps} < 0$ (which corresponds to the absence of free volume which might be taken up by positronium) and $\Delta < 0$, i.e., positronium is not formed.

As shown above, the probability of positronium formation is controlled not only by basic parameters of the Ore gap, but also may be strongly affected by positron attachment in the course of its moderation and by its inelastic moderation due to the interaction with individual molecules and, we may add here, with the entire crystal lattice. All of these processes that reduce the effective upper boundary of the Ore gap, or rapidly draw off positrons under the gap, certainly depend not only on the chemical composition of the substance, but also on the intermolecular interaction. In this hitherto unexplored theory, lies the first possible cause of the effect of phase transitions on the probability of positronium formation.

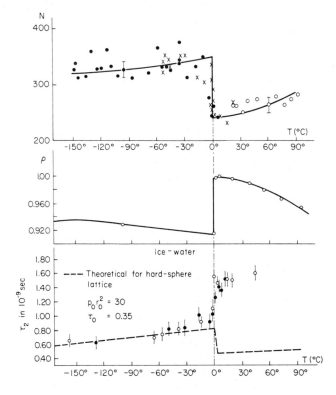

Fig. 8. Change of coincidence counting rate in the angular correlation peak[43] of the lifetime, τ_2, of the long-lived component of the time spectrum of annihilation and the density dependence on the temperature of ice and water.

The second cause is connected with the position of the lower boundary of the Ore gap, i.e., with the affinity of the medium to positronium
or, in other words, with the presence of free volume in which the
positronium atom could be accommodated. This factor, also directly
connected with phase transitions, was noted in many studies, mainly
not in connection with the probability of positronium formation but
rather with its lifetime τ_2 and the basic process of "pickoff" annihilation.

Reduction of τ_2 with a drop in temperature, as well as with compression of the substance, was interpreted as the result of the increased density of the substance, i.e., the reduction of the free
volume in which the positronium atom can accommodate itself. Wallace[47,1e], proposed a simple and wholly descriptive model of a positronium atom in the interstices as set in a potential well caused by
the strong repulsion from the surrounding atoms, and having a wavefunction which is periodic internally and exponentially damped ex-
ternally. The probability of finding the positronium outside of the
well to the probability of finding it inside is given by

$$\frac{k^2/\alpha}{\alpha + 2mVa/\hbar^2}$$

where $\alpha = [2m(V - E)]^{1/2}/\hbar$, $k^2 = 2me/\hbar^2$ and V is the depth of the
well. E is the energy of the level occupied by the positronium and
a is the radius of the well. With a reduction of the well radius a,
ψ^2_{ext} increases, and there is a corresponding increase of the overlap
of the positronium wavefunction with the electron clouds of surrounding molecules, and thus of the rate of "pickoff" annihilation resulting
in a reduction in τ_2. Similar consideration were also discussed in
Reference 43.

A more detailed treatment of positronium formation in molecular
substances on the basis of the "free volume model" was offered by
Brandt, Berko, and Walker.[48] These authors calculated the density
distribution of positronium in the lattice, as sketched in Fig. 9, in
terms of the following simplifying assumptions:

(1) The mutual polarization of Ps and the lattice is to be disre-
garded;

(2) The lattice is to be pictured as a cubic array of potentials
each with a height of U_0, a radius r_0 ("excluded volume," V_0), with
with electron density ρ_0, located at the center of the cell of volume
V_1, with radius r_1. For $r_0 \leq r \leq r_1$, $U_1 = 0$ and $\rho_1 = 0$. In that case,
$V_1 - V_0$ represents "free volume" of the cell. Letting $v^* = V_1/V_0$,
the "reduced" cell volume, equal to the reciprocal fraction of excluded volume; $(1 - 1/v^*)$ is equal to the fraction of free volume;

(3) Ps atoms are considered thermalized, and are assumed to

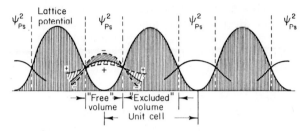

Fig. 9. Schematic diagram showing the density distribution of positronium in a crystal lattice. The distribution of positron and electron densities are also indicated for the case when the positronium atom is polarized by the lattice.[48]

have zero velocity $(\vec{K}_{Ps} = 0)$.

The equation for the rate of "pickoff annihilation" γ_p is

$$\gamma_p = \frac{1}{\tau_2} - \lambda_T = \pi r_0^2 c \rho_0 \int_{(V_0)} \psi_{Ps}\, \psi_{Ps}^*,\, dV$$

(where $\lambda_T = 1/\tau_T = 7.14\ 10^6\ sec^{-1}$), as derived from calculations of the positronium wavefunction for various lattices in the Wigner-Seitz approximation.

The result is given in Reference 48 in the form of

$$\gamma_p = \frac{\pi r_0^2\ c \rho_0}{1 + F(U_0, r_0, r_1)} \tag{4}$$

along with graphs function $F(v^*)$ for various values of the dimensionless scattering parameters $P_0 r_0^2 = 4m U_0 r_0^2 / \hbar^2$, and for three geometric configurations of the lattice-plane, spherical and cylindrical. Increasing v^* from 1 to 1.10, i.e., the appearance in the lattice of "free volume," comprizing in all about 9% of the overall volume, is accompanied by reduction of the "pickoff" annihilation rate by $1.1 \rightarrow 1.6$ times for plane $(P_0 r_0^2 = 5 \rightarrow 30)$, by $1.1 \rightarrow 2.6$ times for spherical $(P_0 r_0^2 = 50 \rightarrow 1000)$ and by $1.1 \rightarrow 5.7$ times for cylindrical $(P_0 r_0^2 = 5 \rightarrow 50)$ lattices. Further enlargements of the free volume increase τ_2 even more strongly.

The authors[48] have offered the comparison of their calculations, with results reached by them in their own experiments on the temperature dependence of τ_2 in water (and in ice), glycerin, and Teflon, in a wide range of temperature from 78 to 340°K. The density value ρ_0 was taken to equal $3.8 \times 10^{23}\ cm^{-3}$, which matches the ion Ps^-: $(\tau_0 = 1/(\pi r_0^2 c \rho_0) = 0.35\ 10^{-9} sec)$. The scattering parameters $P_0 r_0^2$ were selected as equal to $10 \rightarrow 15$ for Teflon, 20 for glycerin, and

30 for water. In the case of the calculation for water, a spherical lattice was assumed. For Teflon and glycerin, the cylindrical form was selected allowing for a much greater dependence of τ_2 on v^*. This dependence of v^* on temperature represents simply the temperature dependence of the reciprocal density of the investigated substance.

Yields for Teflon, glycerin, and ice proved highly consistent with the calculations. However, in the region of the abnormal rise in the density of the water $(0-4°C)$, the amount did not decrease, but, on the contrary, increased sharply, as was shown in Fig. 8.

The amount of I_2 falls upon melting ice from $45 \pm 5\%$ (ice) to $25 \pm 5\%$ (water). Further heating of the water gradually restored the dependence of τ_2 on temperature, as described in the free-volume model. To explain the abnormal τ_2 process with melting ice, the authors of Ref. 48 postulated the possibility of a radical change at this point of the parameters $P_0 r_0^2$ and ρ_0. Experiments in recent years have in general confirmed the fitness of the free-volume model to describe the smooth τ_2 changes with temperature and pressure. However, a series of deviations from this model have been noted, with an indication of its quite restricted application for describing the τ_2 changes during phase transitions. Data on changes of positronium formation probabilities (I_2) with temperature, pressure, and phase transitions remain incompletely explained specially since, generally speaking, it is hardly possible at this time to speak of any definite correlation between positronium formation probability in the condensed phase and its lifetime.

Henderson and Millett,[49] observed the dependence of τ_2 and I_2 on pressure ranging from 1–1250 atm in 22 organic liquids and established the linear increase of τ_2 with the increased ratio of specific volume V/V_0. At phase transition points, sharp changes of τ_2 and decrease of I_2 were noted for three liquids, that solidified under high pressure.

Quite a detailed investigation of a series of liquids was carried out by Wilson, Johnson, and Stump[50] regarding the dependence of τ_2 and I_2 on temperature (up to 200°C) and on pressure (up to 6000 atm). An important result of this study was the separation of the effects of density and temperature. The following type of equation was established in experiments on the change of pressure:

$$\tau_2 = \tau_2^0 \exp(-\mu \Delta V/V_0) \qquad (5)$$

which may be treated also as a linear equation, since $\mu \Delta V/V \ll 1$. Here ΔV is the change in volume; V_0 is the volume at 30°C and one atmosphere. Thus the relation (5) describes the linear increase of τ_2 with the increase of the corresponding normalized volume of the substance V/V_0. The results obtained by Wilson et al.[50] (at 30°C

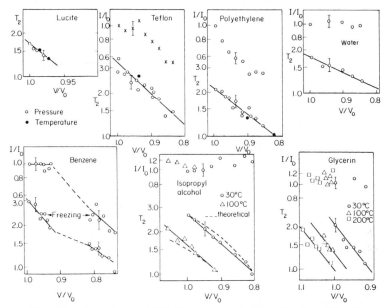

Fig. 10. Dependence of lifetime, τ_2, and intensity, I_2, of the long-lived component of the time spectrum of positron annihilation in Teflon, polyethylene, and lucite, water, benzene, isopropyl alcohol, and glycerin on the compression of these substances (at 30° C when temp. is not shown).[50]

and various pressures) for solids (polymers – Teflon, polyethylene, Lucite) and for liquids (water, isopropyl alcohol, glycerin, and benzene, solidified at high pressures) are given in Fig. 10. The value of the factor varies between μ = 2.5 ± 0.4 (water) and 6.8 ± 0.8 (glycerin): for polymers μ = 4.3 → 5.0.

Positronium formation probability in liquids proved to be independent of pressure, while in solid polymers the ratio I_2 (P)/I_2 (0) decreases with the compression of the substance.

By introducing corrections for the temperature dependence of density in the case of solids, it was possible to establish the presence of complementary τ_2 changes with temperature in the opposite direction from those observed directly in the experiment: The corrected lifetimes of the long-lived positronium τ_2^0 decreases as the temperature rises, as indicated in Fig. 11. Thus τ_2 dependence on temperature agrees, although only qualitatively, with what is expected for the gas-kinetic or diffusion picture of positronium atom collisions with some specific "quenching" agent, or their shifting to vacancies with high probability of "pickoff" annihilation. The authors[50] point out that in liquids a change in pressure or tempera-

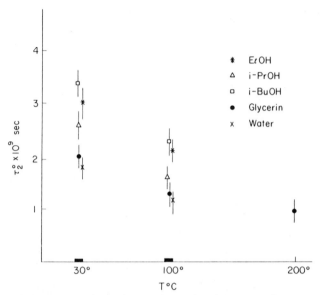

Fig. 11. Temperature dependence of positron lifetime $\tau_2°$, as corrected by taking into account density change for several liquids.[50]

ture may effect both the number and the extent of such vacancies (spherical holes, microregions of reduced density). In a solid, how-ever, the number of vacancies remains constant, with only their size undergoing change.

The mean positronium lifetime τ_2 is determined by

$$\frac{1}{\tau_2} = P_i \lambda_T + P_0 (\lambda_T + \gamma_p) \approx P_0 \gamma_p \qquad (6)$$

where Pi and P_0 stand for the probabilities of positronium occurrence within a vacancy, or outside of it. For vacancies shaped like a square hole, $P_0 \propto V^{0.87}$, so that $\tau_2 = c \cdot V^{0.87}$, where V is the volume of the hole, while the value of c is determined by the depth of the hole and the rate constant of the pickoff annihilation γ_p.

Having taken, on the basis of the compressibility of polymers, 20% as the fraction of the vacuo (cavities – gaps – holes) in uncom-pressed polymers, the authors[50] concluded that $\tau_2 = \tau_2^0 [1 - 5(\Delta V/V)]^{0.87}$, which corresponds with $\mu = 4.35$ in formula (5).

Furthermore, using Frenkel's kinetic theory of liquids to deter-mine the concentration of microcrystallites in the liquid, and to de-termine the number of vacancies, i.e., regions of minimum density (Z) and taking for the overall free volume of the liquid as $(V - b)$, where b is the correction of the Van der Waals type, the authors[50] obtain for the vacancy volume in liquids:

$$v = \frac{V - b}{Z} = \text{const} \left(\frac{V - b}{T^3} \right) \tag{7}$$

and for the corresponding lifetime:

$$\tau_2 = \text{const} \left(\frac{V - b}{T^3} \right)^{0.87} \tag{8}$$

Having determined the value of the constant for isopropyl alcohol at 30°C and 1 atm, the authors[50] derive for this substance the dependence of τ_2 on the pressure for 30 and 100°C. It agrees satisfactorily with the experiment (dotted line in Fig. 10). The data of Clarke and Hogg[51] on the reduction of τ_2 with the lowering of temperature of solid cyclohexane from 0 to − 196°C, qualitatively agree with the free-volume formula. (At − 110°C a break was noted in the dependence of τ_2 upon temperature, an accelerated drop of τ_2 low temperatures, hypothetically related to the phase transition from the cubic to the monoclinic structure.) Reference has already been made to the work of Spirn et al.[13], and their discovery of the presence of three components in the time spectrum of positronium annihilation in polyethylene. With a rise in temperature from 40 to 200°C, the lifetime of the most long-lived of these components (τ_A) is prolonged, according to the free-volume formula, from 2.50 to 3.3×10^{-9} sec, while its intensity (I_A) increases from 25 to 37%. For the two other components ($\tau_B = 0.5 \times 10^{-9}$ sec, $I_B = 30\%$ at 40°C, and $\tau_C = 0.25 \times 10^{-9}$ sec, $I_C = 45\%$ at 40°C), no lifetime dependence on temperature was observed; the thermally increased intensity of long-lived components I_A occurs at the expense of the latter component (I_C). Results also generally interpretable on the basis of the free-volume formula were recently obtained by Groseclose and Loper[52] for three polymers—polystyrene, Lucite, and polyethylene—at temperatures ranging from −200 to +150°C. Polystyrene and Lucite showed a reduction of τ_2 with a temperature decrease which is weakened near the transition point of glass-crystals. However, polyethylene, marked by the presence of type I phase-transition at 130°C and of type II transition at −20°C, showed a sharp unexpected change of slope of $\tau_2(T)$ and a rapid drop in τ_2, just below −20°C. Inasmuch as a change in volume during transitions of the second type should be small, the authors suggested that during the sample preparations the polyethylene chains were lined up oriented, making possible their subsequent contraction below −20°C. As in previous studies,[13-15] the third component in the annihilation spectrum was found by Groseclose and Loper.

Of undoubted interest are the studies of the effects of the irradiation of various materials, the positronium formation within them, and what subsequently happens to the positronium atom. These

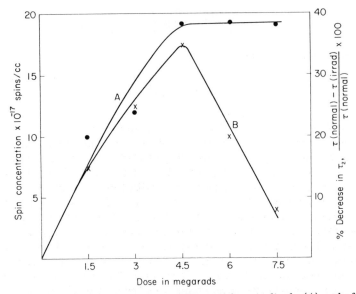

Fig. 12. Dependence of the concentration of free radicals (A) and of the reduction of lifetime of positrons, τ_2, (B) in Teflon upon dosage by Co^{60} radiation.[54]

studies also reinforce qualitatively the argument for the free-volume model. The first experiments in this direction were conducted with Teflon as early as 1957-58;[43] however, they showed no change in the angular correlation curves, and in the long lifetime τ_2 with total neutron irradiations up to $\sim 10^{17} cm^{-2}$. Later Fabri and Germagnoli[53] (see also Ref. 41) studied in greater detail the effect of neutron irradiation on solid anthracene, and established that long-lived components appeared with an integral flux of $4 \times 10^{18} cm^{-2}$, $I_2 \approx 30\%$ and $\tau_2 \approx 6 \times 10^{-10} sec$; with a flux of $2 \times 10^{19} cm^{-2}$, correspondingly $I_2 \approx 50\%$ and $\tau_2 \approx (7.6 \pm 0.5) \times 10^{-10} sec$. There was also a changed configuration of the angular correlation curves—irradiation leads to the appearance of narrow components with an area $10 \rightarrow 15\%$ of the overall size. Thus, irradiated anthracene behaved approximately like a liquid—it differed mainly in that although there is a similar I_2 there is a longer lifetime in liquid anthracene: $\tau_2 \approx 2.25 \times 10^{-9}$ sec[41] (i.e., in liquid anthracene there is an even greater proportion of free volume).

In the work of a group of Indian scientists,[54] the lifetime of positrons in Teflon previously irradiated with γ-rays from Co^{60} were compared with concentrations of free radicals determined by the EPR signal intensity. The results obtained are shown in Fig. 12. It is evident that the dose which yields the maximum concentration of radicals entails also maximum reduction of τ_2, reaching ~35% of the value for τ_2 a nonirradiated polymer; with additional irradiation dosage, τ_2 increases to its original value.

Interpretation of the results[54] is based on the fact that severance of the $C-F$ and $C-C$ bonds leads not only to the forming of free radicals, but also to the formation of vacancies on the sites of fluorine atoms or in a gap in the basic polymer chain, as the result of some contraction of two of its halfs after severance of a $C-C$ bond (type A). Positronium found in these vacancies can be rapidly quenched by a neighboring unpaired electron (lifetime of $\tau_2 < \tau_2^0$). Saturation of a radical yield occurs by their recombination; however, the gaps at the site of the $C-C$ bond break are still preserved. Such gaps as before serve as holes for the trapping of positronium (type B). Now, however, positronium annihilates at a normal rate (lifetime τ_2^0). If N_0 represents the number of the original vacancies (lifetime τ_2^0), S_1 is the number of spaces (vacancies) of type A, and S_2 is the number of spaces of type B, then

$$\frac{1}{\tau_2} = \frac{N_0 + S_2}{N_0 + S_1 + S_2} \frac{1}{\tau_2^0} + \frac{S_1}{N_0 + S_1 + S_2} \cdot \frac{1}{\tau_2} \tag{9}$$

It is not hard to convince oneself that:

$$S_1 = a \cdot \frac{e^{2aID} - 1}{c^{2aID} + 1} \quad \text{and} \quad S_{1_{lim}} = a$$

$$S_2 = gD - a \cdot \frac{e^{2aID} - 1}{e^{2aID} + 1} \tag{10}$$

$$S_1 + S_2 = gD$$

where D represents the dosage and I the intensity of irradiation, g is the radiation yield of radical formation, $a = (gI/K)^{1/2}$, and K is the recombination rate constant.

It is evident that where $N_0 + gD = \frac{1}{4}ae^{2aID}$, a minimal value is obtained for τ_2, while with $D \to 0$ and $D \to \infty$, $\tau_2 \to \tau_2^0$.

It would be interesting to carry further the study of Ref. 54, meanwhile varying the intensity of the irradiation.

However, in view of all that has been said, it would be wrong to assume that the free-volume formula describes currently known cases of τ_2 variations in the condensed phase.

About the most successful cases of the application of the free-volume formula are polymeric substances. Meanwhile, the series of new facts disclosed here (for instance, the presence of three components in the time spectrum of annihilation) show the need to add substantially to the current interpretation of these facts. In a group of cases it is also desirable to set up new experiments in order to eliminate specific discrepancies among the data of various experiments. A good example is that of Teflon, to which the greatest number of studies has been devoted.

Fabri et al.[55] studied the behavior of positronium in Teflon at temperatures ranging from −196 to +280°C, during which they paid particular attention to the effect of phase transitions at about room temperature. Temperature dependences obtained by them for τ_2 and I_2 are presented in Fig. 13. During transition (~ −20°C) from the triclinic to the hexagonal lattice (with appearance of absorption-line λ = 16 μ in the infrared spectrum), τ_2 almost doubles, while I_2 markedly drops. Within the range of high temperatures, therefore, a sharp rise in τ_2, as well as I_2, is noted. Changes in τ_2 and I_2 were reversible only for heating to a temperature much less than 275°C and for slow cooling. The authors[55] show that the change in Teflon density during the aforementioned transition phase (1.23%) is clearly insufficient to explain the sharp drop in τ_2 and I_2.

In the study by Spirn and Brandt,[56] (temperatures ranging from −196 to +340°C), they found, unlike Fabri et al.,[55] the maximum lifetime of the long-lived component (τ_A) for Teflon at about ≈ 200°C, with a subsequent drop to the melting region (~320°C), and a sharp increase only after liquefaction. Both branches of the rise in τ can be explained, in the opinion of the authors[56] by the thermal expansion of Teflon. The intensity of the long-lived component depended little on the temperature of the solid phase (I_A ≈ 15%), but increased sharply due to fusion. The lifetime of the other two components (τ_B and τ_C) increased with heating right up to melting, and decreased above the melting point; meanwhile I_B kept increasing while I_C kept decreasing.

To clear up the problem of the long-lived components of positron annihilation in Teflon, Fabri, Germagnoli, and Randone[57] undertook quite an interesting experiment to determine separately the lifetime of the narrow and the wide components in angular distribution of annihilation γ-rays. However, it is hard to explain their interpretation of the difference of the two time-spectrum, one for annihilation photons emitted at all angles and the other for photons emitted into the restricted angular range: $\pi - \theta$ = 8 ± 2 mrad, by the existence of two alternative kinds of positronium decay. After all, in an analogous situation of the decay of the radioactive isotope

the lifetime of C will not depend on whether the time spectrum is measured for its α or for its β activity.

The following experiments[58] using analogous techniques, apparently quite promising, did not confirm the results of Fabri

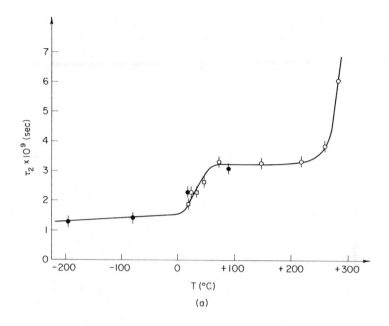

(a)

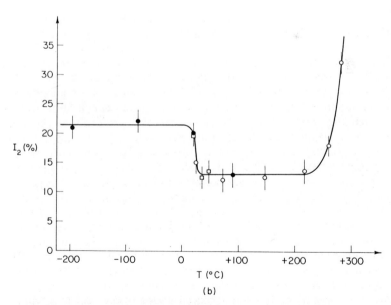

(b)

Fig. 13. Temperature dependence of τ_2 and I_2 for Teflon.[55]

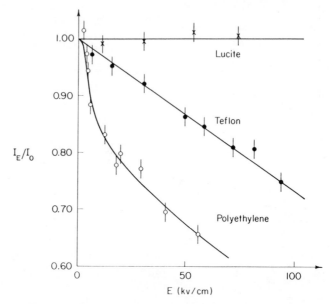

Fig. 14. Dependence of intensity, I_2, of the long-lived
component on static electric field in lucite, Teflon, and
polyethylene.[59]

et al.,[57] i.e., the decay curve for small angles ($\pi - \theta = 0 \pm 2$ mrad)
and large angles ($\pi - \theta > 4$ mrad) proved to be identical.

What remains unclear, meanwhile, is the discovery by the Milan
group[59-60] of the action of static electric fields (about 120 kV/cm) on
positronium formation and decay in Teflon, and in other nonpolar
macromolecules (paraffin, polyethylene). In Reference 59 it was
found that the action of such fields substantially decreases the intensity of long-lived component (see Fig. 14), in Reference 60 was
shown the finding of the reduced lifetime of this component: $\tau_E = \tau_0(1 - \alpha E)$ where $\alpha = (9.3 \pm 1.3) \, 10^{-4}$ cm/kV.

The effects shown were not observed in the case of polar polymers, whose molecules feature the presence of a constant dipole
moment, e.g., Lucite, nylon, polyvinylchloride. At the same time,
absolute values for τ_2 and I_2 for polyethylene and Lucite are nearly
the same,[52] and magnetic quenching of the intensity of the long-
lived component both in Teflon and in Lucite is identical, and tallies
with what is expected for free positronium.[61] Besides Teflon, the ice-
water system was subjected to the most detailed study.

Attention has already been directed above to the fact that when
water is frozen,[48] I_2 increases, and a very narrow peak appears in

the ice, in the angular correlation curve,[43],[44] identifiable with positronium. The moderation of positronium in collisions with hydrogen
atoms should be equivalent in ice and in water, but the energy of the
ground state, occupied by the Ps atom in the three-dimensional
square well, $E = (\pi h^2/16mr^2) = 4.6 \ 10^{-16}/r^2$ eV, should sharply decline[43] with the increase of the radius of the hole r, which may also
speed up positronium thermalization. This is a qualitative argument
in the spirit of the free-volume formula; however, it is actually far
from explaining all the details of the temperature and phase variation of τ_2 (especially of I_2) in all the varieties of water and ice, for
example, the differences in the magnetic quenching of positronium,
which will be dealt with in Section III. The temperature dependence
of τ_2 and I_2 in water and in ice from -30 to $+80°C$ was studied by
Fabri et al.[62] —the results are given in Fig. 15. The basic conclusions here is that changes of τ_2 and I_2 near the fusion point prove
far smoother than, for instance, with naphthalene.[30] The data shows
considerable scatter in the range of $\Delta T \approx 30°C$. Incidentally, the
narrow-peak yield in ice and water also changes smoothly with temperature[43] (see Fig. 8, above). The temperature dependence of the
$I_2\tau_2$ product proved close to that observed earlier[39] for the rate of
3γ coincidence. The authors[62] note that the I_2 difference obtained
by them at $T° = -40°C$ ($I_2 = 0.42 \pm 0.03$) and $+20°C$ ($I_2 = 0.28 \pm$
0.02) agrees with the change in the yield of *para*-positronium
$^1/_3\Delta I_2 = 0.047 \pm 0.013$. At the same time, intensification of the
narrow peak in the angular correlation results of de Zafra and Joyner[43] in ice $(-40°C)$, as compared with water, $(+20°C)$ agrees with

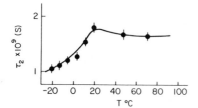
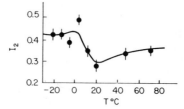

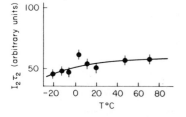

Fig. 15. Temperature dependence
of τ_2, I_2, and product, $\tau_2 I_2$, for ice
and water.[62]

the fraction of *para*-positronium formation 0.077 ± 0.01. Fabri et al.[62] conclude from this that in ice there can occur supplementary *para*-positronium formation attributable to the electromagnetic conversion mechanism: $^3S_1 \rightarrow {}^1S_0$ in a strong dipole field. This had already been suggested by Ferrell.[46]

A quantitative summary of the results enumerated above are given in Table III in order to compare the effects of various factors

TABLE III

Comparison of the Effect of Various Factors
on the Lifetime (τ) and Intensity (I) of the Long-Lived Component
of the Time Spectrum of Positronium Annihilation

Substance	Nature of the action	Type of Change		Ref.	Free-volume model
		τ	I		
Ice	Heating	↑	↑	62	+
	Fusing	↑	↓	48,62	−
Water	Heating to 4° C	↑	↓	48,62	−
	Heating to 20° C	↑	↓	62	
	Heating to 20° C	↓	↑	62	
Cyclohexane (solid)	Heating	↑	—	51	+
Naphthalene	Melting	↑	↑	30	+
Anthracene	Melting	↑	↑	26,41	+
	Irradiation by neutrons	↑	↑	41,53	+
Liquids	Compression	↓	—	49,50	+
Solid polymers	Compression	↓	↓	50	+
Polystyrene Polyethylene Lucite	Heating	↑	↑	13,52	+
Teflon	Heating close to 20° C	↑	↓	55	
	Heating close to fusion zone	↑	↑	55,56	+
Teflon, paraffin, polyethylene, (nonpolar polymers)	Electric field	↓	↓	59,60	
Lucite Nylon Polyvinyl-chloride (polar polymers)	Electric field	—	—	59,60	

on the lifetime and the intensity of the long-lived component of positron annihilation. Decrease, increase, or stability of τ and I are indicated by arrows ↓↑ or —. The last column of Table III specifies
the qualitative agreement of the experimental data with the free-
volume formula. The drop (or rise) in τ with the increase (decrease)
of density, i.e., with the decrease (increase) of the free volume of
the substance, is indicated here by the symbol + in the case of a
correlated change in τ , and I or absence of change in I. The symbol
— stands for cases of an anomalous change of τ . No symbol is used
to indicate the opposite changes of τ and I, nor for experiments with
electric fields.

Evidently, the free-volume formula, with all of its good features,
includes far too few properties of positron annihilation in liquids
and in solids, and apart from the factor of density, an important part
is played by the nature of the intermolecular interaction, and by the
internal order of the structures.

The conclusion that a few changes in density alone cannot clear
up the picture of angular correlation of decayed γ-quanta in various
types of sulfur and quartz was reached by Colombino, Degregori,
Mayrone, Trossi, and DeBenedetti[63],[64] on the basis of their experiments with plastic, rhombic, and monoclinic sulfur;[63] and with four
types of quartz:

   (a) with fused quartz (ρ = 2.1 − 2.3 gm/cm³);
   (b) with crystal quartz (2.65 gm/cm³)
   (c) with tridymite, with about the density of fused quartz; (2.22
gm/cm³) and an ice-type structure;
   (d) with cristobalite, a cubed-ice type structure.

The correlation curves of all three types of sulfur turned out
closely alike, although the density of rhombic was up to 5.5% higher
than for monoclinic, and although in plastic sulfur there is an I_2
component that is not found in monoclinic sulfur.[3]

In the case of quartz, increased yield of the narrow component of
the correlation curve was noted only in fused quartz, with all three
other types giving similar results.

Of course, the free-volume formula is aimed in the first instance
at explaining not the variations in positronium formation but the
changes in its lifetime.

As to the possible effect on positronium lifetime of intermolecular interaction and internal structural regularity, note the very interesting work of Cole and Walker[65] on the positron annihilation in
liquid or in mesomorphic crystals.

There exist two basic types of such crystals—nematic (liquid)
and smectic (fluid), conventionally represented in Fig. 16. In all
liquid crystals, the long axes of the molecules are parallel, but the
higher degree of structural regularity of smectic crystals is due to

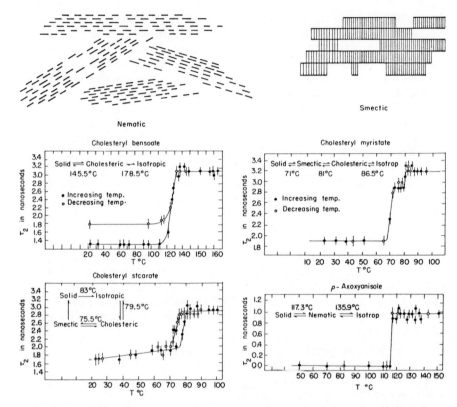

Fig. 16. Schematic representation of nematic and smectic crystals, and temperature dependence of the lifetime of positrons τ_2, for liquid crystals.[65]

the fact that its molecules contain localized centers of strong mutual attraction, whereas in the nematoid phase they are dispersed all along their length. That is why the interaction energy of the molecules of the nematoid phase depends solely on the angle between their long axes, but for the molecules of the smectic phase, the interaction energy depends as well on the shifting of one molecule along the side of another one, as a result of which these molecules form equidistant smetic planes in which, as it were, the molecules are fixed at either end. A special case of the nematic phase is presented by cholesterol crystals, structured from plates of molecules, whose planes are oriented parallel to each other, and lie perpendicular to the symmetry axis of such crystals.

Nematic and smetic crystals occupy an intermediate position between solid and amorpholiquid (isotropic) phases, and during a rise in temperature, there successively occur phase transitions of the first type with a very small exothermal effect:

solid phase $\rightleftharpoons$ smectic phase $\rightleftharpoons$ nematic $\rightleftharpoons$ liquid
                                           (cholesterol   (isotropic
                                           phase)   phase)

The study of Cole and Walker contained a demonstration of the change in τ_2, not only during fusing (i.e., solid-smetic), but also during phase transitions between smectic and cholesteryl phases. Their data for cholesteryl-benzoate, cholesteryl-stearate, cholesteryl-myristate and p-azoxianizol are indicated in Fig. 16. The τ_2 change was noted only in transitions where an abrupt change takes place in the intermolecular, dipolar action, hindering positronium formation and shortening its lifetime. This charge is strongest in the solid phase, especially azoxyanisole, where long-lived components are generally absent.

The results of the Cole-Walker study[65] again compel one to recall the previously mentioned classification of Wallace,[1e] and also the fact that ice and water differ not only in density but also in structural regularity, as well as in the nature of their intermolecular interaction—hydrogen-bonds in ice are rather more ionic than covalent in character; finally, there is the differing effect of the electric field on τ_2 and I_2 in polar and in nonpolar polymers. Structural stability and intermolecular interaction in the condensed phase play, as has already been mentioned, an important part in both positron moderation in the vicinity of the Ore gap (attachment, for instance, to the negative ends of dipoles; inelastic energy losses), and in the properties already noted for positronium—its polarization, and its moderation as it approaches thermal energies. All these factors variously affect positronium lifetime, its formation probability, thermalization, and various transformations, and the nature of the angular correlation of its annihilation γ-quanta. Furthermore, one must take into account a series of anomalies in magnetic quenching of positronium (to be discussed later), and the possibility of the non-positronium origin of a long-lived component of the time spectrum of annihilation. That is why this section may end on the assertion that regardless of the abundance of available experimental data and the undoubted success of the free volume model in explaining many facts, the problems of further observations of positronium behavior, and an overall interpretation of the role of temperature, density, and phase transitions in positronium formation and decay, are becoming increasingly urgent.

III. MAGNETIC QUENCHING OF POSITRONIUM (ACTION OF EXTERNAL MAGNETIC FIELD)

The description of magnetic quenching of positronium requires first of all consideration of the general features of the two ground (1S) states of this atom.[1]

The singlet state of positronium, $^1S_0 (m = 0)$, decays by 2γ quanta. The decay constant of this state is characterized by

$$\lambda_S = \frac{1}{\tau_S} = 4\pi r_0^2 c \, | \psi(0) |^2 \tag{11}$$

where $r_0 = e^2/mc^2$ the classical electron radius, while $|\psi(0)|^2$ is the density of the electron wavefunction at the positron.

In the free positronium atom

$$| \psi(0) |^2 = \frac{1}{\pi n^3 a_B^3} = \frac{1}{\pi n^3} \left(\frac{Me^2}{\hbar^2} \right)^3 \tag{12}$$

where $a_B = \hbar^2/Me^2$ is the radius of the first Bohr orbit, while $M = me/2$ is the reduced mass.

As a result, in the ground $(n = 1)$ positronium state

$$\lambda_S = 4r_0^2 c \left(\frac{Me^2}{\hbar^2} \right)^3 = 8 \times 10^9 \, \text{sec}^{-1} \tag{13}$$

The triplet (ortho) positronium state $^3S_1 (m = +1, 0, -1)$, decays by 3γ quanta, and its decay constant is expressed as:

$$\lambda_T = \frac{1}{\tau_T} = \lambda_S \frac{4}{9\pi} (\pi^2 - 9) \frac{e^2}{\hbar c} = \frac{\lambda_S}{1115} = 7.14 \times 10^6 \, \text{sec}^{-1} \tag{14}$$

The hyperfine splitting of the ground positronium state is characterized by the energy excess of the triplet state (^3W) over the singlet state (^1W)

$$\Delta W = \, ^3W - \, ^1W = \frac{56}{3} \pi \mu^2 \, | \psi(0) |^2 \tag{15}$$

where μ is the magnetic moment of the electron and the positron, equal to $e\hbar/2mc$. This energy consists of two components, the spin-spin splitting of the magnetic interaction $\Delta W_1 = \, ^{32}/_3 \pi \mu^2 |\psi(0)|^2$ (in the case of the hydrogen atom this splitting, $^{32}/_3 \pi \mu \mu_p |\psi(0)|^2$ is unique, and is observed by the emergence of the known line with a 21-cm long wave), and the interaction exchange energy due to the virtual annihilation: $\Delta W_2 = 8\pi\mu^2 |\psi(0)|^2$. For the free positronium atom (where $n = 1$) and if one neglects the radiation electrodynamic corrections, we get:

$$\Delta W = \, ^3W - \, ^1W = \frac{56}{3} \pi \left(\frac{e\hbar}{2mc} \right)^2 \frac{1}{\pi} \left(\frac{me^2}{2\hbar^2} \right)^3 = \frac{7}{12} \left(\frac{e^2}{\hbar c} \right)^4 mc^2 = 8.4 \times 10^{-4} \text{eV} \tag{16}$$

The wavefunction of ground positronium state appears as:

$$\psi_{0,0} = \frac{1}{\sqrt{2}} [\varphi_e(1)\varphi_p(2) - \varphi_e(2)\varphi_p(1)] \qquad m = 0 \qquad {}^1S_0$$

$$\psi_{1,1} = \varphi_e(1)\varphi_p(1) \qquad\qquad\qquad m = 1$$

$$\psi_{1,0} = \frac{1}{\sqrt{2}} [\varphi_e(1)\varphi_p(2) + \varphi_e(2)\varphi_p(1)] \qquad m = 0 \qquad {}^3S_1$$

$$\psi_{1,-1} = \varphi_e(2)\varphi_p(2) \qquad\qquad\qquad m = -1$$

$$(17)$$

The charge parity of positronium is $C = (-1)^{L+S}$, so that from the two 1S ground states of positronium ($L = 0$) the triplet ($S = 1$) appears as charge-odd and the singlet ($S = 0$) as charge-even.

However, the operator for the interaction of Ps with magnetic field $H_m = e\hbar/2mc[\vec{\sigma}_e - \vec{\sigma}_p] \cdot \vec{H}]$ is not invariant to the replacement of an electron by a positron, and therefore does not conserve the charge parity, but mixes singlet and the triplet states with $m = 0$. In a magnetic field $H \gtrsim (2mc/e\hbar)\,\Delta W$, it is no longer the spin of the positronium that proves to be a "good" quantum number, but the magnetic quantum number m: $m \pm 1$ corresponds decay by 3γ quanta, and $m = 0$ decay by 2γ quanta.

Each of these two states, distinguishable by its value of m, is represented in positronium with a weight of 50%, so that the decay events by 2γ quanta with short lifetime in large magnetic fields increases two-fold compared with decay in the absence of any field, while the long-lived $ortho$-state is quenched by $1/3$. The wavefunction of the composite ${}^1S_0$ and ${}^3S_1\,(m = 0)$ states appears as

$$\psi = C_S\,\psi_{0,0} + C_T\,\psi_{1,0}$$

the ratio

$$\frac{C_S}{C_T} = a = \frac{\sqrt{1 + x^2} - 1}{x}$$

where

$$x = \frac{2e\hbar}{mc} \cdot \frac{H}{\Delta W} = 4\frac{\mu H}{\Delta W}$$

The diagram of the splitting of the positronium levels in a magnetic field is given in Fig. 17. The field affects the $m = 0$ sublevel energies as

$${}^3E(m = 0) = \frac{{}^1W + {}^3W}{2} + \frac{\Delta W}{2}(1 + x^2)^{1/2}$$

$${}^1E(m = 0) = \frac{{}^1W + {}^3W}{2} - \frac{\Delta W}{2}(1 + x^2)^{1/2}$$

$$(18)$$

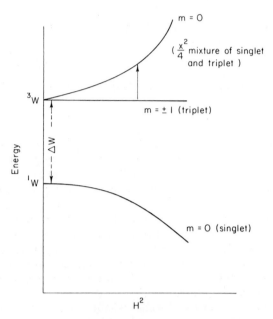

Fig. 17. Diagram of the split-up of positronium levels in the magnetic field.

and the $m = \pm 1$ sublevel energy remains unchanged. As it is clearly
seen from (18) the linear terms are missing in the expression characterizing the energy shift in the magnetic field, i.e., the Zeeman
effect proves to be quadratic. Qualitatively this is explained by the
fact that due to the opposite signs and equal absolute values of magnetic moments of electron and positron on *ortho*-positronium, the
total momentum equals here zero; the total magnetic momentum of
para-positronium equals two (in Bohr magneton units), but its spin
is zero and therefore there is absent here any distinct direction of
the projection of magnetic momentum*.

*Such a distinct direction appears in the presence of an external magnetic
field, whose direction serves as a quantization axis. That is why the weight
of the $m = 0$ orthopositronium substate (equal on the average to $\frac{1}{3}$) depends
on angle θ between the direction of the magnetic field and the plane of the
quanta detected, changing from $\frac{1}{2}$ for $\theta = 90°$ to 0 for $\theta = 0°$. This circumstance, noted in Reference 66, should be kept in mind in interpreting experiments involving magnetic quenching.

This theory offers, for *ortho*-positronium quenching, the following formula which characterizes the fraction of 3γ quanta decays of the triplet state in the magnetic field H:

$$W_{3\gamma} = \frac{2}{3} + \frac{1}{3} \left[1 + \left(\frac{2\mu H}{\Delta W} \right)^2 \frac{\lambda_S}{\lambda_T} \right]^{-1} \tag{19}$$

Obviously, when $H = 0$, $W_{3\gamma} = 1$ and when $\mu H \gg \Delta W$, $W_{3\gamma} \to \frac{2}{3}$. The quenching of orthopositronium can occur not only from an external field, but also from the field of paramagnetic admixtures in the experimental specimen. However, pertinent evaluations lead to the conclusion that even for as paramagnetic a gas as oxygen, the rate constant of such quenching at normal temperature and pressure, should total only $\sim 10^5 \, sec^{-1}$ — two orders of magnitude less than the rate of spontaneous 3γ decay. That is why during a reaction of orthopositronium to paramagnetic admixtures, the direct conversion of $^3S_1 \to {}^1S_0$ always predominates and, incidentally, it does not require a change of the spin state of the impurity itself from $I \geq 1$.[67,68] From this point on, the discussion will be limited entirely to positronium quenching with external magnetic fields.

Such quenching in gases was first obtained by Deutsch[69] in his classical experiments, and later by Wheatley and Halliday[70] by observing the decrease of 3γ coincidences; by Pond and Dicke,[71] by observing the increase of 2γ coincidences; by Hughes, Marder, and Wu[72] via the effect of the magnetic field on the angular spread of 3γ-quanta decay probability, as compared with the calculations of Drisko[66] ; and by Heinberg and Page[73] via increased yield of "narrow components" in the angular correlation of the γ quanta in a magnetic field. Experiments with gases confirmed theoretical predictions as to the energy of hyperfine splitting of ΔW, and the ratio of the constants of singlet and triplet positronium decay. A particularly precise value of ΔW for free positronium was determined in experiments by Deutsch and his co-workers[74,75] by orthopositronium resonance quenching with an rf electromagnetic field, causing transitions $^3S_1 (m = \pm 1) \to {}^3S_1 (m = 0)$, followed by 2γ annihilation.

The first experiments with intensification by the magnetic field of the narrow components of angular correlation of annihilation γ quanta, in the solids, where positronium is formed (Teflon, fused quartz) were performed by Page and Heinberg.[37,38] Subsequently, Telegdi and his co-workers[76] observed in these substances, quenching of 3γ annihilation with magnetic fields.

As is well known, the decay rate of orthopositronium in the condensed phase rises sharply due to "pickoff" annihilation, occurring as a rule with a 2γ-quanta emission. The fraction of the 3γ decays of orthopositronium consequently decreases sharply, comprising in all λ_T / γ_p, where γ_p is the positronium decay constant with respect to "pickoff" annihilation: $\gamma_p \cong 1/\tau_2$; τ_2 is the lifetime of long-lived ($\sim 10^9$ sec) components, in annihilation time-spectra identified with ortho-positronium.

The corresponding fraction of 3γ annihilation in the decay of the $^3S_1 (m = 0)$ component, instead of $[1 + (2\mu H/\Delta W)^2 (\lambda_S /\lambda_T)]^{-1}$ becomes in the condensed phase $\lambda_T /\gamma_p [1 + (2\mu H/\Delta W)^2 (\lambda_S /\gamma_p)]^{-1}$, and the overall fraction of 3γ decay of the triplet state in the magnetic field is now determined by

$$W_{3\gamma} = \left\{ \frac{2}{3} + \frac{1}{3} \left[1 + \left(\frac{2\mu H}{\Delta W}\right)^2 \frac{\tau_2}{\tau_S} \right]^{-1} \right\} \frac{\tau_2}{\tau_T} \qquad (20)$$

and not by Eq. (19).

Experiment shows the dependence of the coincidence counting rate on the external magnetic field, enabling one to determine whether this dependence agrees with the independently determined value of τ_2, since this is required by the formula (20) where ΔW, τ_T, and τ_S have known fixed values.

The term characterizing the efficiency of the magnetic quenching is now equal to $(2\mu H/\Delta W)^2 (\tau_2 /\tau_S)$, instead of $(2\mu H/\Delta W)^2 (\tau_T /\tau_S)$ for the gas (i.e., for free positronium). That is why, in order to assure magnetic quenching in the condensed system, one must take $(\tau_T /\tau_2)^{1/2}$ times greater magnetic field. Experiments with gases were performed with magnetic fields of about 8 kG, in the condensed phase—about 22 kG.

Experiments using the magnetic field to increase the narrow component yield in angular correlation curves [37,38,75,76] give essentially the same information as do experiments with 3γ-decay magnetic quenching or an increase of 2γ coincidence rate.

The narrow component is connected, as is well known, with 2γ annihilation of singlet positronium, and, in the absence of a field, it is $1/4$ of the entire positronium yield. Therefore, the increased yield of the narrow component is determined by that portion of the triplet state, with $m = 0$, that mixes with the singlet state, or specifically:

$$\Delta I_N = \frac{1}{4} \left(\frac{2\mu H}{\Delta W}\right)^2 \frac{\tau}{\tau_S} \left[1 + \left(\frac{2\mu H}{\Delta W}\right)^2 \frac{\tau}{\tau_S} \right]^{-1} \qquad (21)$$

where $\tau = \tau_T$ for free positronium [in a gas], and $\tau = \tau_2$ for the condensed phase.

Similarly, observation of the intensity of the long-lived component I_2 with increase of magnetic field should show a decrease from $^3/_4 P$ to $^1/_2 P$: $I_2 = P[^3/_4 - \Delta I_N]$, where P is the positronium formation probability. The ratio: $R(H) = I_2 (H)/I_2 (0)$ should correspondingly decrease from 1 to $^2/_3$, as was actually determined in a series of experiments [61,62,79,80] performed mainly by Italian scientists.

Finally, it should be noted that magnetic quenching of the $m = 0$ constituent of triplet positronium also shortens its lifetime, while the lifetime of the $m = \pm 1$ remains unchanged. Such a reduction from 2.25×10^{-9} sec ($H = 0$) to 1.2×10^{-9} sec(($H = 22$ kG) has been observed in Reference 79.

According to Reference 61 the lifetime of $m = 0$, $^3S_1$, positronium is

$$\tau^1 = \tau_2 \frac{1 + a^2}{1 + a^2 \tau_2 / \tau_S}$$

and changes from $\tau^1 = \tau_2$ in the absence of a magnetic field ($a = 0$) to $\tau^1 = 2[\tau_S \tau_2/(\tau_S + \tau_2)] \approx 2\tau_S$ with $H \to \infty$, ($a \to 1$).

The calculation of lifetime change leads to some further complication in the equations describing the effect of a magnetic field on orthopositronium. The calculations are found in Ref. 61. We shall not reproduce them here since using these formulas does not change the character of the following discussion.

The list of substances used for observing magnetic quenching of long-lived components of the annihilation time spectrum in the condensed phase, includes several polymers (Teflon, Lucite, polystyrene), fused quartz, water, ice, and also KCl. A summary of the experiments is presented in Table IV. Besides the name of the substance, an index is given of the extent of quenching: n-stands for *normal*, i.e., what is expected for *free* positronium; s-stands for *stronger*; w stands for *weaker*; O-stands for absence of noticeable quenching.

In all the polymers investigated, magnetic quenching proved fully in accord with the above formulas, satisfactorily confirming not only positronium formation in these polymers, but also nearly identical properties of this positronium with those of the free atom. In water, and especially in ice, however, the data obtained prove the complexity of the observed phenomena and of the need for further experiments. In ice, as a rule, the magnetic field did not yield an increase of the narrow component, a fact that basically contradicts the expected "ordinary" positronium[80] behavior, and adds still another anomaly to those discussed earlier regarding the water-ice system.

Inasmuch as even without a magnetic field the configuration of the curves of angular correlation of annihilation quanta is markedly different in water and in ice, and inasmuch as in ice there is a sharply marked narrow peak[43,44] (thermalized positronium), that does not appear in water, it would be extremely desirable to investigate magnetic quenching in ice by another method—by intensity of long-lived components, as was done for water, but also by direct registration of 3γ coincidences.

TABLE IV

Summary of Experiments with Magnetic Quenching of Positronium

Authors	Substances	Research method	Magnetic field (in kG)
Page et al.[37,38]	Teflon Fused quartz	$\theta_{2\gamma}$	up to 16.3
Telegdi et al.[76] 1956	Teflon (n) Fused quartz (n)	$C_{3\gamma}$	0 and 10
Warshaw[77] 1957	Teflon (n)	$\theta_{2\gamma}$	0 and 10
Freitag and Ziock[79] 1958	Polystyrene (n)	I_2, τ_2	0, 14, and 22
Iaci et al.[78] 1962	Water (s) Ice (O)	$\theta_{2\gamma}$	up to 15
Bisi et al.[61] 1962	Teflon (n) Lucite (n)	I_2	up to 18.6
Fabri et al.[62] 1963	Water (s) Ice (O)	I_2	up to 15
Bisi et al.[81] 1964	KCl (w)	I_2	up to 15
Fabri et al.[80] 1964	Teflon (n) Water (s)	$C_{3\gamma}$ Intensity of 511 KeV in photo peak annihilation spectrum	up to 15

In water, the quenching action of the magnetic field turns out more marked than expected for "ordinary" positronium.[62,80] This fact is illustrated in Fig. 18, where experimental data for water, Teflon, and KCl are compared with the theory. Fabri and his co-workers[62,80] show that the discrepancy in one's calculations can be eliminated by making the value ΔW for positronium in water equal 5×10^{-4} eV instead of 8.34×10^{-4} eV, the value from Eq. (16). In other words, these authors propose to reduce $|\psi(0)|^2$ for positronium in water compared with free positronium. This reduction may be connected with the departure from spherical symmetry of the wavefunctions and the "swelling" of positronium because of the polarizing interaction of the positronium atom with water molecules. It must be noted, however, that there is no sense in changing ΔW in formulas of type (20) or (21), regarding this quantity as some disposable parameter and at the same time keeping the old value of τ_S, which also depends on $|\psi(0)|^2$. As it is clear by comparing (11) and (15), $\tau_S \Delta W = 14\mu^2/3r_0^2 c = \hbar c/e^2 \cdot \hbar \cong 137\,\hbar$ = const. Taking this into account, in order to bring the experiments into agreement with the theory of magnetic quenching, ΔW must be reduced for water to 3×10^{-4} eV, which will account for an increase in the linear dimensions of positronium by 40% and a lifetime increase of the singlet by 2.8 times to about 3.5×10^{-10} sec.

Meanwhile, the probability of the increase of para-positronium lifetime not only has not been verified so far experimentally, but it has not even been discussed. It is evidently one of the most important coming questions in research on the behavior of positronium in the condensed phase. In concluding this section, one would like to consider one other important problem in experiments with magnetic quenching of positronium. That is, the investigations which recently have shown an abnormally high probability of 3γ annihilation.[82,84] If the entire long-lived component of the annihilation time spectrum is dependent on positronium formation, then the annihilation probability with emission of 3γ quanta should evidently be described by

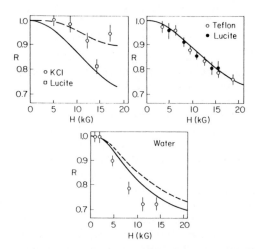

Fig. 18. Quenching of the long-lived component of the time spectrum of positron annihilation in a magnetic field. Along the Y-axis, the ratio of the intensity of this component, I, in field H and without a field. The continuous line denoting the theoretical curves corresponds to the quenching of "normal" positronium: ($\Delta W = 8.34\ 10^{-5}$ eV). (a) water[80] — strengthened quenching; (b) teflon[61] — normal quenching; (c) KCl[81] — weakened quenching.

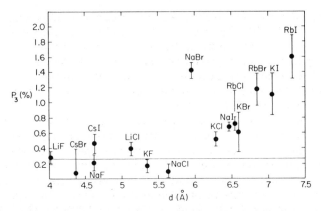

Fig. 19. The dependence of probability of positron annihilation with emission of 3γ quanta upon the lattice spacing of the halide crystals of the alkali metals.[82,83]

$$P_{3\gamma} = I_2 \frac{\tau_2}{\tau_T} + (1 - \tfrac{4}{3} I_2) \frac{1}{372} \qquad (22)$$

With $I_2 = 0$ (free annihilation), the probability of $P_{3\gamma}$ is minimal, constituting 0.27%. The value of $P_{3\gamma}$ should not be any greater in all cases where the long-lived component is caused not by free positronium but by some other source, for instance, the formation of a compound of the $e^+ A^-$type, or the usual covalent two-electron bond binding positronium compounds, the fraction of the 3γ annihilation in P_S^- should be $^1/_{1116}$. Meanwhile, Gainotti et al.,[82,83] have found that for alkali halide crystals with a lattice-parameter greater than 6Å, the probability of 3γ annihilation is noticeably greater than 0.27%, and also increases with the increase of the lattice parameter (see Fig. 19), rising to 1.6% in RbI ($d = 7.33$A).

Even more remarkable results have been obtained with oxides of alkali-earth metals by Bussolati and Zappa,[84] who noted not only a 3γ-annihilation probability, from the γ-quanta spectrum, but also lifetime and intensity of long-lived components. Experimental values for τ_2 and I_2 and $P_{3\gamma} \%$, and the partial lifetime of triplet positronium for 3γ-annihilation, calculated by them from $P_{3\gamma} = I_2 (\tau_2 / \tau_{T3})$, are listed in Table V. First and foremost it must be mentioned that all the experiments in previous studies[82-84] were performed not by direct observation of 3γ coincidences but by comparing the 0.51 MeV peak intensity in the compounds being studied, with this intensity in substances where positronium is certain not to be formed,[82-83] or peak-to-valley ratio of γ-ray spectra.[84] However, processes of the type of $e^+ e^- e^- \rightarrow \gamma + e^-$ and $e^+ e^- e^- \rightarrow 2\gamma + e^-$ in multielectronic systems (as well as secondary scattering of the annihilation γ quanta, including the above-mentioned single-quantum annihilation) may cause both change in intensity of the 0.51 MeV peak compared with the standard (the single-quantum annihilation which gives a more energetic γ quanta), and also a reinforcement of the valley region of the γ-quanta spectrum ($e^+ e^- e^- \rightarrow 2\gamma + e^-$ and the secondary scattering).*

If, however, the data[82-84] really refer to 3γ annihilation, then they merely support the possibility of the existence not only of the "swollen" positronium postulated for water, but also of the "compressed" positronium most evidently represented in the case of BeO. The probability of such positronium compression in a solid was mentioned in Dixon and Trainor's[85] discussion of the $2S$ state. However, to explain a time τ_T reduction as strong as that in Table V, one must also presuppose the destruction of the spherical symmetry of the positronium wavefunction by some polarizing forces, since uniform spherical compression of positronium by its surrounding molecules with effective pressure of about 10,000 atm can only curtail positronium lifetime by 25% according to figures given by Brandt et al.[48] Corresponding to a triplet lifetime of τ_T = 4.8 10^{-9} sec would be a singlet lifetime of τ_S = 4.3 $\times 10^{-12}$ sec, and a positronium radius in the $1S$ state of about 0.35 Å (instead of 1.06 Å), and thus about 5.4 times weaker, than the normal, quenching action of the magnetic field. Perhaps this very fact explains in large measure the very weak effect of the magnetic field on the long-lived component of the time spectrum of annihilation of positrons in KCl ($P_{3\gamma}$ = 0.52 $\pm$ 0.09%)[82] as reported earlier in the work of Bisi, Fiorentini, and Zappa[81] (see Fig. 18), and the absence of magnetic quenching of positronium in ice.

A material suitable for the formation of compressed positronium with the required polarized wavefunction might have a dielectric constant $\epsilon < 1$, and an anomalous dispersion in the adjacent ultraviolet

TABLE V
Data of Bussolati and Zappa[84] on the Anomalous 3γ Annihilation

Substance	$\tau_2 \times 10^9$ sec	I_2 (%)	$P_{3\gamma}$ (%)	$\tau_{T_3} \times 10^9$ sec
BeO	3.46 $\pm$ 0.26	8.4 $\pm$ 0.2	6.18 $\pm$ 0.38	4.8 $\pm$ 0.5
MgO	4.86 $\pm$ 0.52	2.5 $\pm$ 0.1	2.33 $\pm$ 0.11	5.4 $\pm$ 0.7
CaO	3.75 $\pm$ 0.28	3.3 $\pm$ 0.3	0.75 $\pm$ 0.11	19 $\pm$ 4
BaO	3.20 $\pm$ 0.27	0.74 $\pm$ 0.08	0.42 $\pm$ 0.07	7 $\pm$ 2

* According to the estimates of Smirnov, the rates for different modes of annihilation from the PS^- state ($e^+ e^- e^-$) are: $W_{2\gamma} \approx 4\ 10^9$ sec^{-1}, $W_{3\gamma} \approx 10^7$ sec^{-1}, $W_{1\gamma} < 7\ 10^5$ sec^{-1}. Thus, single photon annihilation is unimportant.

region. All that has been said renders urgent the problem of studying the 3γ coincidence directly, and to find out the effect of magnetic fields on these coincidences, most of all in such substances as BeO. Besides, in connection with the presence of many unexplained questions concerning the role of density, temperature, pressure, and phase transitions in positronium formation and decay, it appears quite desirable to study systematically the effect of all these factors on magnetic quenching of positronium, as well as a comparison of data on the effects of electric and magnetic fields.

IV. CHEMICAL QUENCHING OF POSITRONIUM

"Positronium quenching" comprises all processes leading to the shortening of positronium lifetime. These processes include

$$\text{ortho-para conversion } (^3S_1 \rightarrow \ ^1S_0{}^*) ,$$

"pickoff" which is annihilation of the positron in the positronium atom with "foreign" electrons during collision with molecules of the medium, and chemical quenching, i.e., variants of chemical interaction, like the reactions of oxidation $(Ps + Ox \rightarrow e^+ + Red)$, addition $(Ps + M \rightarrow PsM)$, and substitution $(Ps + RM \rightarrow PsM + R)$ of positronium.

In the case of oxidation, a positron is released and annihilates rapidly afterwards in free collisions, or through attachment to anions or neutral molecules. Addition or substitution induce rapid positron annihilation, with one of the electrons of the bond.

Briefly referred to was the possibility of positron attachment to molecules or anions with formation of products of type e^+M or e^+A^-. Obviously, these products also may be designated as positronium compounds — PsM^+ or PsA. The rate of positronium decay (i.e., positron annihilation) in such compounds, as well as in compounds formed in reactions with free positronium atoms is quite high $(\lambda \ge 10^{10} \sec^{-1})$, and that is why bound positronium is practically no longer subject to supplementary quenching. These observations in most cases refer also to free parapositronium, although on the basis of its small mass and correspondingly considerable velocity of thermal motion, it can, with greater probability than the positronium compounds, successfully effect some interaction during the time shorter than the intrinsic value of $\tau_s = 1.25 \ 10^{-10} \sec$. Thus, in the condensed phase, with quencher concentration $n = 10^{22} \operatorname{cm}^{-3}$, and

---

* The rate of the reverse process $^1S_0 \rightarrow \ ^3S_1$ as a rule, is less than the rate of spontaneous decay, and thus, reverse conversion produces no quenching, for, on the contrary, it results in an increased positronium life-time.

geometric cross section of interaction $\sigma = 10^{-15} cm^2$, and positronium thermal velocity $v \approx 10^7 cm/sec$, the interaction time becomes $\tau_b = 1/n\sigma v = 10^{-14} sec$. However, this extreme case is not typical of positronium quenching. Moreover, at such great rate of interactions of parapositronium, the actual annihilation rate will no longer be determined by the interaction rate itself, but by the annihilation rate of the positrons in the positronium compounds being formed, which is normally only slightly in excess of λ_s. Hence, in the vast majority of cases, positronium quenching need be considered only for its long-lived triplet state.

Annihilation experiments of positrons in the gas phase showed to all appearances three varieties of positronium quenching. One of the most important proofs of the very existence of positronium quenching was the demonstration by Deutsch[86] of positronium quenching with admixture of NO to nitrogen, and Freon by the mechanism of conversion of $^3S_1 \rightarrow {}^1S_0$ by the unpaired electron of nitrogen oxide. Furthermore, the action of NO was studied both via increased 2γ coincidence rate,[87] and decrease of 3γ annihilation probability, with addition of nitrogen oxide to argon. Values of $2 \times 10^{-17} - 8 \times 10^{-17} cm^2$ are given for the cross section of *ortho-para* conversion by nitrogen oxide. Evidently, an analogy to NO quenching mechanism occurs also with NO_2. Positronium quenching in the gaseous oxygen appeared in previous studies[2,3,88,89] with a much smaller cross section than with nitrogen oxide $\sigma \approx 1 \times 10^{-19} - 4 \times 10^{-19} cm^2$. The authors[88] postulated that this quenching depends on the paramagnetic properties of the oxygen, and arises also through the conversion mechanism with or without spin inversion of the oxygen molecule.[67] Furthermore, Paul, on the basis of his experiments with the quenching of positronium with oxygen additives in liquid argon,[90] derived a fully plausible hypothesis[91] on the possibility of the addition reaction: $Ps + O_2(+M) \rightarrow PsO_2(+M)$. Deutsch obtained experimentally the bimolecular rate constant for the reaction of Ps with O_2, the value $3.1 \times 10^{-12} cm^3/sec$, which at atmospheric pressure of O_2 accounts for the reasonable value of the trimolecular rate constant $(\sim 10^{-31} cm^6/sec)$. Positronium quenching with oxygen in a series of organic liquids proves to be two magnitudes higher than in the gas,[92] which also would account for a significant yield of the addition reaction in the gas-phase quenching. Moreover, in oxygen, at any rate, a conversion mechanism is also partially functioning. This can be judged by the fact (see surveys[1e,1f]) that the presence of NO and O_2 increases positronium quenching in those gases by magnetic fields, presumably due to transitions $^3S_1 (m = 1) \rightarrow {}^3S_1 (m = 0)$. A similar effect is absent in the case of positronium quenching with halogens. The strongest positronium quenching in the gas phase was observed[88] with chloride $\sigma \approx 10^{-16} cm^2$, as well as, judging by survey[1a] with bromine and iodine. In this case, the authors[88] assumed positronium recombination with chlorine. Another quenching variant is also in principle possible, namely the substitution reaction Ps + Cl_2 → Cl + PsCl. The probability of such a reaction depends on activation energy. Thus in order to obtain additional verification of the mechanism of gas-phase reactions of positronium with oxygen and halogens, it should be useful to carry out experiments on the temperature dependence of their annihilation rates. In view of the very small mass of positronium, one may expect a marked manifestation of the tunnel effect, which should lead to the absence of the observed activation energy in exothermic reactions (about which more will be said later), and to the equality of the activation energy of the endothermic reactions with their thermal effect. The latter circumstance, incidentally, may open the way to the direct determination of the bonding energy of positronium with sundry atoms and radicals.

Actually, the bonding energy e^-e^+ in positronium is 6.8 eV, the electron affinity of chlorine is 3.8 eV. If the bonding energy e^+Cl^- in positronium chloride is 3.8 eV, as was estimated by Simons[93], the energy, gained in the bonding of Ps with Cl would be ~ 0.8 eV. The strength of Cl-Cl bond is 2.5 eV, therefore the above estimate of Simons corresponds to the energy balance of substitution reaction equal to $Q \approx -1.7$ eV. At such a great activation energy ($E \geq$ 1.7 eV) the process Ps + Cl_2 → Ps Cl + Cl could not play any role for thermalized positronium at room temperature.

The role of free radicals, oxygen, and halogens (iodine), as quenchers of positronium, has also been studied in the liquid phase. Pond[94,95] for the first time observed such quenching by a very small rise in the magnitude of the 2γ-coincidence rate (because of diminution of probability of 3γ-annihilation), with addition to benzene (of about 100 mg/cm)^3 of the free radical-diphenylpicrylhydrazyl. He estimated the cross section for such quenching at $1.1 \times 10^{-17} cm^2$, with the adhesion mechanism, or $4.4 \times 10^{-17} cm^2$ with the conversion mechanism.

Berko and Zuchelli[96,97] studied the action of diphenylpicrylhydrazyl, DPPH, with different techniques. They reduced τ_2 in benzene ($\tau_2 = 2.67 \times 10^{-9}$ sec) by adding 3% DPPH ($\tau_2 = 5.3 \times 10^{-10}$ sec). These authors analyzed in detail two types of kinetic equations of positronium formation and quenching:

$$\frac{dP_f}{dt} = -(\lambda_f + 4\gamma_c) P_f$$

$$\frac{dP_S}{dt} = \gamma_c P_f - (3\gamma + \lambda_S) P_S + \gamma P_T \qquad (23)$$

$$\frac{dP_T}{dt} = 3\gamma_c P_f + 3\gamma P_S - (\gamma + \lambda_T) P_T$$

and

$$\frac{dP_f}{dt} = -\lambda_f P_f$$

$$\frac{dP_S}{dt} = -(3\gamma + \lambda_S)P_S + \gamma P_T \tag{24}$$

$$\frac{dP_T}{dt} = 3\gamma P_S - (\gamma + \lambda_T)P_T$$

where $P_f(t)$, $P_S(t)$, and $P_T(t)$ represent the probabilities of finding
a free positron, singlet positronium, and triplet positronium at time
t; and λ_f, λ_s, and λ_T are the rate constants of free positron annihilation, and that of singlet ($8 \times 10^9 \sec^{-1}$) and triplet ($7.14 \times 10^6 \sec^{-1}$)
positronium; γ_c is the rate constant of positronium formation, while
γ is the constant of conversion, leading to "premature" decay of
orthopositronium. Evidently, $\gamma = K[\text{conv}]$ refers to concentration of
the admixture causing conversion and $K(\text{cm}^3/\sec)$ is the bimolecular
rate constant equal to the product of a conversion cross section at a
corresponding positronium velocity: $K = \sigma v$. A similar description
fits other bimolecular reactions of positronium quenching.

Equations (23) satisfy the hypothesis concerning the competition
between free positron annihilation and positronium formation. The
initial conditions here are: $P_f(0) = 1$, $P_S(0) = P_T(0) = 0$.

Equations (24), first discussed by Dixon and Trainor,[85] according to Berko and Zuchelli,[97] better satisfies the experimental data,
and follows from the initial conditions:

$$P_f(0) = I_1, \qquad P_S(0) = \tfrac{1}{4}I_2, \qquad P_T(0) = \tfrac{3}{4}I_2.$$

In this case:

$$P_f(t) = A_f\, e^{-\lambda_1 t}$$
$$P_S(t) = B_S\, e^{-\lambda^1 t} + C_S\, e^{-\lambda_2 t} \tag{25}$$
$$P_T(t) = B_T\, e^{-\lambda^1 t} + C_T\, e^{-\lambda_2 t}$$

where coefficients A_F, B_S, B_T, C_S, and C_T are functions of I_2, γ,
λ_S, and λ_T. Equation $\lambda_2 = 1/\tau_2$ gives the decay rate of the long-
lived annihilation component, wherein

$$\lambda_2 = \alpha - (\alpha^2 - \beta^2)^{1/2}, \qquad \lambda^1 = \alpha + (\alpha^2 - \beta^2)^{1/2}$$

$$\alpha = 2\gamma + \frac{\lambda_S + \lambda_T}{2}, \qquad \beta^2 = \gamma\lambda_S + \lambda_S\lambda_T + 3\gamma\lambda_T$$

Elaborating their data with the aid of their adduced equations, the authors[97] have concluded that $\sigma v = 9.7 \times 10^{-11}$ cm^3/sec, which accounts, at the thermal velocity of positronium, for the quenching cross section $\sigma = 1.2 \times 10^{-17}$ cm^2. They concluded that 69% of the positrons annihilate in benzene in free collisions; 25% in positronium with τ_2 and 6% in positronium with $\tau^1 = 1/\lambda^1$.

However, it must be borne in mind that both Eqs. (23) and (24) take into account neither *pickoff* annihilation nor the various chemical reactions of positronium, nor the possibility of positron capture in various nonpositronium complexes at different stages of moderation. Calculating these processes, materially complicates the original equation, but by the utilization of the full aggregate of the experimental data (the ratio of 2γ and 3γ annihilation; the lifetime and intensity of the various components; the angular correlations, curves, etc.,) similar systems of kinetic equations, solved with the aid of computers, can help materially to interpret all the results.

In his studies of the quenching action of DPPH in benzene, (about 5% admixture), de Zafra[98] applied the technique of angular correlation. This showed that contrary to the expected narrowing of the correlation curves due to the *ortho-para* conversion mechanism, those curves widened. Moreover, the widened correlation curves for benzene with admixture of DPPH, $(C_6H_5)_2 NH - N(C_6H_2(NO_2)_3)$, also proved to be the same as for admixtures of diphenylpicrylhydrazin, $(C_6H_5)_2 NH - NH(C_6H_2(NO_2)_3)$, which does not have an unpaired electron.

Hence, the quenching action of DPPH is to be explained best not by *ortho-para* conversion, but by the attachment of positronium to one of the benzene rings.

It is to be noted that the widening of the angular correlation curves was observed in the work of de Zafra[98] not only in connection with positronium quenching, but also with the inhibition of positronium formation due to such admixtures as NO$_3$ and NO$_2$ − anions in water,[2] and chloroform in benzene,[32] In this sense, inhibition from positron capture above the Ore gap, or in the vicinity of the gap, leads to the same result as positronium quenching by its attachment. However, the data of Tao, Bell, and Green[12] for condensed argon, show that these processes can be separated in time. Hence, experiments set up to observe angular correlation simultaneously with measurement of positron lifetimes[57,58] could, in principle, help materially to differentiate between the processes of positronium inhibition or positronium quenching.

Positronium quenching by oxygen was observed in liquid argon,[90,91] and recently it was also detected in a series of organic liquids, (acetone, heptane, hexane, benzene, toluene, alcohols),[92] with rate constants $\sigma v = 3.3 - 8.3 \times 10^{-11}$ cm^3/sec. A conclusion regarding quenching by oxygen was arrived at by Lee and Celitans,[92] on the basis of an appreciable increase in τ_2, with careful degassing of the above-mentioned liquids. For instance, in pure ethyl alcohol, $\tau_2 = 3.60 \times 10^{-9}$ sec; when saturated by air, $\tau_2 = 2.9 \times 10^{-9}$ sec; and when saturated by oxygen, $\tau_2 = 2 \times 10^{-9}$ sec. Calculation of the quenching constants were made assuming the concentration of oxygen in solution to be equal to tabulated values. Having noted how close the rate constants of oxygen quenching of positronium were to those of the oxygen quenching of excited molecular states in these liquids,[99] Lee and Celitans[92] concluded that the calculated quenching rate observed in both situations is dependent upon oxygen diffusion, and that positronium is evidently solvated. However, this conclusion was not confirmed in a direct experiment observing the temperature dependence of positronium quenching. Finally, one cannot exclude the fact that the similarity of the two quenching rates for oxygen[92],[99] may prove accidental, since with speed-up of the diffusion rate possible for free positronium, the quenching reaction can cross over from the diffusion to the kinetic region.

The authors[92] have suggested that positronium in organic liquids is quenched by oxygen by a triplet to singlet conversion. They did not discuss the possibility of an addition of postronium to the oxygen molecule.

In the last studies of the series,[100] on the basis of the comparison of the shape of angular correlation curves of annihilation γ quanta for hexane-degassed, air-saturated and oxygen-saturated, a conclusion was reached as to the impossibility of explaining such quenching by positronium *ortho-para* conversion.

Hatcher and Millett[27] studied the quenching of positronium with admixtures of iodine (about 0.35%) in heptane, which also causes some inhibition of positronium formation. In this instance, $\sigma v = 1.1 \times 10^{-10}$ cm^3/sec, which is close to the case of DPPH in benzene.[97]

Somewhat by itself in the series of studies of liquid-phase positronium quenching stands the work of Hogg et al,,[101] who noted a decreased τ_2 due to the dissolving of sodium and potassium in liquid ammonia (at $-$ 65°C) and in ethylene diamine (at 20—24°C). In the saturated solution of sodium in ammonia, there occurred full quenching of long-lived components ($\tau_2^0 = 1.7 \pm 0.2 \times 10^{-9}$ sec); saturation of ethylene diamine with sodium reduced τ_2 from $\tau_2^0 = 1.8 \pm 0.2 \times 10^{-9}$ sec to $\tau_2 = 1.2 \pm 0.2 \times 10^{-9}$ sec; the more soluble potassium gave the $\tau_2 -$ value up to $\tau_2 = 0.7 \pm 0.2 \times 10^{-9}$ sec. An active factor in these quenching systems, to all appearances, were solvated electrons.

A wide range of studies of positronium quenching in aqueous solutions was initiated by the findings of Berko and Zuchelli, by the addition to water of ions of Mn^{2+} (see Survey 1c), and a detailed study by Green and Bell.[102] These authors investigated the quenching effect of a series of paramagnetic ions and the ion Sb^{3+}. Their results are enumerated below in Table VI. Chlorides of these ion were used for, in the case of NaCl, the absence of postronium quenching was established for anions of Cl. An example of experimental data[102] and their analysis is offered in Fig. 20. This analysis was done on the basis of Eq. (24), it being assumed in one of the two methods of analysis that in pure water, the value of τ_2 is determined by *ortho-para* conversion alone, and in the other computation, by pickoff annihilation.

Maximum quenching (at very great concentrations of admixtures) corresponds to $\tau_2{}^\infty = 4\tau_S = 5 \times 10^{-10}$ sec in the case of conversion in pure water, and to $\tau_2{}^\infty = 4[\lambda_S + \gamma_p + 3(\lambda_T + \gamma_p)]^{-1} = 3.9 \times 10^{-10}$ sec in the case of pickoff annihilation (for water it was found that $\tau_2 = 1.8 \times 10^{-9}$ sec, i.e., $\gamma_p = 5.5 \times 10^8$ sec^{-1}). As seen in Fig. 20, the pickoff analysis for water comes out better than the conversion. At present, in fact, pickoff annihilation is considered the fundamental mode of orthopositronium decay in the condensed phase; there are in addition different processes of positronium quenching by admixtures.

The results obtained by Green and Bell[102] are adduced in Table VI. The computations of quenching cross sections offered in this Table were based on the assumption of the conversion mechanism for this quenching. Calculation of the quenching cross section from the rate constant σv cm^3/sec, uses the value v as equal to the thermal velocity of thermalized free positronium.

In the last column of Table VI are listed values for quenching cross sections, taken from the book by Green and Lee,[f] to determine whether to use, not the concentrations, C, of the ions, but their thermodynamic activities, A. With large concentrations, $A \ll C$, and, accordingly, $\sigma_Q{}^A \gg \sigma_Q{}^C$. In deriving the values $\sigma_Q{}^A$, Green and Lee[f] also point out the similarity of the consequence of $\sigma_Q{}^C$

TABLE VI

Cross Section of Positronium Quenching by Various Ions in Aqueous Solutions[102]

Ion	Compounds	Number of unpaired electrons	$\sigma_Q^\epsilon \times 10^{19}$ (cm^2)	$\sigma_Q^A \times 10^{18}$ (cm^2)
Cr^{3+}	$CrCl_3$	3	6.3	33.2
Mn^{2+}	$MnCl_2$	5	2.5	1.92
	$MnSO_4$	5	1.8	8.76
Fe^{3+}	$FeCl_3$	5	38	18.9
Fe^{2+}	$FeCl_2$	4	4.8	2.79
Co^{2+}	$CoCl_2$	3	5.3	2.8
Ni^{2+}	$NiCl_2$	2	5.6	3.03
Cu^{2+}	$CuCl_2$	1	11	5.04
Nd^{3+}	$NdCl_3$	3	0.4	
Sb^{3+}	$SbCl_3$		3.7	

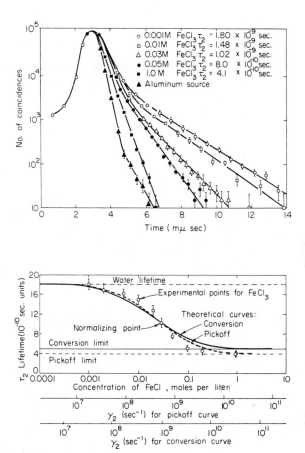

Fig. 20. Experimental curves of the time distribution of positron annihilation in aqueous solution[102] containing $FeCl_3$ and the dependence of τ_2 vs $FeCl_3$ concentrations.

values for paramagnetic ions as quenchers of orthopositronium, and of their effectiveness as quenchers of the triplet excited state of naphthalene (according to data),[68] and indicate that positronium in aqueous solutions perhaps is not completely thermalized, that is its behavior should approximate the behavior of hot atoms (in such a case there is no point in working with quenchers' activities instead of with their concentrations).

The conversion mechanism of quenching for Mn^{2+} and Co^{2+} was further confirmed in the work of de Zafra,[98] indicating that with the admixture of these ions to water, the narrow component of the angular correlation curves is reinforced. Using the kinetic equations (24) modified with the addition of pickoff annihilation, and operating

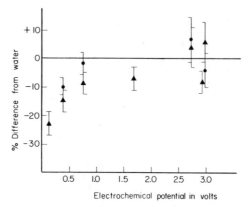

Fig. 21. Effect of various cations on change of counting rate of 3γ coincidence in $2M$ aqueous solutions of chlorides (▲) and sulfates (●). Along the X-axis are the standard oxidation-reduction potentials of the cations[103] (left to right: Sn^{2+}, Cd^{2+}, Zn^{2+}, Al^{3+}, Na^+, K^+, Li^+).

with concentrations of ions (not with ion activities), de Zafra[98] obtained quenching cross sections $\sigma_Q = 8 \times 10^{-20} - 8 \times 10^{-19} cm^2$ for Co^{2+} (optimal value $2 \times 10^{-19} cm^2$) and $\sigma_Q = 2 \times 10^{-19} - 8 \times 10^{-18} cm^2$ for Mn^{2+} (optimal value $8 \times 10^{-19} cm^2$). Meanwhile on the basis of the absolute value of the half-width of the narrow component of correlation curves in water, $(\Delta\theta = 1.8$ mrad) the positronium velocity turned out 5 times greater than the equivalent thermal rate, so that upon comparison with the data in Table VI, the adduced value of σ_Q for Co^2 and Mn^{2+} must be increased five-fold.

However, one can hardly expect the positronium conversion mechanism for all ions enumerated in Table VI. In fact, according to Ferrell,[67] the cross section of conversion quenching should be proportional to $1/_{12} n(n + 2)E^2$, where n represents the number of unpaired electrons, while E represents the amplitude for exchange scattering. As evident from Table VI, no relation between σ_Q and n is discernible. Moreover, the diamagnetic ion Sb^{+3} also turned out to be a "quencher." A considerable advance in the description of positronium quenching was made in the work of McGervey and De-Benedetti.[103] Measuring the counting rate of 3γ-coincidence $C_{3\gamma}$ in pure water and in various solutions, these authors subdivided the admixtures studied by them into 3 groups—paramegnetic ions $(Mn^{2+}, Co^{2+}, Ni^{2+}, Cu^{2+})$—reducing $C_{3\gamma}$ by $20-35\%$; nitrates (cations of which in combining with Cl^- did not affect $C_{3\gamma}$) reducing $C_{3\gamma}$ by $18-42\%$, and a group of sulfates and chlorides, the action of which on $C_{3\gamma}$ depended generally on the position of the cations in the electrochemical voltage series, as illustrated in Fig. 21. The authors[103] introduced another hypothesis about quenching, viz. oxidation, occurring for several cations (for instance, Cd^{2+} + Ps → Cd^+ + e^+), and also for anions NO_3^-: NO_3^- + $4H^+$ + Ps → NO + $2H_2O$ + e^+. Acceleration of decay of orthopositronium due to oxidation is conditioned by the formation of free positron and its subsequent rapid annihilation.

As a result, the kinetic equation for the free positron and for positronium intermix in a complementary way, a factor which certainly complicates the determination of either. In Fig. 22 is presented the diagram of the processes of the formation of positronium and of different varieties of its decay (taking into account also the oxidation) derived from Ref. 104. The rate constant for oxidation has been set by the authors as proportional to the oxidation-reduction potentials. This point of view was developed by Trumpy,[105] who studied the effect of various paramagnetic salts and other additives in aqueous solutions on the angular distribution of annihilation quanta. On the basis of the dependence of the intensity of the narrow components in the correlation curves upon the standard oxidation-reduction potential of diamagnetic additives in aqueous solutions (as shown in Fig. 23), Trumpy draws the conclusion that the potential of positronium itself is near zero, since a weakening of the narrow components by oxidation was observed for the admixtures with a positive potential, of $SbCl_3$ (regarded as SbO^+), NO_3^-, ClO_3^-, MnO_4^-, H_2O_2, Cu^{2+}, and Fe^{3+}. Upon analyzing his data for paramagnetic additives having narrowed the correlation curves compared with pure water, Trumpy points out that in several cases studied by Green and Bell,[102] the oxydation action must have exceeded their conversion action, and therefore the calculation offered above, $\tau_{2\,min} \approx 3.9 \times 10^{-10}$ sec, was incorrect,

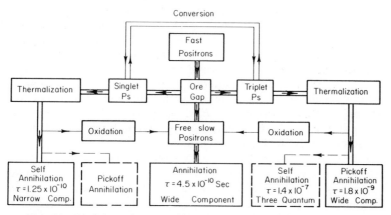

Fig. 22. Diagram of positronium interaction in aqueous solutions taking into account the possibility of its oxidation.[104]

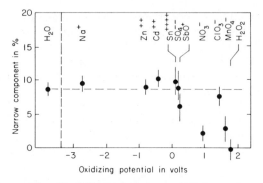

Fig. 23. Effect of various admixtures in
aqueous solutions on the yield of the narrow
component in angular correlation curves.
Along the x-axis, standard oxidation-reduction potentials of diamagnetic admixtures.[105]

and its agreement with the experiment, accidental. By way of examples, Trumpy adduces $FeCl_3$ (see Fig. 20), $CuCl_2$, for which the
quenching cross sections (Table VI) are particularly high, and the
diamagnetic salt $SbCl_3$.

The description of positronium oxidation rate, based on oxidation-
reduction potentials, encountered a series of objections:[106] (1) Because of the rapid annihilation of positrons, chemical processes of
the type Ox + Ps → Red + Ps$^+$ (Ox: Oxidizer; Red: reducer; Ps =
$e^+ e^-$, Ps$^+ = e^+$) prove essentially irreversible; (2) For that reason,
and because of the exceptionally small steady-state concentration
of Ps and Ps$^+$, one must not use for analyzing positronium reactions
potentials of multielectron transitions of type: Me^{2+} + 2Ps → Me +
2Ps$^+$ (Me: metal); and (3) in reactions with positronium participation,
no macroscopic metal phase is formed—a factor that does not jus-
tify operating with standard metal-ion potentials. In order to demonstrate the essentially kinetic nature of the action of various substances
on positronium annihilation in aqueous solutions, and to arrive at a
systematic comparison of such action with oxidation-reduction and
magnetic properties of various ions, we carried out[106] a series of experimental studies of 3γ annihilation of positrons in aqueous solutions.
We will indicate only the basic results:

(1) Table VII shows the decreased 3γ-annihilation rate as compared
with pure water under the action of various admixtures (basically different cations with anion Cl$^-$). In the face of the general tendency toward the decrease of the $C_{3\gamma}$ counting rate as far as stronger oxidizing
agents are used, there also occur serious deviations from such a sequence. Partly, these deviations may be caused by the conversion of

$^3S_1 \to {}^1S_0$ by unpaired electrons of paramagnetic ions, but between the magnetic properties of ions and the value of $C_{3\gamma}$ there is also no simple correlation. Therefore, regardless of agreement of the data in the table with other results,[103,105] we do not consider as an established fact the systematic variation of $C_{3\gamma}$ with the standard oxidation-reduction potentials of the admixtures.

(2) In line with the results,[106,105] we also found in[106] a strong quenching of the C_γ counting rate with anion admixtures of the NO_3^- oxidizer, and also, we found that MnO_4^- reacts even more strongly. But the MnO_4^- action $(0.01M)$ proved quite the same in strongly acid (pH = 2), neutral (pH = 7), and alkaline (pH = 12) solutions: accordingly, $C_{3\gamma}$ = 5.13 ± 0.16; 5.01 ± 0.16 and 5.15 ± 0.27 min^{-1} (with the value 6.04 ± 0.09 for water). This conclusively demonstrates the decisive role of the concentration of MnO_4^-, and not of the oxidation-reduction potential of the system. We arrived at an analogous conclusion also from the data on $C_{3\gamma}$ rates in admixtures of Fe^{3+} and Fe^{2+} with various concentrations, but with fixed ratios of these concentrations.

(3) The counting-rate, $C_{3\gamma}$, dependence on the concentration of MnO_4^- (in a neutral solution) is shown by the following figures:

TABLE VII

Action of Various Admixtures in Aqueous Solutions
on the Counting Rates of 3γ Coincidence[106]

Substance	Concentration moles/1	Standard oxidation-reduction potential (volts)	Number of unpaired electrons	Difference between $C_{3\gamma}$ (min^{-1}) in relation to water
KOH	1	−2.92		−0.02 ± 0.31
BaCl$_2$	2	−2.92		−0.55 ± 0.39
NaCl	2	−2.71		+0.07 ± 0.25
MnCl$_2$	2	−1.10	5	−0.57 ± 0.26
ZnCl$_2$	2	−0.76		+0.24 ± 0.34
FeCl$_2$	0.1	−0.44	4	−0.99 ± 0.27
CrCl$_3$	2	−0.41	3	−1.70 ± 0.28
TlNO$_3$	Saturation	−0.34		−1.24 ± 0.29
CoCl$_2$	2	−0.27	3	−1.17 ± 0.40
NiSO$_4$	2	−0.23	2	−1.03 ± 0.36
CuCl$_2$	2	+0.34	1	−1.85 ± 0.31
FeCl$_3$	2	+0.77	5	−2.62 ± 0.33
FeCl$_3$	0.1	+0.77	5	−1.41 ± 0.28
KMnO$_4$	Saturation	+1.63		−2.44 ± 0.42
H$_2$O$_2$	30 wt.-%	+1.78		−1.55 ± 0.28

Concentration, Saturated

MnO$_4^-$, mole/L:	solution	0.1	0.01	0.001	0 (water)
$C_{3\gamma}$, min^{-1}	3.6 ± 0.42	5.08 ± 0.45	5.08 ± 0.12	5.50 ± 0.30	6.04 ± 0.09

Evidently, the $C_{3\gamma}$ quenching effect develops strongly enough even with low concentrations. In experiments with high concentrations of strongly-reacting admixtures, the value of $C_{3\gamma}$ tends towards the limit common to all oxidizing admixtures, in line with the yield of free 3γ annihilation. That is why a quantitative comparison of the effect of various admixtures on positronium formation and conversion requires low concentrations of such admixtures as an experimental prerequisite. Positronium oxidation is always determined not by the equilibrium condition but by the rate of this reaction— at the first glance not by the thermal effect but by the activation energy.

However, because of its small mass, positronium may pass through a potential barrier by the tunnel effect. For that reason, the effective activation energy of exothermal oxidation reactions is equal to zero, while for endothermal reactions, it coincides with the thermal effect.

Because the oxidation potential is stronger for most oxidizers than for Ps, it has here no effect on the reaction rate, but for weaker oxidizers (endothermal reactions), it begins to determine this oxidation rate itself (but not the equilibrium condition).

In their study,[104] McGervey, Horstman, and DeBenedetti independently took essentially the same line of reasoning as ours[106] (adopted also by Green and Lee[1f]). That study examined the effect of admixtures of various chlorides on the lifetime τ_2 of positrons in aqueous solutions. The summary of the results is given in Fig. 24. The authors point out that some τ_2 decrease in concentrated AlCl$_3$-type solutions may be explained simply as increased density of the solution (about 1.18 gm/cm^3), and to the corresponding increase of pickoff annihilation. The kinetic equations used in Ref. 104 to determine the annihilation picture with the presence of oxidative admixtures, were

$$\frac{dP_f}{dt} = -\lambda_f P_f + \gamma_0 P_T$$

$$\frac{dP_T}{dt} = -\gamma_p P_T - \gamma_0 P_T$$

(26)

where γ_p and γ_0 are rate constants of pickoff annihilation and oxidation. One gathers from this that rate constants of the decay of the long-lived components, $\lambda_2^\infty = 1/\tau_2^\infty$ within the compass of large admixture concentrations is equal to $\lambda_2^\infty = \gamma_p + \gamma_0$ with $\gamma_p + \gamma_0 \leq \lambda_f$ or $\lambda_2^\infty = \lambda_f$ with $\gamma_p + \gamma_0 \leq \lambda_f$.

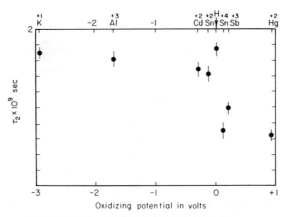

Fig. 24. Effect of various chlorides in aqueous so
solutions on the lifetime, τ_2, of positrons, Along the
X-axis, standard oxidation-reduction cation potentials.[104] Concentration of various admixtures from
$1M$ to $2M$.

In the following study in this series,[107] the oxidation rate of positronium was measured in aqueous solutions with ions of MnO_4^-, IO_3^-,
and Hg^{2+}. Oxidation shortened the τ_2 value down to the $\tau_2 = 4.3 \times$
10^{-10} sec, equal to the short life time τ_1 in pure water and treated
from Eq. (26) as the annihilation time of free positrons: $\tau_2^\infty = 1/\lambda f$.
In this same study, still another example is noted of the inhibition of
positronium formation in water (reduced I_2 without noticeable changes
in τ_2) by the action of $Pb(ClO_4)_2 3H_2O$, which was not noted in the case
of other perchlorates, and hence should be ascribed to the cation Pb^{2+}.
The oxidation potential of Pb^{2+} equals 0.126 eV, and if the potential of
positronium, according to Trumpy,[105] is close to zero, then the oxidation reaction in this given case should be endothermic. Since it is
hard to assume positron attachment to the positively charged cation,
the authors[107] elaborate another viewpoint, whereby in the case of
Pb^{2+} there occurs not a decreased probability of positronium formation, but a very rapid oxidation of "hot" positronium long before its
thermalization, as a result of which part of the positronium atoms
fall out of the long-lived components. This viewpoint calls for further
consideration of the action of admixture of NO_3^-.
    Among the results[107] must be noted also the discovery of a few de-
viations from the additivity of the oxidation action of the cations and
the anions. Thus, the salt $Hg(ClO_4)_2 \cdot 9H_2O$ proved to be a weaker
oxidizer than $HgCl_2$. At the same time, both anions — ClO_4^- and
Cl^- — showed no effect on the lifetime of positrons. The mixture of
$\frac{1}{16} M HgCl_2$ and $\frac{1}{32} M KMnO_4$ proved to be the weaker oxidizer, than

it was expected on the basis of the oxidation action of each admixture separately. The authors[107] consider these facts explained by the weakened oxidative abilities of cations and anions upon formation and strengthening of their associative bonds.

A series of new experiments on chemical quenching of positronium was also carried out in our own laboratories in recent years. Methods were evolved for observing both the lifetime and intensity of the long-lived component of positron annihilation and independently the angular correlation of annihilation γ quanta. Thereby different ways of quenching were identified since the conversion caused a narrowing of the correlation curves, whereas in chemical quenching these curves become wider.

As in all other analogous studies, we considered that the total rate of destruction of orthopositronium atoms in aqueous solutions, with admixtures of some acceptor (concentration $[Ac]$), equals:

$$-\frac{d[P_s]}{dt} = \lambda_{aq}[P_s] + K[Ps][Ac] = [Ps](\lambda_{aq} + K[Ac]) \qquad (27)$$

where $\lambda_{aq} \approx 6 \times 10^8 \, sec^{-1}$ (the total rate of spontaneous annihilation $\lambda_T = 7.14 \times 10^6 \, sec^{-1}$, plus pickoff annihilation in pure water), while K is the pertinent rate constant of the interaction of positronium with the acceptor. The total $(\lambda_{aq} + K[Ac])$ enters as a factor along with P_T into the different kinetic equations for dP_T/dt of type (24) or (26). The list of the acceptors employed (mainly of the chloride or sulphate groups) and the corresponding rate constant values of $K(cm^3/sec)$, obtained in our work[108] from data on shortening of lifetime τ_2, is presented in Table VIII.

In comparing data on lifetime and angular correlation,[109] the change in yield of the narrow component (ΔI_N) was calculated by two methods — by subtraction of the angular correlation curves, normalized in terms of the area for water, from the curve for the solution (the method of de Zafra)[98] and by the direct passage from the experimental angular distribution to the momentum distribution of the centers of the mass of annihilating pairs (Trumpy's method).[105] The second method has the advantage that the results of the calculation depend less on the change of shape of the curves of angular correlation for each of the components. The kinetic equations chosen for working out the available data were those of Dixon-Trainor[85] of type (24), supplemented generally by terms describing the oxidation of positronium with admixtures. Experimental data for conversion ($MnSO_4$) and oxidation ($KMnO_4$), along with calculated curves, are presented in Fig. 25. The minimal value for $\tau_2{}^{\infty}$ in water, presented in Fig. 25 (3.9×10^{-10} sec) corresponds to the case for pure conversion by an admixture in the presence of pickoff annihilation in

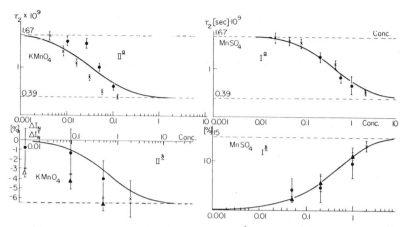

Fig. 25. Effect of additives $MnSO_4$ (I^a, I^b) and $KMnO_4$ (II^a, II^b) on the lifetime, τ_2, and on the intensity of the narrow component in the angular correlation curve. The lifetime data indicated by dots is from Ref. 109, by crosses comes from Ref. 102 ($MnSO_4$) and from Ref. 107 ($KMnO_4$). The dots on the ΔI diagrams have been calculated by Trumpy's method,[105] the triangles by de Zafra's method.[98]

water (see p. 229). In the case of purely oxidative action of an admixture, as was indicated on page 229, $\tau_2{}^\infty = 1/\lambda_f = 4.3 \times 10^{-10}$ sec. However, both these values of $\tau_2{}^\infty$ are sufficiently close, and choosing between them on the basis of concentration dependence of τ_2 is made difficult. In this connection the data on the angular correlation involved are quite significant. For admixtures subject to conversion, ΔI_N is positive in that it approaches

$$\Delta I_N = \frac{I_2}{\left(1 + 4\dfrac{\gamma_p}{\lambda_s}\right)\left(1 + \dfrac{\gamma_p}{\lambda_s}\right)} \approx 15\% \qquad \text{for aqueous solutions}$$

For oxidizing admixtures, ΔI_N is negative, and approaches

$$-\Delta I_N = \frac{I_2}{3}\left[\frac{\lambda_s}{\lambda_s + \gamma_p} - \frac{\lambda_s}{\lambda_s + \gamma_p + \gamma_0}\right] \approx 7\%$$

for aqueous solutions within the range of very rapid oxidation, when not only the triplet but the singlet positronium succeeds in getting into the oxidative reaction. This very case is represented in Fig. 25 for $KMnO_4$, and was also observed by us for other strong oxidizers, $Cr_2O_7{}^{2-}$, $CrO_4{}^-$, $UO_2{}^{2+}$, Ti^{4+}, Ce^{4+}, Sn^{4+}, Cu^{2+}. Related admixtures with strong conversion action investigated by us are the paramagnetic ions Mn^{2+}, Fe^{2+}, Co^{2+}, and Ni^{2+}. Such paramagnetic

TABLE VIII
Rate Constants of Positronium Quenching in Aqueous Solutions[108]

Acceptor	Concentration (M/l)	No. of unpaired electrons	K (cm³/sec)	Acceptor	Concentration (M/l)	No. of unpaired electrons	K (cm³/sec)
				Strong interaction with positronium (shortening of τ_2)			
Fe^{3+}	0.01 0.03 0.05	5	2×10^{-11}	$Cr_2O_7^{2-}$	0.005 0.01 0.015	0	1.5×10^{-10}
Cu^{2+}	0.02 0.06 0.2	1	8×10^{-12}	CrO_4^{2-}	0.03 0.06 0.3	0	1.5×10^{-11}
Ti^{4+}	0.05 0.15 0.40	0	3.3×10^{-12}	MnO_4^{-}	0.025 0.05 0.01	0	2.7×10^{-11}
UO_2^{2+}	0.01 0.03 0.1	0	1.2×10^{-11}	Fe^{2+}	0.1 0.3 0.5	4	3.5×10^{-12}
Ce^{4+}	0.03 0.1 0.3	0	2.8×10^{-11}	Mn^{2+}	0.2 0.6 1.0	5	2.5×10^{-12}
Sn^{4+}	0.025 0.05 0.1	0	0.9×10^{-11}	Ni^{2+}	0.07 0.15 0.3	2	2.75×10^{-12}
Cr^{3+}	According to data[102]	3	3.3×10^{-12}	Co^{2+}	According to data[102]	3	3.3×10^{-12}

Ion	Concentration		
U^{4+}	0.03 0.1 0.3	2	$< 10^{-14}$
Ti^{3+}	0.05 0.15 0.40	1	$< 10^{-14}$
Ce^{3+}	0.03 0.1 0.3	1	$< 10^{-14}$
Pb^{2+}	0.25 1.0	0	$< 10^{-14}$
Nd^{3+}	According to data[102]	3	$\sim 10^{-13}$

Weak interaction with positronium			
H_2SO_4	0.01 1.0 1.0	0	$< 10^{-14}$
Na_2SO_4	0.05 0.2 1.0	0	$< 10^{-14}$
$NaCl$	0.1 0.5 1.0	0	$< 10^{-14}$
$Fe(CN)_6^{4-}$	0.1 0.3 0.5	0	$< 10^{-14}$

ions as U^{4+}, Ti^{3+}, Ce^{3+}, showed practically neither any conversion (regardless of the presence of unpaired electrons) nor any oxidative reaction. Composite oxidative conversion reaction (however, with strong preponderance of oxidation) was observed for Fe^{3+}.

Substances whose interaction constants with positronium atoms do not exceed $10^{-14} cm^3/sec$, are ions of lowest and constant valences (for instance, Na^+, hydrogen ions). A change of acidity of solutions of Fe^{2+} from $5M\,H_2SO_4$ to pH ~ 2, as also admixtures of considerable amounts of Na_2SO_4, did not appreciably change the rate constant of the reaction with Fe^{2+}, which confirms the negligibly low rate constant, under the given conditions, of the Ps reaction with H^+ and Na^+.

Let us now pause to examine in greater detail the results obtained for Fe^{3+} and Fe^{2+}, which are of special interest, for they may be compared with analogous data for hydrogen atoms. For a positronium reaction with Fe^{3+} and Fe^{2+}, the rate constants of K_{Ps} at room temperature was equal to $2 \times 10^{-11} cm^3/sec$ and $3.5 \times 10^{-12} cm^3/sec$, respectively. At one time, Riesz and Hart[110] had found the rate constants K_H of analogous reactions of hydrogen atoms in aqueous solutions to be: $0.8 \times 10^{-14} cm^3/sec$ for Fe^{3+} and $1.1 \times 10^{-15} cm^3/sec$ for Fe^{2+}. And so, hydrogen-like positronium in both instances reacts approximately 2500-3000 times faster than hydrogen.

In interpreting this result, we have primarily proceeded from the assumption that both positronium and hydrogen reactions with various acceptors in aqueous solutions operate in the kinetic region. Then the rate constant of reaction is $K_0 = \sigma_0 \epsilon v \; cm^3/sec$, where σ_0 is the geometric cross section, ϵ is the probability of attachment during collision, and v is the velocity of thermal motion. If neither the positronium nor the hydrogen is hydrated, then

$$\frac{v_{Ps}}{v_H} = \left(\frac{M_H}{M_{Ps}}\right)^{1/2} \approx 30$$

if hydration occurs, $v_{Ps\text{-}aq} \approx v_{H\text{-}aq}$. At any rate, the increase of even two orders of magnitude of the speed of the Ps reaction compared with hydrogen may be explained only by quantum effects, viz., as an increase in λ_{Ps} above the geometric dimensions of the molecules (an increase in σ_0) and, most important, the tunneled penetration of positronium atoms through the activated potential barrier due to their tiny mass (increase of ϵ).

Based on the above assumption, comparison of the rate constants for the reactions of hydrogen and positronium yielded the estimate for the activation energy of reactions of H atoms with iron ions: $E \approx 4500 \; cal/mole$ for both Fe^{3+}, and for Fe^{2+}.[108] Taking into account the data later obtained by us, and the results given below for experiments with the temperature dependence of reaction rates of positronium quenching,[111] which make clear the presence here of a diffusion mechanism and possible also positronium hydration, the indicated amounts of energy must be considered as lower limits (the upper limit $E \approx 8500$ cal/moles).

According to the above assumptions (see, e.g., Ref. 12), the reaction of H with Fe^{2+} goes by two stages: $H + Fe^{2+} \rightarrow HFe^{2+}$ and $HFe^{2+} + H^+ \rightarrow H_2 + Fe^{3+}$; and the rate of reaction is limited by the first stage, i.e., the formation of a complex. In the case of positronium, *ortho-para* conversion may also proceed analogously via formation of a hydride-type complex (positronides) with subsequent internal conversion. In an oxidation reaction of the type $H + Fe^{3+} \rightarrow H^+ + Fe^{2+}$, two variants of the mechanism are possible — formation of a complex, and the comparatively long distant tunneling of an electron from the hydrogen to the iron. The question as to whether or not such a tunneling of the electron occurs is being widely discussed in theoretical chemistry. The equality of the ratios of hydrogen and positronium reactions rates with Fe^{2+} and Fe^{3+}, i.e., the presence of significant activation energy also for reaction $H + Fe^{3+}$, serves as a convincing argument in favor of the formation in both cases of the complex with hydrogen, and against the "tunneled" transmission of the electron during hydrogen oxidation. That being the case, other experiments previously described[108] support the conclusion formulated by Frumkin and his co-workers[113] in their studies of electroreduction of anions.

Continuing these experiments with Fe^{2+} and Fe^{3+},[114] we compared τ_2 and I_2 for perchlorates of Fe^{2+} and Fe^{3+} , where complex formation is practically nonexistent; for sulfates, containing in the sulfate solution a commensurate number of ions of Fe^{3+} and complex iron ions, and for ferro- and ferricyanides of potassium (the liability constants of these complex ions are 10^{-35} and 10^{-42}, respectively). The data for sulfates and perchlorates Fe^{2+} and Fe^{3+} simply coincided with those in Table VIII for ferrous chlorides. At the same time, however, there was found some inhibition of positronium formation (i.e., reduction of I_2) by an anion of ClO_4, which somewhat undermines the above line of argument of the authors[107] regarding the specific inhibiting actions of cations of Pb^{2+} . For anion $[Fe(CN)_6]^{3-}$ $K_{Ps} = 2 \times 10^{-11}$ cm^3/sec, i.e., it also coincides with the value for the constant of the oxidation of positronium by ion Fe^{3+} , whereas $K_H = 6.5 \times 10^{-17}$ cm^3/sec,[115] i.e., much less than for Fe^{3+} , so that $K_{Ps}/K_H = 3.1 \times 10^5$. In the case of the diamagnetic anion $[Fe(CN)_6]^{4-}$ there could be observed neither positronium quenching $(K_{Ps} \ll 10^{-14}$ $cm^3/sec)$, nor interaction with hydrogen atom $(K_H \ll 10^{-17}$ $cm^3/sec)$.[116]

It is noteworthy that for trivalent iron, the rate constant of the reaction with positronium remains practically unchanged, independent of complex formation, i.e., with high spin, just as with low-

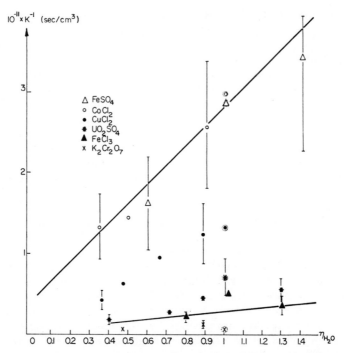

Fig. 26. Dependence of reciprocal rate constant of positronium reaction with various acceptors in water versus viscosities (temperatures varied).

spin compounds. Such constancy may be explained by the fact that
the oxidation constant in any given case constitutes the main part of
the observed rate constant of interaction with positronium. The extension of the width of the activation barrier is compensated by the
increase in the geometric cross section of the ion interacting with
the positronium, which permits one to interpret the result obtained
within the framework of the hypothesis elaborated earlier,[108] regarding the preponderant role played, as a whole, in positronium reactions by tunnelling of positronium. In this connection, it is easy to
understand the differences of two orders of magnitude of the rate constant of the reactions of Fe^{3+} and $[Fe(CN)_6]^{3-}$ with the hydrogen
atom, because tunnelled transmission is completely negligible.

An extensive series of experiments[111] was devoted to the study of
temperature dependence of positronium reactions with ions Cu^{2+},
Fe^{2+}, Co^{2+}, UO_2^{2+}, Fe^{3+}, and $Cr_2O_7^{2-}$ in aqueous solutions, and also
with Cu^{2+} in acetone, glycerin, ethyl alcohol, and tetrahydrofuran.
The reaction rate of positronium within a wide temperature range
(e.g., from 25 to 150°C for $CuCl_2$ in glycerin, from −80 to +60°C for

$CuCl_2$ in ethyl alcohol, etc.) was compared with the viscosity and electroconductivity of the solutions. As is clear from Figs. 26 and 27, in all solvents the reciprocal rate constant of positronium reactions increase linearly with viscosity η.

This being the case, diffusion factors materially affect the reaction rate, and the measured rate constant K is everywhere below the kinetic value limit $K_0 = \sigma_0 \epsilon v$.

The first and quite important conclusion to be drawn from the observed dependence of the rate of positronium quenching appears to be the fact that positronium does not enter into such reactions in aqueous reactions as a hot atom. The presence of a temperature dependence seems a weighty argument favoring thermalization before quenching.

Let us also remember that the hypothesis regarding the effect of diffusion factors on positronium quenching in various liquids via oxygen was advanced by Lee and Celitans,[92] without experimental

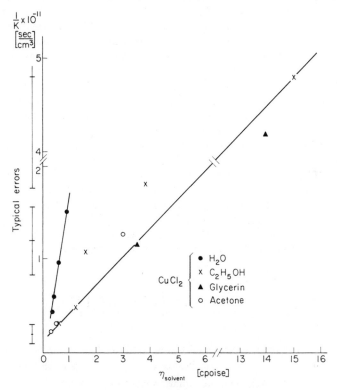

Fig. 27. Dependence of reciprocal rate constant of positronium reaction with $CuCl_2$ in various solvents upon viscosity.

data on the dependence of quenching rate on temperature. Therefore the question remains an open one.

In the mixed diffusion-kinetic range $1/K = 1/K_0 + 1/K_D*$ so
that the diffusion-constant

$$K_D = 4\pi(D_{Ps} + D_{Ac})(r_{Ps} + r_{Ac}) + \frac{4\sigma_{Ac}D_{Ps}^{1/2}}{(\pi t)^{1/2}}$$

in cm³/sec, where D_{Ps} and D_{Ac}, r_{Ps} and r_{Ac} are the diffusion coefficients and radii of the positronium and acceptor respectively.
σ_{Ac} is the cross section of the quenching reaction and t is the time
from the moment of positronium formation. The second term in K_D,
depending on the time factor, is negligible small as a rule already
when $t \ll \tau \approx 10^{-9} - 10^{-10}$ sec.

The direct relationship of rate constants of the quenching reaction of positronium with the viscosity of solvents is unique testimony
of the occurring of these reactions in the diffusion region. The absolute values of rate constants ($K = 3 \times 10^{-12} - 10^{-10}$ cm³/sec at
20°C, and $K = 10^{-11} - 2 \times 10^{-10}$ cm³/sec at 80°C) are nearly that
obtained by Lee and Celitans[92] for positronium in reaction with oxygen, agreeing with the values $Dr_0 \approx 10^{-12}$ cm³/sec at room temperature. Under those conditions, the diffusion coefficient of positronium
in water and in other solvents does not exceed ~10^{-4} cm²/sec. To us,
however, it seems that this is still not reason enough to affirm that
positronium is strongly solvated, not to mention the fact that the
solvating properties of various solvents are distinctly different, and
whereas diffusion coefficients at a given viscosity are everywhere
alike, there is no basis for expecting a high speed-up of free positronium diffusion in a liquid because of its small mass (in contrast
with gases, where $D \sim 1/m^{1/2}$). An interesting and important problem is the precise extrapolation of the rate constant of positronium
interaction with strong quenchers (of type $Cr_2O_7^{2-}$) approaching zero
viscosity, i.e., determining the values of $K_0 = \sigma_0 \epsilon v$, which should be
perceptibly higher for free, nonsolvated positronium.

*In the general case

$$\frac{1}{K} = \frac{1}{K_D K_0} \frac{\lambda_f(K_D + K_0) + K_D K_0[Ac]}{\lambda_f - \lambda_{aq}}$$

where λ_f(sec^{-1}) is the rate constant of the annihilation of free positrons during collisions (in water $\lambda_f \approx \lambda_{aq}$). Obviously, if λ_f exceeds the lesser of two
values K_D(Ac) or K_0(Ac), then the equation advanced in the text, $1/K =$
$1/K_D + 1/K_0$, is quite sufficiently fulfilled, which tallies with the linear
dependence $1/K = 1/K_0 + \beta\eta$, if one disregards the comparatively weak
change of $1/K_0$ with temperature (about 17% in the range of $0-100°$C).

To determine decisively whether or not positronium is solvated to various solvents (note that the absence of solvation of positronium implies also the definite nonsolvating of hydrogen atoms), of particular importance are experiments with strong quenchers, and also the precise extrapolation of rate constants of quenching to zero viscosity, i.e., the reliable determination of the value $K_0 = \sigma_0 \epsilon v$. As already studied in Ref. 111 for the case of the $Cr_2O_7^{2-}$, the rate constant $K_0 > K_{80°C} \approx 2 \times 10^{-10}$ cm³/sec, which for hydrated positronium yields $\sigma_0 \epsilon > 3.5 \times 10^{-15}$ cm². A similar value for $\sigma_0 \epsilon$, even where $\epsilon = 1$, lies at the borderline of the possible, and therefore serves as an argument for the existence in water of free or — more probably — weakly bound positronium (at hydration energy or, in other words, the depths of positronium "traps" is commensurate with kT, and thus positronium should have spent a considerable time in a free state with corresponding increase of velocity, v).

It would be desirable to establish also the nondependence of the quenching rate on viscosity for very weak quenchers where, because of the smallness of ϵ, the reaction occurs within the kinetic region. A special problem is presented by the comparison of positronium quenching rates in various solvents. Our recent experiments in the study of positronium quenching with free radicals, 2.2.6.6. tetramethyl-4-oxy-piperidin-1-oxyle in nonpolar solvents of the decalin type and benzene, confirmed the fact that the quenching rate is determined here, not by temperature itself but by the viscosity of the medium. In Fig. 27 are shown rate constants of positronium quenching by a salt $CuCl_2$ in water, ethyl alcohol, glycerine, and acetone. The fact that the rate constant of positronium reaction with $CuCl_2$ is the same at equal concentrations of this salt and viscosities of the solutions in water, acetone, tetrahydrofuran, regardless of the sharp (10 to 100 fold) reduction of conductivity during transition from water to the two previously named solvents, seems to indicate that positronium quenching is independent of whether there occurs an actual extensive separation of cations and anions, as in polar solvents, or whether they are bonded within a single molecule, as in nonpolar solvents. The indicated characteristic of positronium reaction offers an opportunity to study valence states independently of the complicating phenomena of dissociation and solvation.

Let us note, finally, that positronium quenching by $CuCl_2$ was observed[111] in ice also, at $-6°C$, with constant $K = 10^{-12}$ cm³/sec (in water at $20°C$ $K \approx 8 \times 10^{-12}$ cm³/sec).

From the data discussed in this last section, it is clear that the observation of positronium quenching, as well as the inhibition of its formation, reveals the interesting possibility of studying the elementary processes of radiation chemistry, the mechanism of oxidative reactions, and the role of quantum effects in chemical kinetics.

The chemistry of positronium and the positron is still in its early infancy. We do not doubt the fact that in the hands of chemists positron annihilation will prove a highly valuable method and will offer a great deal of information essential not only for the study of the properties of positrons and their transformations, but also for theoretical chemistry as a whole.

REFERENCES

1. Surveys of Annihilation of Positrons:
   (a) Deutsch, M., *Progr. Nucl. Phys.* **3**, 131 (1953).
   (b) DeBenedetti, S., and H. C. Corben, *Am. Rev. Nucl. Sci.* **4**, 191 (1954).
   (c) Berko, S., and F. L. Hereford, *Rev. Modern Phys.* **28**, 299 (1956).
   (d) Simons, L., *Handbuch Phys.* **34**, 139 (1956).
   (e) Wallace, P. R., *Adv. Solid State Phys.* **10**, 1 (1960).
   (f) Green, J. H., and J. W. Lee, "Positronium Chemistry," Academic Press, London and New York, 1964.
2. Green, R. E., and R. E. Bell, *Canad. J. Phys.* **35**, 398 (1957).
3. Bell, R. E., and R. L. Graham, *Phys. Rev.* **90**, 644 (1953).
4. Celitans, G. J., and J. H. Green, *Proc. Phys. Soc.* **83**, 823 (1964).
5. Celitans, G. J., and S. J. Tao, and J. H. Green, *Proc. Phys. Soc.* **83** 833 (1964).
6. Bisi, A., A. Fiorentini, and L. Zappa, *Phys. Rev.* **131** 1023 (1963).
7. Goldanskii, V. I., A. V. Ivanova, and E. P. Prokop'ev, ZhETF **47**, 659 (1964).
8. Ivanova, A. V., and E. P. Prokop'ev, ZhETF **48**, 1155 (1965).
9. Goldanskii, V. I., and E. P. Prokop'ev, Fisika Tverdogo Tela **6**, 3301 (1964).
10. Paul, D. A. L., and R. L. Graham, *Phys. Rev.* **106**, 16 (1956).
11. Wackerle, J., and R. Stump, *Phys. Rev.* **106** 18 (1956).
12. Tao, S. J., J. Bell, and J. H. Green, *Proc. Phys. Soc.* **83**, 453 (1964)
13. (a) Spirn, I., W. Brandt, G. Present, A. Schwarzchild; (b) A. W. Sunyar, *Bull. Am. Phys. Soc.* **9** 394 (1964).
14. Tao, S. J., and J. H. Green, *Proc. Phys. Soc.* **85**, 463 (1965).
15. Garwin, R. L., *Phys. Rev.* **91**, 1571 (1953).
16. Ore, A., Univ. Bergen Årbok, Naturvidenskap Rekke No. 9 (1949).
17. Craggs, J. D., and H. S. W. Massey, *Handbuch Phys.* **37**, 314 (1959).
18. "Atomic and Molecular Processes" (edited by D. R. Bates). Academic Press New York and London (1962).
19. Buchelnikova, N. S., *Uspekhi Fyz. Nauk.* **65**, 351 (1958).
20. Goldanskii, V. I., T. A. Solonenko, V. P. Shantarovich, Doklady *Acad. Sci USSR* **151**, 608 (1963).
21. Deutsch, M., *Phys. Rev.* **83**, 866 (1951).
22. Marder, S., V. W. Hughes, C. S. Wu, and W. Bennett, *Phys. Rev.* **103**, 1258 (1956).
23. Teutsch, W. B., and V. W. Hughes, *Phys. Rev.* **103**, 1266 (1956).
24. Paul, D. A. L., and L. Saint-Pierre, *Phys. Rev. Letters* **11**, 493 (1963).
25. Goldanskii, V. I., and Yu. S. Sayasov, *Phys. Letters* **13**, 300 (1964).

26. Hatcher, C. R., W. E. Millett, and L. Brown, *Phys. Rev.* **111**, 12 (1958).
27. Hatcher, C. R., and W. E. Millett, *Phys. Rev.* **112**, 1924 (1958).
28. Hatcher, C. R., T. W. Falkoner, and W. E. Millett, *J. Chem. Phys.* **32**, 28 (1960).
29. Hatcher, C. R., *J. Chem. Phys.* **35**, 2266 (1961).
30. Landes, H. S., S. Berko, and A. J. Zuchelli, *Phys. Rev.* **103**, 828 (1956).
31. Berko, S., and A. J. Zuchelli, *Phys. Rev.* **102**, 724 (1956).
32. Ormrod, J. H., and B. G. Hogg, *J. Chem. Phys.* **34**, 624 (1961).
33. Kerr, D. P., and B. G. Hogg, *J. Chem. Phys.* **36**, 2109 (1962).
34. Vojevodskii, V. V. and Yu. N. Molin, *Rad. Research* **17**, 366 (1962).
35. Graham, R., and A. T. Stewart, *Canad. J. Phys.* **32**, 678 (1954).
36. Page, L. A., M. Heinberg, J. Wallace, and T. Trout, *Phys. Rev.* **98**, 206 (1955).
37. Page, L. A., M. Heinberg, J. Wallace, and T. Trout, *Phys. Rev.* **99**, 665 (1955).
38. Page, L. A., and M. Heinberg, *Phys. Rev.* **102**, 1545 (1956).
39. Wagner, R. T., and F. L. Hereford, *Phys. Rev.* **99**, 593 (1955).
40. Stewart, A. T., *Phys. Rev.* **99**, 594 (1955).
41. Cottini, C., G. Fabri, E. Gatti, and E. Germagnoli, *Nuovo Cimento* **14**, 454 (1959).
42. Cottini, C., G. Fabri, E. Gatti, and E. Germagnoli, *J. Phys. Chem. Solids* **17**, 65 (1960).
43. de Zafra, R. L., and W. T. Joyner, *Phys. Rev.* **112**, 19 (1958).
44. Colombino, P., S. DeBenedetti, I. Degregori, and L. Trossi, *Nuovo Cimento* **8**, 508 (1958).
45. Stump, R., *Bull. Am. Phys. Soc.* **2**, 173 (1957).
46. Ferrell, R. A., *Rev. Modern Phys.* **28**, 308 (1956).
47. Wallace, P. R., *Phys. Rev.* **100**, 738 (1955).
48. Brandt, W., S. Berko, and W. W. Walker, *Phys. Rev.* **120**, 1289 (1960).
49. Henderson, G. A., and W. E. Millett, *Bull. Am. Phys. Soc.* **7**, No. 2, J8 (1962).
50. Wilson, R. K., P. O. Johnson, and R. Stump, *Phys. Rev.* **129**, 2091 (1963).
51. Clarke, H. C. and B. G. Hogg, *J. Chem. Phys.* **37**, 1898 (1962).
52. Groseclose, B. C., and G. D. Loper, *Phys. Rev.* **137**, A939 (1965).
53. Fabri, G., and E. Germagnoli, *Nuovo Cimento* **23**, 572 (1962).
54. Chandra, G., V. G. Kulkarni, R. G. Lagu, A. V. Patankar, and B. V. Thosar, *Phys. Letters* **16**, 40 (1965).
55. Fabri, G., E. Germagnoli, and G. Randone, *Phys. Rev.* **130**, 204 (1962).
56. Spirn, I., and W. Brandt, *Bull. Am. Phys. Soc.* **10**, No. 1, BA 13 (1965).
57. Fabri, G., E. Germagnoli, and G. Randone, *Phys. Letters* **3**, 6 (1962).
58. McGervey, G., and V. F. Walters, *Phys. Rev. Letters* **13**, 408 (1964).
59. Bisi, A., F. Bisi, A. Fasana, and L. Zappa, *Phys. Rev.* **122**, 1709 (1961).
60. Bisi, A., A. Fasana, and L. Zappa, *Phys. Rev.* **124**, 1487 (1961).
61. Bisi, A., A. Fiorentini, E. Gatti, and L. Zappa, *Phys. Rev.* **128**, 2195 (1962).

62. Fabri, G., E. Germagnoli, I. F. Quercia, and E. Turrisi, *Nuovo Cimento* **30**, 21 (1963).
63. Colombino, P., I. Degregori, L. Mayrone, L. Trossi, and S. De Benedetti, *Phys. Rev.* **119**, 1665 (1960).
64. Colombino, P., I. Degregori, L. Mayrone, L. Trossi, and S. De Benedetti, *Nuovo Cimento* **18**, 632 (1960).
65. Cole, G. D., and W. W. Walker, *J. Chem. Phys.* **42**, 1692 (1965).
66. Drisko, R. M., *Phys. Rev.* **95**, 611 (1954).
67. Ferrell, R. A., *Phys. Rev.* **110**, 1355 (1958).
68. Porter, G., and M. R. Wright, *Discussion Faraday Soc.* **27**, 18 (1959).
69. Deutsch, M., and E. Dulit, *Phys. Rev.* **84**, 601 (1951).
70. Wheatley, J., and D. Halliday, *Phys. Rev.* **87**, 235 (1952).
71. Pond, T. A., and R. H. Dicke, *Phys. Rev.* **85**, 489 (1952).
72. Hughes, V., S. Marder, and C. Wu, *Phys. Rev.* **98**, 1840 (1955).
73. Heinberg, M., and L. Page, *Phys. Rev.* **107**, 1589 (1957).
74. Weinstein, R., M. Deutsch, and S. Brown, *Phys. Rev.* **94**, 758 (1954).
75. Weinstein, R., M. Deutsch, and S. Brown, *Phys. Rev.* **98** 223 (1955).
76. Telegdi, V. L., Y. C. Sens, D. D. Yovanovich, and S. D. Warshaw, *Phys. Rev.* **104**, 867, (1956).
77. Warshaw, S. D., *Phys. Rev.* **108**, 713 (1957).
78. Iaci, G., I. F. Quercia, and E. Turrisi, *Nuovo Cimento* **24**, 746 (1962).
79. Freitag, D., and K. Ziock, *Z. Phys.* **153**, 124 (1958).
80. Fabri, G., G. Poletti, and G. Randone, *Phys. Rev.* **135**, A80 (1964).
81. Bisi, A., A. Fiorentini, and L. Zappa, *Phys. Rev.* **134**, A328 (1964).
82. Gainotti, A., E. Germagnoli, G. Schianchi, and L. Zecchina, *Nuovo Cimento* **32**, 880 (1964).
83. Gainotti, A., E. Germagnoli, G. Schianchi, and L. Zecchina. *Phys. Letters* **13**, 9 (1964).
84. Bussolati, C. and L. Zappa, *Phys. Rev.* **136**, A657 (1964).
85. Dixon, W., and L. Trainor, *Phys. Rev.* **97**, 733 (1955).
86. Deutsch, M., *Phys. Rev.* **82**, 455 (1951).
87. Pond, T. A., *Phys. Rev.* **85**, 489 (1952).
88. Gittelman, B., E. P. Dulit, and M. Deutsch, *Bull. Am. Phys. Soc.* **1**, 69 (1956).
89. Heymann, F. F., P. E. Osmon, J. J. Veit, and W. F. Williams, *Proc. Phys. Soc.* **78**, 1038 (1961).
90. Paul, D. A. L., *Canad. J. Phys.* **36**, 640 (1958).
91. Paul, D. A. L., *Canad. J. Phys.* **37**, 1059 (1959).
92. Lee, J., and G. J. Celitans, *J. Chem. Phys.* **42**, 437 (1965).
93. Simons, L., *Phys. Rev.* **90**, 165 (1953).
94. Pond, T. A., *Phys. Rev.* **93**, 478 (1954).
95. Pond, T. A., *Phys. Rev.* **94**, 758 (1954).
96. Berko, S., and A. J. Zuchelli, *Phys. Rev.* **99**, 1652 (1955).
97. Berko, S., and A. J. Zuchelli, *Phys. Rev.* **102**, 724 (1956).
98. de Zafra, R. L., *Phys. Rev.* **113**, 1547 (1959).
99. Ware, W. R., *J. Phys. Chem.* **66**, 455 (1962).
100. Kerr, D. P., H. M. Cooper, and B. G. Hogg, *Canad. J. Phys.* **43**, 963 (1965).

101. Hogg, B. G., T. Sutherland, D. A. L. Paul, and J. Hodgins, *J. Chem. Phys.* **25**, 1082 (1956).
102. Green, R. E., and R. E. Bell, *Canad. J. Phys.* **36**, 1684 (1958).
103. McGervey J., and S. DeBenedetti, *Phys. Rev.* **114**, 495 (1959).
104. McGervey, J., H. Horstman, and S. DeBenedetti, *Phys. Rev.* **124**, 1113 (1961).
105. Trumpy, G., *Phys. Rev.* **118**, 668 (1960).
106. Goldanskii, V. I., O. A. Karpukhin, and G. G. Petrov, Zh. Eksp. Theor. Fiz. **39**, 1477 (1960).
107. Jackson, J. E., and J. D. McGervey, *J. Chem. Phys.* **38**, 300 (1963).
108. Goldanskii, V. I., V. G. Firsov, and V. P. Shantarovich, *Doklady Akad. Nauk SSSR* **155**, 636 (1964).
109. Goldanskii, V. I., B. G. Egiazarov and V. P. Shantarovich, "Fyzika Elementarnykh Chastite" (Physics of Elementary Particles) p. 48, Atomizdat. Moscow, 1966.
110. Riesz, P., and E. J. Hart, *J. Phys. Chem.* **63**, 868 (1959).
111. Goldanskii, V. I., and V. P. Shantarovich, Paper B-2, at 20th International Congress on Pure and Applied Chemistry, Moscow, July, 1965.
112. Czapski, G., G. Gortner, and G. Stein, *J. Phys. Chem.* **65**, 960 (1961).
113. Frumkin, A. N., O. A. Petrii, and N. N. Nikolaeva-Fedorovich, *Electrochim. Acta* **8**, 177 (1963).
114. Goldanskii, V. I., V. G. Firsov, and V. P. Shantarovich, Kinetika i Kataliz **6**, 564 (1965).
115. Dolin, P. I., and A. V. Egunov, *Dokl. Akad. Nauk SSSR* **154**, 1153 (1964).
116. Egunov, A. V., and P. I. Dolin, *Dokl. Akad. Nauk SSSR* **148**, 140 (1963).

Research Developments

Research Developments

Calculated Core Annilation Momentum Distributions for Several Metals[*]

D. M. Rockmore and A. T. Stewart

University of North Carolina, Chapel Hill, North Carolina

In the use of positron annihilation as a research tool in metals most workers have been primarily concerned with the properties of the conduction electrons. It is well established, however, that positrons also annihilate with the core electrons. Since these inner electrons are more tightly bound than the conduction electrons, they have, correspondingly, momentum distributions which are of significant magnitude over a range of values of momentum, considerably exceeding the Fermi momentum of the metal. In addition to an intrinsic interest in core annihilation properties, it is also desirable to be able to separate the annihilations with conduction electrons from that of core electrons. For example, this is particularly necessary in order to make reliable measurements of the so-called "higher momentum components." As experimental techniques improve and yield more and more detailed data, the question of interpretation of results becomes both more difficult and more important. As will be shown, results so far obtained in calculating core annihilation momentum distributions, and comparison to experiment, indicate that core annihilation poses some problems of interest in itself.

In the work reported here the procedure was similar to that of Berko and Plaskett.[1] Hartree-Fock wavefunctions with exchange were taken from the literature[2] for Al^{+3}, Be^{+2}, Ca^{+2}, Cu^+, K^+, Mg^{+2}, Na^+, and potentials were then calculated taking the conduction electrons into account by the approximation of assuming them to have constant density, and normalizing them to the volume of the Wigner-Seitz sphere for the material concerned.

The ground state positron wavefunction was then determined using these potentials and the Wigner-Seitz approximation requiring spherical symmetry and zero slope at the Wigner-Seitz radius. Correlation effects between the positron and electrons were not taken into account. The positron wavefunction thus computed was

[*]Work supported in part by the National Science Foundation and Advanced Research Projects Agency.

normalized such that there was a probability of unity of finding it in the Wigner-Seitz sphere. Other results obtained in the computational process were energy eigenvalues, radial momentum distributions, and the z component momentum distributions. The latter two are formed by transforming the positron and core electron wavefunction product into the momentum representation for the radial distribution, and a further integration over the x- and y-momentum components to obtain the z-momentum distribution. The program has several internal checks for self-consistency. In addition, the fact that the calculated potential at the Wigner-Seitz radius should be almost zero and the similarity between our calculations for aluminum and copper to those of Berko and Plaskett[1] provide additional checks on the validity of the computational process.

The z-momentum distributions have been compared with experimental data. A typical comparison is shown in Fig. 1 where the calculated and experimental results for magnesium are shown. The actual form of the experimental data is shown in the inset in the lower left-hand corner of Fig. 1. The customary interpretation is that a free-electron parabola due to the conduction electrons is added to the broad distribution due to the core electrons. The parabola cuts off, or meets the core distribution, at the Fermi momentum for magnesium. Due primarily to temperature effects and instrument resolution there is a smear making this junction a smooth curve instead of a curve with discontinuous slope. The procedure used in making

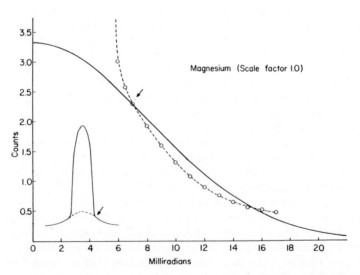

Fig. 1. Direct comparison of calculated and experimental results for magnesium.

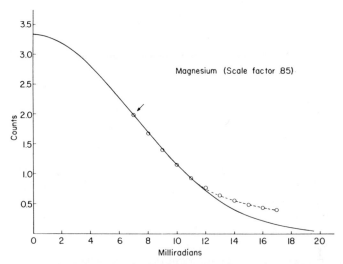

Fig. 2. Comparison of calculated and experimental results for magnesium. The calculated momentum distribution has been reduced in width by 15%.

the comparison of experimental and calculated results was as follows: A point near, but outside, the region of smear on the experimental core distribution was picked, and an ordinate scale determined to make it and the corresponding point of the calculated core distribution coincide. The same scale was then used to plot the remaining points of the experimental core distribution. As can be seen, the resulting fit shown in Fig. 1, in this case, is relatively poor. However, if the theoretical results are plotted along an abcissa whose scale is 0.85 times that of the original one, it is seen that the fit is much improved with deviations occurring only at the tail of the distribution. The same procedure was followed for the other materials, and various scale factors were determined which allowed good fits between experimental and calculated results. In fact, the fit shown in Fig. 2 is worse than that obtained in all other cases, most of which show no appreciable deviation between calculated and experimental data over the entire range of available experimental data.

Table I shows the scale factors required in comparison to the positions of the metals in the periodic table. It appears that in going to the right in the table the scale factor approaches unity, and that the heaviest elements shown have the scale factors closest to unity. Beryllium, at first glance, appears to behave anomalously but, we believe, its behavior has a simple explanation in view of the interpretation of the results which follow.

It has been mentioned that the calculated results were obtained

TABLE I

		Be	0.9		
Na	0.8	Mg	0.85	Al	0.86
K	0.92	Ca	1.0		

by ignoring positron-electron correlation effects. If one looks at the calculated positron wavefunctions one notices that the positron does not penetrate very far into the core, due to coulomb repulsion. Thus, the positron essentially represents a cloud of positive charge surrounding the ion core. The electrons are attracted by this positive charge and tend to move towards it and away from the nucleus. This results in a lowering of their mean kinetic energy, and hence a reduction in the amplitude of the portions of their momentum distributions corresponding to the higher momenta. In other words, the effect of positron-electron correlation is to shift the momentum distribution to lower values of momentum. This shows up as a shrinking of the original momentum scale. Qualitatively one would expect that the more tightly bound the electrons, the less the effect of the positrons, and also the greater the number of electrons to be affected, the less the effect.

The anomalous behavior of beryllium thus could be explained by the fact that the $1S$ electrons are very tightly bound, while the $2S$ and $2P$ electrons of sodium, magnesium, and aluminum are more affected even though there are eight of them, compared to beryllium's two $1S$ electrons.

To summarize, it appears that the procedure used to calculate core annihilation distributions is reasonably good for the elements in the middle of the periodic table, and can be extended to lighter elements by adjusting the scale of the abscissa. It would be of interest to check the interpretation given by computations which determine from first principles the effect of positron-core electron correlations. The deviation of calculated and experimental data at high momentum for magnesium and calcium requires explanation, and it would be well to extend the experimental data over a greater range for the other elements to see if they too deviate from the calculated results at higher momenta. Evidence from comparison with Argon data indicates that this deviation may be due almost entirely to our failure to subtract background counts before comparing theoretical and experimental results. This would also affect the values obtained for the scale factors.

We would like to thank J. J. Donaghy for the use of his experimental data for sodium and lithium, J. B. Shand for the beryllium data, J. H. Kusmiss for magnesium, aluminum, and calcium data, and S. M. Kim for copper data.

REFERENCES

1. Berko, S., and J. S. Plaskett, *Phys. Rev.* **112**, 1877 (1958).
2. Al^{+3}: C. Froese, *Proc. Cambridge Phil. Soc.* **53**, 206 (1957); Be^{+2} and Ca^{+2}: D. R. Hartree and W. Hartree, *Proc. Roy. Soc. (London)* **A149**, 210 (1935); Cu^{+}: D. R. Hartree and W. Hartree, *Proc. Roy. Soc. (London)* **A157**, 490 (1936); K^{+}: D. R. Hartree and W. Hartree, *Proc. Roy. Soc. (London)* **A166**, 450 (1938); Mg^{+2}: W. J. Yost, *Phys. Rev.* **58**, 557 (1940); Na^{+}: D. R. Hartree and W. Hartree, *Proc. Roy. Soc. (London)* **A193**, 299 (1948).

Core Annihilation in Sodium[*]

J. P. Carbotte[†]

Cornell University, Ithaca, New York

It is well known from recent work[1,2] that enhancement effects resulting from the direct coulomb coupling between the annihilating
pair are critical in determining the lifetime of positrons in a conduction electron gas. However, these effects have never been discussed in past investigations of core annihilation where the possible polarization of the cores by the positron is always ignored.
On the basis of the ladder approximation for the electron-positron
propagator, we have derived a formula for core annihilation which
includes the direct electron-positron coupling to all orders. It is not
our intention to describe the derivations[3] here, nor will we need to
specify in detail our final formula. Only its general structure is of
interest.

Past treatments[4-7] of core annihilation involve matrix elements
that are products of a thermalized positron, and a single core electron wavefunction. We find additional matrix elements entering the
theory that are just as important. They are overlap integrals of the
unoccupied electron Bloch functions $\psi_{\mathbf{k}}(\mathbf{x})$ with a tight-binding core
state modulated by a plane wave momentum $\mathbf{p} - \mathbf{k}$, i.e.,

$$\langle \psi_{\mathbf{k}} | e^{i(\mathbf{p}-\mathbf{k})\cdot\mathbf{x}} | \varphi_{\text{core}} \rangle$$

These occur, of course, only when one takes into account the virtual
transitions of the core electrons to unoccupied conduction states induced by the positron coulomb field. More precisely, we find that
the partial annihilation rate $R_{\mathbf{p}}$ is proportional to the square of the
sum of two terms: the usual positron-core electron overlap integral
plus

[*]Research supported by the Office of Naval Research under Contract
NONR-401(38), Technical Report #7.

[†]*Present address:* Department of Physics, McMaster University, Hamilton, Ontario, Canada.

$$\sum_{\mathbf{k}} \langle \psi_{\mathbf{k}} | e^{i(\mathbf{p}-\mathbf{k})\cdot\mathbf{x}} | \varphi_{\text{core}} \rangle \Phi_{\mathbf{p}}(\mathbf{k}) \tag{1}$$

where $\Phi_{\mathbf{p}}(\mathbf{k})$ plays the role of an effective enhancement factor, the exact nature of which does not concern us. The sum over $\mathbf{k}$ is to extend over all unoccupied states.

It should be pointed out that although our formula for $R_{\mathbf{p}}$ is based on the sum of the ladder graphs, some further simplifying assumptions were made to get it in the form (1). These involve neglecting band effects in computing matrix elements between states, both of which are almost plane wave-like. This restricts the theory to simple metals, although for sodium errors from this source are certainly less than 5%. On the other hand, it is difficult to make a good estimate of overlap integrals of the form (1), since their value is sensitive to the precise deviations of $\psi_{\mathbf{k}}(\mathbf{x})$ from a plane wave inside the ion core. We do not want to stress these difficulties here, however, and we make the simplest possible approximation for the $\psi_{\mathbf{k}}(\mathbf{x})$'s, namely,

$$\psi_{\mathbf{k}}(\mathbf{x}) = \frac{1}{\sqrt{V}} e^{i\mathbf{k}\cdot\mathbf{x}} u_0(\mathbf{x}) \tag{2}$$

where $1/\sqrt{V}u_0(\mathbf{x})$ is the exact Bloch state for an electron at the bottom of the conduction band $(3s)$. The calculation now simplifies greatly since, in this case, the matrix elements appearing in (1) become independent of $\mathbf{k}$, and can be pulled out of the summation. We cannot, of course, expect to get accurate quantitative results in this way. Nevertheless, the model certainly gives the correct qualitative picture of the underlying physics, and contains all of the important features of a more exact calculation.

On this model, the contribution to $R_{\mathbf{p}}$ coming from the (nl) shell is

$$R_{\mathbf{p}}^{nl} = 8\pi(2l + 1)R^0 \frac{1}{V} |J_{nl}^+(\mathbf{p}) + \chi_{nl}(\mathbf{p})J_{nl}^-(\mathbf{p})|^2 \tag{3}$$

where R^0 is the Sommerfeld total annihilation rate. The overlap integrals $J^{\pm}$ are given by

$$J_{nl}^{\pm}(\mathbf{p}) = \int_0^{\infty} dr\, j_l(pr) P_{nl}(r) R_0^{\pm}(r) \tag{4}$$

where $j_l(pr)$ is the spherical Bessel function of order l, and $P_{nl}(r)$ the Hartree-Fock wavefunction for the (nl) shell of the free Na^+ ion.[8] The quantity $R_0^+(r)/r$ is the positron Wigner-Seitz wavefunction for a particle of zero crystal momentum[9] and $R_0^-(r)$ is simply $ru_0(r)$.[10]

The effective enhancement factor $\chi_{nl}(\mathbf{p})$ appearing in (3) is given by $1/V \sum_{\mathbf{m}} \Phi_{\mathbf{m};\,\mathbf{p}-\mathbf{m}}^{nl}$, where Φ satisfies the familiar[1,2] integral equation

$$\Phi^{nl}_{m;\,p-m} = \frac{\theta(m - p_F)}{m^2 + (p - m)^2 + \Delta_{nl}}\, u^s(p - m)$$

$$+ \frac{\theta(m - p_F)}{m^2 + (p - m)^2 + \Delta_{nl}}\, \frac{1}{V} \sum_{q} u^s(q)\, \Phi^{nl}_{m+q;\,p-m-q} \tag{5}$$

with $\theta(m - p_F)$ being a step function equal to zero for $m < p_F$ and one otherwise, and $u^s(q)$ being the qth component of the Fourier transform of the effective electron-positron force. The Δ_{nl}'s give the energy gap between the bottom of the conduction band and the (nl) core level.

The most important results to come out of the calculation are as follows. The $1s$ electrons make negligible contributions to R_p. Although the large energy parameters $\Delta(\Delta_{2s} = 60$ eV, $\Delta_{2p} = 27$ eV) appear in the denominators of (5), the Born approximation is still inadequate to get reasonable $\chi_{nl}(p)$, especially for small p's. The variation of $\chi_{nl}(p)$ with p is not insignificant, but it is sufficiently slow for the momentum dependence of R_p to be essentially determined by that of the overlap integrals $J^{\pm}(p)$. Since the core electrons are sharply localized around each lattice site, the $J^{\pm}(p)$ extend considerably beyond p_F in momentum space. Thus, long tails arise in the two photon counting rate. However, the $J(p)$'s are quite distinct functions of momentum, and do not for instance carry the same sign for all p's. Some destructive interference between the two terms in (3) occurs.

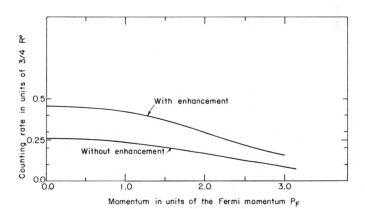

Fig. 1. The contribution to the two photon counting rate $R_{p_z = p_F \gamma_z}$, in units of $\frac{3}{4} R^0$, coming from annihilation with the core electrons. Notice that around $3p_F$ the upper curve levels off slightly, while the lower curve drops to zero linearly.

The results for the counting rate R_{p_z}, in units of $\frac{3}{4} R^0$, are plotted in Fig. 1, where they are compared with the rate from $J^+(\mathbf{p})$ alone. The variation with momentum of these two curves is similar, although the areas under them are different. In the first instance, we find a total annihilation rate of $R^{core} = 2.23\ R^0$ to be compared with $1.02\ R^0$ when enhancement effects are neglected. These two values differ approximately by a factor of two. This may seem low, since the enhancement factors $\chi_{nl}(\mathbf{p})$ are typically of the order of 0.8, while the $J(\mathbf{p})$'s have roughly the same magnitude. There is, however, considerable interference between $J^+(\mathbf{p})$ and $J^-(\mathbf{p})$, as previously mentioned.

Finally, it is tempting to compare our results with experiment. The best value for the total rate coming from the conduction electrons found in the work of Carbotte and Kahana[2] is $R^{cond.} = 14.03\ R^0$. Thus, $R^{total} = R^{core} + R^{cond.} = 16.26\ R^0 = 3.12 \times 10^9\ \text{sec}^{-1}$, which is in good agreement with the experimental result of Bell and Jørgensen.[11] The agreement with the two photon counting rate most recently reported by Stewart[12] is poor. Our model calculation accounts for little more than half of the tails. A better calculation is necessary, although a small part of the events beyond p_F, no doubt, come from lattice effects in the conduction electron gas.

REFERENCES

1. Kahana, S., *Phys. Rev.* **129**, 1622 (1963).
2. Carbotte, J. P., and S. Kahana, *Phys. Rev.* **139**, A213 (1965).
3. It will be submitted for publication elsewhere.
4. Berko, S., and J. S. Plaskett, *Phys. Rev.* **112**, 1877 (1958).
5. Daniel, E., *J. Phys. Chem. Solids* **6**, 205 (1958).
6. Wallace, P. R., "Solid State Physics" (Seitz and Turnbull, eds.), Vol. 10, p. 1. Academic Press, London and New York, 1960.
7. Rose, K. L., and S. DeBenedetti, *Phys. Rev.* **A138**, 927 (1965).
8. These functions are tabulated in D. R. Hartree and W. Hartree, *Proc. Roy. Soc. (London)* **A193**, 299 (1948).
9. One essentially uses a Hartree field to determine this function. For details, see J. P. Carbotte, Ph.D. Thesis, McGill University, 1964 (unpublished).
10. This function is tabulated in J. Callaway, *Phys. Rev.* **123**, 1255 (1961).
11. Bell, R. E., and M. H. Jørgensen, *Canad. J. Phys.* **38**, 652 (1960).
12. Stewart, A. T., private communication.

On Positron Lifetimes vs. Two Gamma Correlations in the Alkali Metals[*]

J. H. Terrell, H. L. Weisberg, and S. Berko

Brandeis University, Waltham, Massachusetts

It is well known that the theoretical angular distributions of 2-γ annihilation radiation calculated in the one-electron approximation are often in good agreement with experiment. Whereas the area under the theoretical angular distribution gives directly the annihilation rate, this rate is smaller than the experimental rate by an order of magnitude. It is the purpose of this paper to attempt a reconciliation of these two aspects of positron annihilation in the alkali metals Li, Na, K, and Cs.

Figure 1 shows the positron wavefunctions for the various metals. We followed the prescription of Berko and Plaskett[1] by computing the functions in the Wigner-Seitz (W.S.) approximation. For a given potential the radial Schrödinger equation was solved using computer programs which automatically imposed the proper boundary condition, normalized the function, and stored it for future use. The potential was constructed from self-consistent Hartree-Fock-Slater[2] (H.F.S.) potentials. Although the positron potential in this calculation has exchange, it is well known that this has little effect on the shape of the wavefunction.[1] The abscissa is plotted in units of r_s (W.S. sphere radius). We notice the following features of these curves: (a) as the nuclear charge increases, the positron is pushed away from the nucleus; and (b) since the W.S. radius, r_s, also increases for heavier elements, the amplitude of the positron is correspondingly decreasing in order to satisfy the boundary condition and normalization.

The matrix element for the probability for 2-γ annihilation of an electron and positron is proportional to the Fourier transform of the electron and positron wavefunctions. The electrons were separated into a core and valence part. The core electrons were treated in the Bloch tight-binding approximation and numerical H.F.S. self-consistent atomic functions were used.[2] The angular distribution

[*]Work supported by the National Science Foundation and the U.S. Army Research Office, Durham, North Carolina.

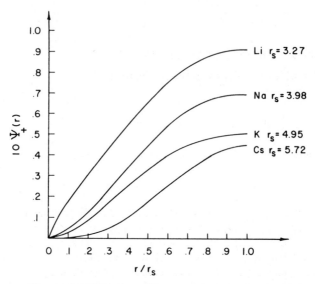

Fig. 1. Positron wavefunctions for Li, Na, K, and Cs computed in W.S. approximation.

of 2-γ annihilation radiation due to core electrons is as follows (see Ref. 1 for a derivation of this result):

$$I_c(p_z = mc\theta) = \sum_l 4\pi\, 2(2l + 1) \iint dp_x\, dp_y$$
$$\times |\int_0^\infty \psi_-^l(r)\, \psi_+(r)\, j_l(pr)\, r^2\, dr|^2$$

where $\psi_-^l(r)$ is an atomic electron function of angular momentum l, and $\psi_+(r)$ is the positron wavefunction. $j_l(pr)$ is the spherical Bessel function of order l. $I_c(\theta)$ was computed for all core electrons which overlapped with the positron function.

The valence electron was treated in the W.S. approximation. The radial Schrödinger equation was solved by computer with an appropriate potential. An eigenvalue was found that put the proper number of nodes in each wavefunction with the proper boundary condition. The angular distribution due to the valence electron is as follows:[1]

$$I_v(p_z = mc\theta) = \sum_K \iint dp_x\, dp_y\, 2|A_{K(0)}|^2$$

where

$$A_K(0) = \int_{cell} e^{-i\mathbf{K}\cdot\mathbf{r}}\, \psi_+(r)\, u_-^0(r)\, d\mathbf{r}$$

The sum is over all reciprocal lattice vectors **K**. $u_-^{\,0}(r)$ is the periodic part of the Bloch electron wavefunction. $I_v(\theta)$ was calculated by drawing Fermi spheres in reciprocal space for five reciprocal lattice vectors. Since we used the experimental angular distribution of Stewart[3] for polycrystalline samples to compare with theory, an average was performed for p_z cutting in the (100), (110), and (111) directions. Table I gives the square of the Fourier coefficients for W.S. electron and positron for each element.[*]

Figure 2 shows the theoretical and experimental angular distributions. The theoretical result is the solid curve and is made up of valence and core parts. The lower curve for each element is the contribution from the core electrons. The amount of high momentum is overestimated, but the shape of the high momentum part follows the experimental trend from metal to metal. It is interesting to note that the ratios of the average contribution to $I_v(\theta)$ for Li at $\theta = 0$ mrad and $\theta = 7$ mrad for the W.S. electrons and the valence contribution using Orthogonalized Plane Wave electron functions calculated by Melngailis,[4] are within 4% of each other.[*] The theoretical and experimental curves for each metal are normalized to have the same areas. Notice that in each curve the theoretical angular distributions overestimate the experimental tails.

The total annihilation rate in the one-electron theory is as follows:

$$\lambda_t = \frac{\pi r_0^2 c}{8\pi^3} (A_v + A_c)$$

where

$$A_v = \int I_v(p_z)\, dp_z \quad \text{and} \quad A_c = \int I_c(p_z)\, dp_z$$

r_0 is the classical electron radius and c is the velocity of light. Since the single particle rate is too small, we assume that we can enhance the one-electron rates by introducing *angle-independent* factors E_v and E_c for valence and core electrons, respectively. The rate to be compared to experiment is now as follows:

$$\lambda_t = \frac{\pi r_0^2 c}{8\pi^3} (E_v A_v + E_c A_c)$$

The fraction of the experimental annihilation rate due to valence electrons alone is called λ_v:

$$\lambda_v = \frac{\lambda_{\exp}}{1 + \dfrac{A_c}{A_v} \cdot \dfrac{E_c}{E_v}}$$

*See note added in proof on page 275.

TABLE I*
Values of $|A_K(0)|^2$ for Li, Na, K, and Cs

K	Li	Na	K	Cs
(000)	0.98	0.955	0.866	0.785
(110)	0.003	0.002	0.011	0.012
(111)	0.019	0.018	0.029	0.016
(200)	0.014	0.014	0.019	0.006
(220)	0.001	0.001	0.002	0.002

*See note added in proof on p. 275.

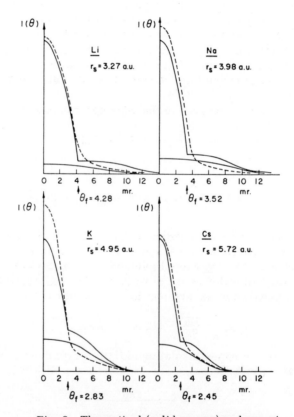

Fig. 2. Theoretical (solid curves) and experimental (dashed curves) angular distributions normalized to same area. $E_v/E_C = 1$ for theoretical curves. (See note added in proof on p. 275.)

where λ_{exp} is the experimental rate. One way of bringing about better agreement between theory and experiment for both the angular distributions and the annihilation rates is to make $E_v/E_c > 1$. This is physically reasonable since no doubt the valence electrons can correlate more easily with the positron than the core electrons.

The object now is to see what E_v/E_c should be to (a) keep the best possible agreement between theoretical and experimental angular distributions and (b) at the same time remain in reasonable agreement with the experimental annihilation rate values. It was not clear whether or not the entire valence part (inverted "parabola" + "tail") was to be enhanced by the same amount or only the inverted "parabolic" part. Since we do not want to introduce a *third* enhancement factor for the tail of the valence part, we decided to enhance first of

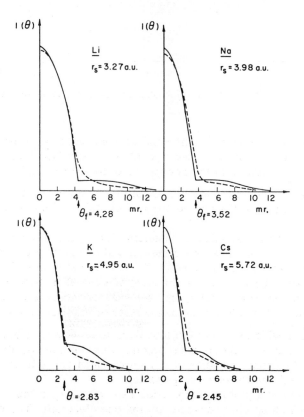

Fig. 3. Theoretical (solid curves) and experimental (dashed curves) angular distributions normalized to same area. $E_v/E_c = 4$ for theoretical curves. (See note added in proof on p. 275.)

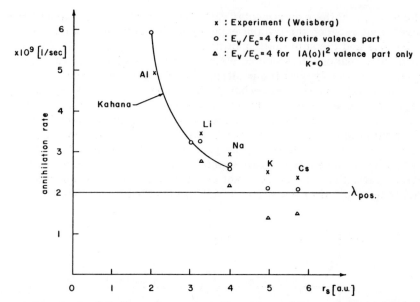

Fig. 4. Annihilation rate vs. r_s .* The errors of the experimental points are ±5%.

all the entire valence part together and as a second trial to enhance the contribution from the inverted "parabolic" part (1st Fourier coefficient $|A(0)|^2_{K=0}$) alone. In the second case the valence tail was added to the core part. The exact answer should be found by a many-body computation similar to the one performed by Kahana,[5] but using Bloch waves.

Figure 3 shows the results of enhancing the entire valence part by making E_v/E_c = 4. The experimental and theoretical curves were normalized to have the same areas. The agreement is seen to be much better except possibly for the case of Cs.* Even better agreement was obtained by enhancing only the valence contribution at K = 0 $(|A(0)|^2_{K=0})$ but this led to an estimate of the rate due to valence electrons which was far too low. It is to be noted, however, that we are using old experimental angular distributions of Stewart[3] which have a tendency (because of his short counters) of underestimating the high momentum components.

Figure 4 shows a plot of annihilation rate vs r_s (r_s is the radius of a sphere which on the average contains one electron). The experimental points are from the work of Weisberg[6] and the spin averaged

*See note added in proof on page 275.

TABLE II*
Enhancement Factors Calculated From
Experimental Rate Values of Weisberg

	Li	Na	K	Cs
E_v	7.80	11.96	16.12	31.12
E_c	1.95	2.99	4.03	7.78

positronium rate (λ_{pos}) is the straight line. Enhancing only the valence contribution at $\mathbf{K} =$ 0 $(|A(0)|^2)$ made λ_v go below λ_{pos} for K and Cs, and much below the theoretical curve of Kahana[5] for Li and Na. We see that enhancing the entire valence part by a factor of 4 is not unreasonable.

If the theoretical curve of Kahana[5] is extended in a smooth way towards Cs, one sees that the values for λ_v follow roughly Kahana's theory except for K.

Using the experimental annihilation rate results of Weisberg[6] we can now obtain values for E_c and E_v for the various metals. The values found for $E_v/E_c = 4$ (entire valence part enhanced) are given in Table II.*

What we have shown is that we can obtain better agreement with experimental angular distributions and at the same time obtain reasonable values for the valence annihilation rate by introducing one parameter, namely, the ratio of valence to core enhancement factors. It will be interesting to see if these phenomenological values for the enhancement factors (Table II) fit in with future theoretical, many-body calculations.

REFERENCES

1. Berko, S., and J. S. Plaskett, *Phys. Rev.* **112**, 1877 (1958).
2. Herman, F., and S. Skillman, "Atomic Structure Calculations," Prentice-Hall, Englewood Cliffs, New Jersey, 1963.
3. Stewart, A. T., *Canad. J. Phys.* **35**, 168 (1957).
4. Melngailis, J., Ph.D. Thesis, Carnegie Institute of Technology, 1965.
5. Kahana, S., *Phys. Rev.* **129**, 1622 (1963).
6. Weisberg, H., Ph.D. Thesis, Brandeis University, 1965.

*Note added in proof: In checking the proof we have discovered that due to an unfortunate oversight we have computed the (111) instead of the (211) contributions in Table I. The corrected computations lower the high momentum contribution of the valence electrons, but leave the core contributions unchanged. The values of Table II are changed somewhat, but their trend and the conclusions of the paper remain unaltered; in fact the recomputed theoretical distributions of Fig. 3 fit the experimental curves better.

Positron Lifetime Measurements with Homogenized Sources in Metals

Teuvo Kohonen

Institute of Technology, Otaniemi, Finland

It has been reported by several authors that the distributions of lifetimes of positrons, which are diffused in certain metals, possess a longer-lived component (τ_2) with an intensity of a few per cent or less. The occurrence of the component is forbidden by the usual theories of metals. The observed components resemble those due to bound positron states in amorphous solids and liquids, and the decay time is of the order 0.5-1 nsec.[1] Latest measurements have shown some indications that the long-lived components of positrons could be due to annihilations in the impure surface layers, or defects of the sample, possibly through the formation of some kind of bound states. It has been shown that the art of preparation of the positron emitter on to the surface of the metal sample has an effect on the intensity of the τ_2 component.[2] Therefore, it was considered to be necessary to homogenize the positron emitter in the samples by metallurgical means. For metals which have a higher melting point than the most useful positron emitter, which is Na^{22} in the form of NaCl, the sintering process was selected to get the source into the metal matrix. Among those metals which have good sintering properties we selected Cu, Ni, and Co. In two other metals which had a lower melting point than NaCl, namely Pb and Zn, the source was homogenized by melting.

The preparation of the samples was started by mixing the active NaCl with the finely divided metal powder. Then the powder was pressed into briquets using a pressure of 7-10 tons/cm². The sintering was performed in a hydrogen atmosphere. The metals which had no good sintering properties, Pb and Zn, were rapidly fused. After the samples were cut to a suitable size and the surface contamination was removed, the samples were covered with a thin layer of the corresponding inactive metal to stop the positrons emitted near the surface.

As the detectors we used plastic scintillators of the type Nuclear Enterprises NE 102 A, 1 × 1 in., in connection with the photomultipliers 56 AVP. A head-on location of the detectors was used, and the source displaced so that both of the annihilation gamma rays could not be captured simultaneously. The anode pulses from the photomultipliers were shortened and limited by hot-carrier and snap-off diodes, as shown in Fig. 1a. The time-to-amplitude converter in these measurements was a circuit using tunnel diodes and working on the start-stop principle. The integral linearity was better than 20 ps of a 10 nsec scale and the stability was better than 20 ps/week. The calibration of the time scale was performed with the aid of air-insulated coaxial lines. Weisberg[3] has used a similar circuit lately. Our version is shown in Fig. 1b. The triggering level of the fast pulse generators was optimized experimentally so as to get the best time resolution. At optimum conditions, a FWHM of 0.34 nsec was obtained for the prompt coincidences between Co^{60} gamma rays, and the apparent

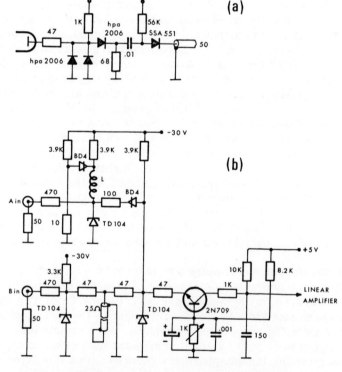

Fig. 1. (a) Fast limiter. (b) Time-to-amplitude converter. The length of the time scale (10 nsec) is determined by two parallel shorted clipping cables, 50 Ω each (RG-174/U). L is an air-cored coil made of copper wire gage No. 23, 3 turns with a diameter of 4 mm, 4 mm long.

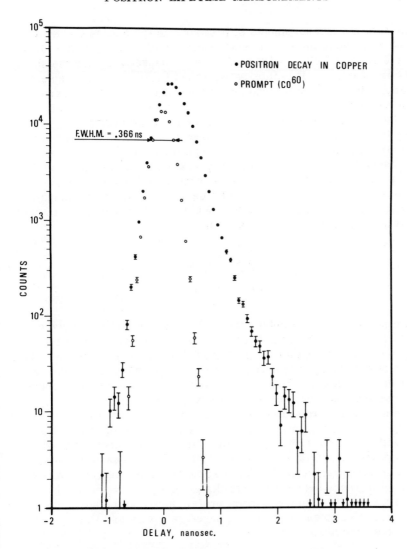

Fig. 2. Lifetime distribution of positrons in copper (solid points) together with the prompt resolution curve (open points).

"half life" of the slope was 4.0×10^{-11} sec. Neither pulse height compensation nor a pile-up rejection circuit were thereby used. Since we had fast pulse height analyzers in the "slow" side channels of a conventional fast-slow arrangement, we did not detect any pile-up of these pulses over almost four decades. The width of the side-channel windows was about 20%. Due to the fast side-channel electronics, it was not practicable to introduce any pulse height compensation.

The lifetime measurements of positrons in the metals Cu, Ni, Co, Pb, and Zn yielded the values 1.98 ± 0.10, 1.58 ± 0.10, 2.12 ± 0.10, 2.47 ± 0.10, and $2.19 \pm 0.10 \times 10^{-10}$ sec, respectively, for the short-lived component τ_1. It is interesting to note that our measurements give approximately similar values as obtained earlier for Cu and Ni, but the three latter values are somewhat larger.

In these measurements none of the metals showed a larger τ_2 intensity than about 2%. This is a smaller value than that obtained with the usual preparation techniques. Though the component still exists, it has been shown that the method of preparation has an effect on the τ_2 components, and hence, that the residual components have no fundamental importance. They may well be due to bound state formation in impurities, e.g., in metal oxides. We can state that their relative intensities are probably no larger than

1.3% for Cu;
1.5% for Ni;
1.6% for Co;
1.3% for Pb; and
1.9% for Zn.

It could not be verified whether the distribution of the long-lived components was exponential, but the mean lives were around 0.7 nsec. One example of the measurements (in Cu) is shown in Fig. 2, together with one run of the prompt resolution curve. The pulse-height window settings were identical for both curves. The source strength was about $1 \mu C$, and the counting time was 1 week.

A comparison of the values for τ_1 given by the centroid-shift and the slope methods was made. If, when taking the prompt resolution curve with the aid of Co^{60} gamma rays, the side-channel settings were kept identical with those used in the positron measurements, and if a differential window width of some 20% was used in both channels, no difference between the results given by the two methods was observed. We would, however, prefer the slope method since it is less sensitive to changes in the source geometry and to long-term drift of the time scale.

ACKNOWLEDGMENT

The author is indebted to Mr. A. Tamminen for the development of the fast electronic circuitry, and for his help during the measurements.

REFERENCES

1. Bell, R. E., and M. H. Jørgensen, *Canad. J. Phys.* **38**, 652 (1960).
2. Kohonen, T., *Ann. Acad. Sci. Fennicae A. VI* No. 130 (1963).
3. Weisberg, H. L., *Nuclear Instrum. Meth.* **32**, 133 (1965).

Positron Annihilation in Magnesium-Indium and Indium-Lead Alloys[*]

B.T.A. McKee, G.F.O. Langstroth, and I.K. MacKenzie

Dalhousie University
Halifax, Nova Scotia, Canada

INTRODUCTION

Previous investigation of the temperature dependence of the angular correlation of two quantum annihilation radiation in several metals has indicated an anomalous behavior in indium, zinc, and cadmium.[1] As the temperature of these three metals is raised from room temperature towards the melting point, there occurs a continuous decrease in the proportion of annihilations which carry away momentum greater than the Fermi momentum. The angular distribution curves of all the metals investigated exhibit small changes with increase in temperature which can be simply explained as a consequence of thermal expansion. It has, however, not been possible to offer a definite explanation for the large temperature effects in indium, zinc, and cadmium.

One common feature of these three metals is their anisotropic thermal expansion.[2] This characteristic does not provide a direct explanation of the anomalous temperature effect because some other anisotropic metals, such as bismuth, exhibit when heated only the small changes in angular correlation associated with lattice expansion.

Indium, zinc, and cadmium have Fermi surfaces that overlap energy discontinuities in the band structure, and the features of this electron overlap will vary considerably under anisotropic thermal expansion. Such an argument has been advanced as explanation of an anomalous temperature dependence of the Knight shift in cadmium.[3] Of course, positrons annihilate with electrons throughout the Fermi sea, and variations in the shape of the Fermi surface would not be expected to result in large changes in the annihilation radiation angular correlation. The high momentum annihilations, however, are not fully understood, and before excluding anisotropic

*Supported by the National Research Council of Canada.

281

expansion and changes in electron overlap as joint cause of the
anomalous temperature effect, it seemed worthwhile to perform
some angular correlation measurements in alloy systems.

EXPERIMENTAL DETAILS AND RESULTS

It is possible to produce anisotropic lattice variations and consequent changes in electron overlap by forming dilute alloys. Addition
of about two atomic percent indium to magnesium introduces overlap
at the second Brillouin zone boundary.[4] Indium is one of the metals
which exhibits the anomalous temperature effect. Addition of lead to
indium will produce anisotropic lattice changes somewhat equivalent
to thermal expansion.[5]

The phase diagram for the indium-lead system is very simple—
an (In) phase for low lead concentrations, a large (Pb) phase, and one
intermediate phase. Thus the system also offers an opportunity to investigate the change in the indium-temperature effect among alloys
containing widely varying percentages of lead. Samples containing 0,
12, 28, 35, 68, and 100 at.-% lead were used. Alloy concentrations
were checked by specific gravity measurements.

The angular correlation measurements were made using a linear-
slit geometry. 5-in. by $1/_{10}$-in. slits 75 in. from the sample resulted
in an angular resolution of 1.3 mrad. Because the primary interest
is a comparison of curves with approximately similar shapes, no
correction was made for the instrumental resolution.

Figure 1 shows the temperature dependence of angular correlation in indium, and the attempted simulation of this behavior by alloying indium into magnesium. At the top of the figure is a pair of
angular correlation curves—indium at 25° and at 135°C. These
correspond to previously reported results, but have been included
here for convenient comparison. The vertical scale has been arbitrarily chosen to give the room-temperature curve a height of 100
units at peak, and the higher temperature curve has been normalized so that the areas under the two curves are equal. The pre-
dominant feature is a decrease in the tail region and an increase in
the low momentum region of the curve, as the temperature is increased. This effect has been found to be continuous between the
temperatures selected here.

The second pair of curves in Fig. 1 shows angular correlation
measurements for magnesium and an alloy of 9 at.-% indium in
magnesium. These curves are also normalized to equal areas. The
alloy curve is very similar to that for pure magnesium. An increase
of about 1% in the Fermi momentum of the alloy is evident, and
would arise from the increased number of free electrons.

The lines shown for these two pairs of curves are visual fits to

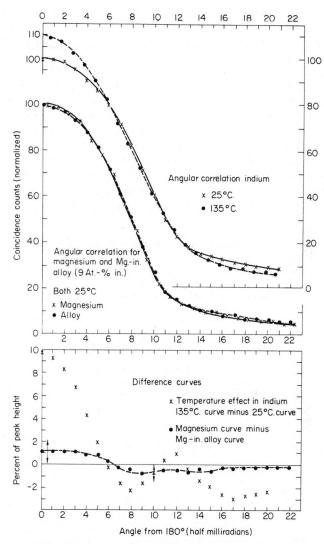

Fig. 1. Temperature dependence of angular correlation in indium, and attempted simulation of this behavior by alloying indium into magnesium.

the experimental points. They were used to obtain the two difference curves which are shown in the bottom section of Fig. 1. These
difference curves serve to emphasize the features of the angular
correlation curves which concern us. The high-temperature minus
room-temperature indium difference curve reflects the high-temperature decrease in the tail region and increase in the low momentum region. The magnesium minus magnesium alloy difference curve
reflects the similarity of those two angular correlation curves. The
line drawn for the one difference curve is only an indication of the
shape. The double-headed arrows represent the square root of the
sum of the squares of the statistical standard deviations of corresponding points in the original angular correlation curves from which
the difference curves were derived. Because the difference curves
were obtained using smoothed values, the scatter of the points is

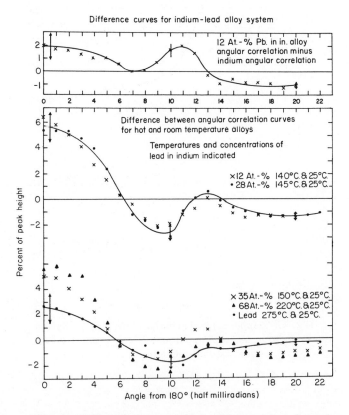

Fig. 2. Difference curves obtained from pairs of angular
correlation curves to illustrate some features of positron annihilation in the indium-lead alloy system.

considerably less than the statistical uncertainty indicated by these arrows. Errors other than those due to counting statistics may be present in the difference curves. Normalization and centering of the angular correlation curves are rather critical. Perhaps the double-headed arrows provide a general measure of confidence for the difference curves.

Figure 2 contains difference curves for the indium-lead alloy system. Normalization has been carried out as described for Fig. 1, and the double-headed arrows have the same meaning. Lines have been drawn through only three sets of points to avoid ambiguity.

The top section presents the angular correlation curve for an alloy of 12 at.-% lead in indium, minus the curve for pure indium. As in the previous figure for the dilute magnesium alloy, there is no large change in the alloy's angular correlation. The remainder of Fig. 2 is 5 temperature difference curves of various alloy concentrations at temperatures indicated. The temperature difference curve of pure indium in Fig. 1 is necessary to complete the set. It is apparent from these difference curves that the indium temperature effect is present in reduced proportion, even in an alloy containing 65 at.-% lead.

DISCUSSION

From the results presented in Figs. 1 and 2, pertaining to angular correlation in dilute alloys of magnesium and indium, it is evident that these alloys do not produce changes in the angular correlation similar to the anomalous temperature effects, even though the alloy proportions were selected to produce anisotropic variations of lattice parameters resembling in magnitude those due to thermal expansion in indium.

From the temperature difference curves in Fig. 2 it is evident that the indium-lead system shows temperature effects corresponding to those of pure indium, with the size of the effect almost proportional to the amount of indium present.

It seems certain that the temperature dependence of positron annihilation in indium is not due to thermal expansion of the lattice, and is not a characteristic of the lattice phase.

Mention might be made of a tentative explanation, which we have not yet had time to investigate, of the temperature effect. There is a possibility that in the metals indium, zinc, and cadmium, the equilibrium dislocation density is high enough at elevated temperatures to have an appreciable effect on the angular correlation curves. The effect on positron annihilation angular correlation of dislocations in plastically deformed metals and alloys has been noted recently.[6] Possibly the temperature effect is really a dislocation effect.

REFERENCES

1. MacKenzie, I. K., G. F. O. Langstroth, B. T. A. McKee, and C. G. White, *Canad. J. Phys.* **42**, 1837 (1964).
2. Childs, B. G., *Rev. Modern Phys.* **25**, 665 (1953).
3. Seymour, E. F. W., and G. A. Styles, *Phys. Letters* **10**, 269 (1964).
4. F. W. von Batchelder and R. F. Raeuchle, *Phys. Rev.* **105**, 59 (1957).
5. Hansen, M., "Constitution of Binary Alloys," p. 855. McGraw-Hill, New York, 1958.
6. Dekhtyar, I. Ya, D. A. Levina, and V. S. Mikhalenkov, *Soviet Phys. - Dokl.* **9**, 492 (1964).

Positron Annihilation in Holmium Single Crystals

A. R. Mackintosh, *R. W. Williams, and T. L. Loucks*

Iowa State University, Ames, Iowa

We have measured the angular correlation of the photons from two-quantum positron annihilation in two single crystal discs of holmium, whose faces are normal to the c-axis (0001) and b-axis (10$\bar{1}$0). The results at 300°K, in the paramagnetic phase, are shown in Fig. 1. The resolution of the apparatus is approximately 0.25 mrad, and the number of counts at the peak is over 100,000 for the c-axis is crystal and over 20,000 for the b-axis crystal, which is being studied further.

The large anisotropy in the results is in accord with the results of recent band calculations on hexagonal close-packed rare earth metals,[1] and the structure in the angular distribution for the c-axis crystal indicates that holmium can provide a sensitive test of the independent-particle theory of positron annihilation. Accordingly, we are calculating the angular distribution of the photons using energy bands, electron wavefunctions derived by the augmented plane-wave method,[2] and a numerically calculated positron wavefunction. These calculations yield energy bands and a Fermi surface very similar to those of gadolinium, and preliminary results on the angular distribution in the c direction manifest the rapid drop at low angles and the bulge at about 3 mrad which are observed in the experimental results. The complete calculation should reveal the extent to which the independent particle model must be modified to take account of the effect of the particle interactions on the angular distribution of the photons.

We have also studied the c-axis crystal at 60°K and the results, shown in Fig. 2, are significantly different from those at room temperature. The magnetic moments in holmium at this temperature form a spiral, and we, therefore, ascribe the change in the results to the modification of the electron distribution by magnetic superzone planes[3] normal to the c-axis. Further experiments on holmium and other rare earth metals are in progress.

*Alfred P. Sloane Research Fellow.

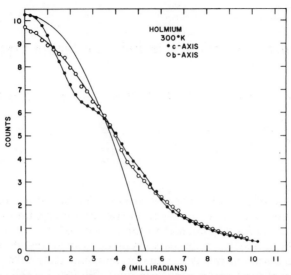

Fig. 1. Angular correlation distributions in holmium single crystals at 300°K, normalized to equal areas. Also shown is the parabola corresponding to three free electrons per atom in holmium, normalized to the peak of the c-axis curve.

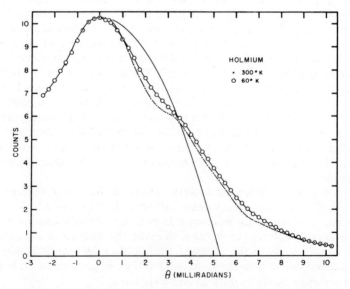

Fig. 2. Angular correlations in the paramagnetic and spiral phases in a c-axis holmium single crystal.

It is a pleasure to acknowledge the assistance of Dr. D. R. Gustafson, who constructed most of the apparatus used in this investigation.

REFERENCES

1. Dimmock, J. O. and A. J. Freeman, *Phys. Rev. Letters* **13**, 750 (1964); Loucks, T. L., (to be published).
2. Slater, J. C., *Phys. Rev.* **51**, 846 (1937).
3. Mackintosh, A. R., *Phys. Rev. Letters* **9**, 90 (1962).

Band Gap in Beryllium[*]

J. B. Shand[†] *and A. T. Stewart*

University of North Carolina, Chapel Hill, North Carolina

INTRODUCTION

The angular correlation of annihilation photons from positrons annihilating in metal single crystals depends on the Fermi surface and the energy discontinuities in k space at Brillouin zone boundaries. The Fermi surface for beryllium is known and we have obtained the angular correlation for several crystal directions. The purpose of this paper is to find the energy gap at one of the zone boundaries. Calculations have been made of one of the angular correlations, referring to the known Fermi surface, and assuming various values of the relevant energy gap, in order to find that value of the energy gap that gives the best fit to experiment.

THEORY

The wavefunction of a conduction electron in a metal may be written in a form which explicitly guarantees orthogonality to the core states[1]

$$\psi_k' = \Phi_k' - \sum_\alpha (\psi\alpha, \Phi_k') \psi_\alpha$$

where Φ_k' may be called the pseudo wavefunction and ψ_α, the core state.

The wavefunction can be described as consisting of a smooth, plane-wave-like part Φ_k', and the orthogonalization terms $\sum_\alpha (\psi_\alpha, \Phi_k') \psi_\alpha$, which give rapid oscillations in the vicinity of the cores. In positron annihilation with these electrons, the Φ_k' term gives the central portion of the angular correlation, which often looks like an inverted parabola; the core-state terms contribute to the broad, slowly-varying background. According to Cohen,[2] we may write Φ_k' as a Bloch function. The Bloch function may be expanded in plane waves:

[*]Supported in part by the National Science Foundation.
[†]*Present address:* University of Georgia, Athens, Georgia.

$$\Phi_{\mathbf{k}} = \sum_i a_i \, (\mathbf{k}') \, e^{i \, (\mathbf{k}' \, - \, \mathbf{Q}_i) \cdot \, \mathbf{r}}$$

where $\mathbf{Q}_i$ is a reciprocal lattice vector. Assume the positron wavefunction is constant. Following DeBenedetti[3] and Berko and Plaskett,[4] it can be shown that the wave vector distribution for annihilation with the Bloch function above is

$$P_{\mathbf{k}'} (\mathbf{k}) \approx \text{const.} \times \sum_i |a_i|^2 \; \delta_{\mathbf{k}\text{-}\mathbf{k}', \mathbf{Q}_i}$$

which means "spikes" at $\mathbf{k} = \mathbf{k}' - \mathbf{Q}_i$, weighted by the $|a_i|^2$. If this distribution is summed over all occupied $\mathbf{k}'$, the result is "clouds" of distribution with the shape of the Fermi sea, centered about each point in the reciprocal lattice, with different weights.

The positron annihilation apparatus is similar to one described elsewhere.[5] The coincident counting rate at some particular $\theta(k_z)$ is proportional to $N(k_z) = \iint P(\mathbf{k}) \, dk_x \, dk_y$.

In free-electron theory, this means the area of a slice through the Fermi sea. Here the situation is more complicated: $N(k_z)$ is the total probability of finding an electron in k space with z component of momentum k_z. The slice is taken through all of reciprocal space, and the contributions must be added up from each distribution cloud that is intersected. Here we will make the nearly-free-electron approximation, which restricts the integral in k space to the nearest zones.

THE EXPERIMENT

The angular correlation of annihilation photons from single crystal beryllium oriented with the c axis[†] as the z direction has been presented in previous papers.[6,7] New measurements have been made on a higher resolution machine, at $100°K$, in order to examine the fine structure more closely. The data are presented in Fig. 1. The background has been subtracted, and all the data have been plotted on one side of the line of symmetry, $k_z = 0$. The data do not differ significantly from the earlier low-resolution data.

[†]For hcp beryllium, the reciprocal lattice is generated by two reciprocal lattice vectors (RLD) $\mathbf{b}_1^*$ and $\mathbf{b}_2^*$ 60° apart in the basal plane and $\mathbf{b}_3^*$ along the c axis. Then (n_1, n_2, n_3) means the RLV $n_1 \mathbf{b}_1^* + n_2 \mathbf{b}_2^* + n_3 \mathbf{b}_3^*$. Here it is also used to describe the Brillouin zone boundary which bisects this RLV perpendicularly.

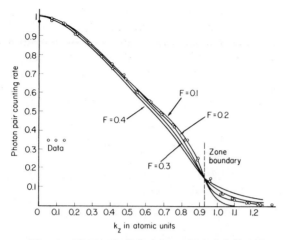

Fig. 1. Theoretical and experimental distribution of annihilation photons from positrons annihilating in single-crystal Be. The z direction is along the c axis. The counting rate is in arbitrary units.

TECHNIQUE OF CALCULATION

Figure 2 shows a cross section of the 2nd Brillouin zone for beryllium, with some of the nearby reciprocal lattice points. The Fermi sea just about fills this zone, overlapping slightly around the equator and leaving small hole regions in the corners. When a positron annihilation experiment is performed with the detectors set to detect coincident photons with total z component of wave vector equal to k_z, as shown in the figure, the counting rate is not proportional to the area of the slice through the Fermi sea. The Fermi sea is "depleted," the depletions going into distributions around the other reciprocal lattice points, so the slice must be taken through the other

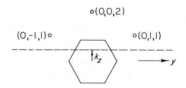

Fig. 2. Cross section of 2nd Brillouin zone of beryllium, showing nearby reciprocal lattice points and a slice through all of reciprocal space at k_z.

distributions, too. In the case of beryllium, it is assumed that the contributions from the distributions around $(0,-1,1)$ and $(0,1,1)$ reciprocal lattice points, balance the depletion of the Fermi sea when the slice is being taken parallel to the $(0,0,2)$ zone boundary. It is then possible to neglect all zone boundaries except $(0,0,\pm 2)$, in calculating the angular correlation.

The wavefunction for Φ_k is a Bloch function, and may be expanded in a Fourier series:

$$\Phi_k = e^{i\mathbf{k}\cdot\mathbf{r}}u_k(\mathbf{r}) = \sum a_i(\mathbf{k})e^{i(\mathbf{k}-\mathbf{Q}_i)\cdot\mathbf{r}}$$

For states near the $(0,0,2)$ zone boundary, Φ_k maybe written in the nearly-free-electron approximation as

$$\Phi_k = \omega^{-1/2}[a_0 e^{i\mathbf{k}\cdot\mathbf{r}} + a_1 e^{i(\mathbf{k}-(0,0,2))\cdot\mathbf{r}}]$$

where ω is the crystal volume. The coefficients a_0 and a_1 are functions of the energy gap at the $(0,0,2)$ boundary, as well as of $\mathbf{k}$. The $(0,0,1)$ zone face may be ignored since its energy gap is only a tiny spin-orbit splitting.

The equation obeyed by Φ_k is a modified Schrödinger equation, where the effective potential is a weak pseudopotential.[8] Substituting, Φ_k into this equation[9] we can show that the energy gap at the $(0,0.2)$ zone boundary is

$$2|V_{002}| = 2|\omega^{-1}\int_\omega V_{EFF}\, e^{-i(0,0,2)\cdot\mathbf{r}}d\mathbf{r}|.$$

Using the relation $|a_0|^2 + |a_1|^2 = 1$, we can obtain expressions for $|a_0|^2$ and $|a_1|^2$ as functions of k_z and of $4|V_{002}|/(0,0,2)\cdot(0,0,2)$, which we call F.

To predict the relative height of the angular correlation curve, when the crystal is oriented with the z direction, normal to the $(0,0,2)$ zone boundary, we do one of two things. For $k_z \leq k_{\text{zone boundary}}$ $(= 0.928$ atomic units) we find $|a_0(k_z; V_{002})|^2$ and multiply by the area of a slice through the Fermi sea at k_z, normal to the $(0,0,2)$ direction. To find the relative height for $k_z > k_{ZB}$ we find $|a_1(k_z - 1.856; V_{002})|^2$, and multiply by the area at $k_z - 1.856$.

A plot of Fermi surface cross sectional area was calculated from Watts[10] de Haas-van Alphen Fermi surface. This smooth curve was "smeared" by the method described above, using a certain value of $F = 4|V_{002}|/(0,0,2)\cdot(0,0,2)$. This procedure was repeated several times with different values of F. A further calculation was made to take account of resolution effects, including temperature, but no appreciable changes in the curves resulted.

RESULTS AND INTERPRETATION

The results are shown in Fig. 1. All curves have been normalized to 1 at $k_z = 0$, as has also the smooth curve (not shown) drawn through the data points. The data points are seen to lie somewhere between the curves for $F = 0.1$ and $F = 0.3$, definitely not near either. Thus we take $F = 0.2 \pm 0.1$, or $V_{002} = 0.17 \pm 0.08$, and the energy gap at the $(0,0,2)$ zone boundary, is $E = 2 | V_{002} | = 0.34 \pm 0.16$ Ry.

DISCUSSION OF ERRORS AND CORRECTIONS

The data deviate from all the theoretical curves in the immediate vicinity of the $(0,0,2)$ zone boundary. It was found that energy gaps at slant zone faces such as $(0,1,1)$ have appreciable effects on this region of the angular correlation. A correction term, assuming an energy gap of 0.5 Ry for the slant zone faces, can account for the discrepancy.

SUMMARY

By fitting theoretical curves to the data a value has been obtained for the energy gap at the $(0,0,2)$ zone boundary of beryllium, which is $E = 0.34 \pm 0.16$ Ry. This estimate may be compared to theoretical values from two full OPW band calculations. Herring and Hill[11] list an energy gap at this boundary equal to 0.493 Ry. Loucks and Cutler[12] present a diagram from which it is possible to extract their value of the energy gap, which seems to be 0.35 ± 0.01 Ry. Watts[13] has obtained a value of 0.22 Ry from our positron annihilation data, but has not given details. A simplified OPW calculation[14] has obtained a value of 0.34 Ry.

REFERENCES

1. Herring, C., *Phys. Rev.* **57**, 1169 (1940).
2. Cohen, M. H., "The Electron Theory of Simple Metals and Alloys," a talk presented to the Special Session on Concentrated Solid Solutions of the Cleveland meeting of the ASM on October 21, 1963.
3. DeBenedetti, S., C. E. Cowan, W. R. Konneker, and H. Primakoff, *Phys. Rev.* **77**, 205 (1950).
4. Berko, S., and J. S. Plaskett, *Phys. Rev.* **112**, 1877 (1958).
5. Stewart, A. T., *Canad. J. Phys.* **35**, 168 (1957). Stewart, A. T., and N. K. Pope, *Phys. Rev.* **120**, 2033 (1960).
6. Stewart, A. T., J. B. Shand, J. J. Donaghy, and J. H. Kusmiss, *Phys. Rev.* **128**, 118 (1962).
7. Berko, S., *Phys. Rev.* **128**, 2166 (1962).
8. Harrison, W. A., *Phys. Rev.* **126**, 497 (1962).

9. Mott, N. F., and H. Jones, "Properties of Metals and Alloys," pp. 59-63. Oxford Univ. Press (Clarendon), London and New York, 1936.
10. Watts, B. R., *Phys. Letters (Netherlands)* **3**, 284 (1963).
11. Herring, C., and A. G. Hill, *Phys. Rev.* **58**, 132 (1940).
12. Loucks, T. L., and P. H. Cutler, *Phys. Rev.* **133**, A819 (1964).
13. Watts, B. R., *Proc. Roy. Soc. (London)* **A282**, 521 (1964).
14. Shand, J. B., unpublished.

An Orthogonalized Plane Wave Calculation
of Positron Annihilation in Lithium

S. DeBenedetti and J. Melngailis

Carnegie Institute of Technology
Pittsburgh, Pennsylvania

Recent measurements by Stewart reveal anisotropies in the momentum distribution of positron annihilation radiation from Li single crystals. These results are often interpreted as simply connected to the shape of the Fermi surface. In reality, the angular correlation pattern is affected not only by the shape of the Fermi surface but also by the necessary departure of the electron wave functions from plane waves. Both these effects have been evaluated for Li, using an OPW (orthogonalized plane wave) method. The conduction electron wavefunction for a given wave number, k, was expanded as a sum over orthogonalized waves (orthogonal to the state of the atomic core) for 19 points, K, of the reciprocal lattice vector, and the expansion coefficients were determined as usual by requiring that the wavefunction be a solution of the Schröedinger equation in a suitable periodic potential. The energy $E(k)$ for the lowest band was also computed with the same method. In this manner both the Fermi surface, $E(k) = E_F$, and the wavefunctions were evaluated from the theory. The observed anisotropies cannot be explained if the Fermi surface shape alone is considered. When the effect of nonplane wave conduction electron wavefunction is included, the calculated anisotropies closely resemble the experimental ones. Finally, if we consider annihilation with core electrons, and introduce an estimate of electron positron attraction—using Kahana's enhancement factor—quantitative agreement between theory and experiment is obtained.

Effective Mass of the Positron in Metals

Chanchal K. Majumdar[†]

Carnegie Institute of Technology, Pittsburgh, Pennsylvania

ABSTRACT

An experiment to determine the effective mass of the positron in metals is discussed. It is well known that the Coulomb force of the positron causes major changes in the electronic motion. Nevertheless, in the angular correlation curve for the annihilation γ-rays there occurs a "break" precisely where one would expect it in the absence of the electron-positron interaction. The break is an image of the Fermi surface of normal metals. At finite temperature such a kink disappears, as the electrons and the positron are thermally excited. Since the electrons are degenerate, their contribution to the rise in the intensity of the coincident γ-rays at the angle corresponding to the Fermi momentum is much smaller than that due to the positron, which behaves essentially as a classical particle with an effective mass m^*. At low temperature the latter gives a characteristic $T^{1/2}$ behavior to the increase in intensity. The experiment to determine the effective mass consists in a study of the temperature dependence of the angular correlation curve and observation of the $T^{1/2}$ behavior. Several electronic effects, such as finite mean free path and thermal expansion of the solid, are considered, and shown to be small and to have different temperature dependence. Materials suitable for the experiment are examined. Finally, theoretical calculations of the effective mass from first principles are also discussed.

A knowledge of the effective mass of the positron in metals is very helpful in understanding the interactions it undergoes in them. This has recently been obtained in sodium by studying the temperature dependence of the angular correlation curve for the singlet state annihilation γ-rays.[1] The high value of $m^* = (1.9 \pm 0.3)m_e$ is another indication of the strong electron-positron correlation, as already revealed in the lifetime measurements.

[†] Supported in part by the National Science Foundation.

THEORY OF THE EFFECTIVE MASS EXPERIMENT[2]

Following the detailed calculation of Lee-Whiting,[3] we assume that the positrons become thermalized in the metal, and come to equilibrium at the same temperature as the metal itself. Since the annihilation rate is practically velocity independent, the final momentum distribution for low concentration of positrons can be taken to be a Maxwellian characteristic of the temperature T of the metal:

$$g(\mathbf{p}) = \frac{1}{(2\pi m * k_B T)^{3/2}} \exp[-\mathbf{p}^2/2m* k_B T] \tag{1}$$

This equation provides an operational definition of the effective mass $m*$.

It has been proved that for normal metals the angular correlation curve will manifest a sharp "break" at the Fermi momentum in the limit of zero temperature.[2] At nonzero temperature, when the diffuseness of the Fermi surface due to the spread of the electronic momenta is still negligible, the finite momentum of the positron will cause the intensity of the γ-rays to rise at the Fermi momentum above that expected at the zero temperature. The rate of rise will be shown to be proportional to $T^{1/2}$, and is quite different from that due to other effects, such as mean free path or thermal expansion which will be proportional to T or higher powers of T.

To calculate the probability that the γ-rays have a momentum K_z in the z direction, we fold the momentum distribution of the electrons, given by the usual Fermi function, with that of the positron (1), and then integrate over K_x, K_y

$$P(K_z) = \lambda \int_{-\infty}^{\infty} dK_x \, dK_y \int_{-\infty}^{\infty} d\mathbf{p} \, \frac{\exp[-(\mathbf{k} - \mathbf{p})^2/2m*k_B T]}{(2\pi m*k_B T)^{3/2}}$$

$$\times \frac{1}{\exp[(E_\mathbf{p} - \mu)/k_B T] + 1} \tag{2}$$

assuming spherical energy surfaces for the electron, $E_\mathbf{p} = \mathbf{p}^2/2m$, and the Fermi energy $\mu = k_F^2/2m$. λ is a constant depending on experimental factors like source intensity. We eliminate this by comparing the intensity at two point $K_z = 0$ and k_F. For a temperature $T \ll T_F$ (Fermi temperature), we get

$$\frac{P(k_F)}{P(0)} = \frac{1}{\pi^{1/2}} \left(\frac{m*T}{m_e T_F}\right)^{1/2} - \frac{1}{4} \frac{m*T}{m_e T_F} + \frac{1}{2\pi^{1/2}} \left(\frac{m*T}{m_e T_F}\right)^{3/2}$$

$$+ \frac{\pi^{3/2}}{24} \left(\frac{m_e}{m*}\right)^{1/2} \left(\frac{T}{T_F}\right)^{3/2} + \cdots \tag{3}$$

The effect of finite mean free path, 1, can be studied by calculating the momentum distribution of the free electron gas in the presence of static impurities. Thermal expansion is easily accounted for from a knowledge of the coefficient of thermal expansion. Since both these effects are *at most* proportional to T, they are found to be small. Including these, the final formula becomes

$$\frac{P(k_F)}{P(0)} = \frac{1}{\pi^{1/2}} \left(\frac{m^* T}{m_e T_F}\right)^{1/2} - \frac{m^* T}{4 m_e T_F} + \frac{\hbar u_F}{\hbar k_B T_F l}$$

$$+ \frac{m^* T}{T_F} \ln 2 - \int_0^T \alpha(T') \, dT' \tag{4}$$

u_F is the Fermi velocity and α the coefficient of linear thermal expansion. The positron effect is dominant from around the Debye temperature to almost the melting point. At extreme low temperatures the instrumental resolution masks everything. Since thermalization is assumed, it is *imperative* to check the $T^{1/2}$ dependence.

Choice of experimental material is guided by the following criteria: (1) high ratio of the Debye temperature and the melting point to the Fermi temperature; (2) good electrical conductivity; and (3) nearly spherical Fermi surface to avoid complications of thermal expansion. It is found that the three alkali metals Li, Na, K, and also Ca, fulfill the quantitative requirements very well, and it is hoped that experiments in all these will eventually be performed.

THEORETICAL CALCULATION OF THE EFFECTIVE MASS OF THE POSITRON IN SODIUM

The effective mass will differ from the bare value because of two effects: (1) the positron moves in a periodic potential ("band effective mass") and (2) it interacts with electrons and phonons in solids. We have made preliminary studies of the band mass in sodium and the change in mass due to interaction with electrons; the phonon part has not yet been investigated but is expected to be small.

One expects the band mass of the positron to be very close to one, in agreement with the estimate of Dresselhaus.[4] In calculating this, the electronic charge distribution is left unaltered by the positron. The solid as a whole is electrically neutral, and the potential experienced by the positron is repulsive in each unit cell. However, this repulsion is concentrated in a very small region in each unit cell, and the electrons screen out the nuclear repulsion almost completely over most of the volume. The potential seen by the positron may thus be regarded as weak and the positron wave function not very different from the plane wave. This is confirmed in a general way by the calculations we have made in the standard Wigner, Seitz, and Bardeen method.[5]

This calculation takes no account of the distortion of the electronic charge distribution due to the strong Coulomb force of the positron. This is particularly true of the conduction electron wavefunctions, since they will respond very easily to the positronic attraction, and will tend to screen it effectively. The core electrons will also be distorted, but not as much as the conduction electrons. An improvement on the above calculation would result if we allow for the distortion of the electronic charge in a self-consistent way in the presence of the attractive positron charge distribution. We have followed a slightly different approach. Since the band mass is so close to one, we shall ignore the lattice altogether. It is also known from the lifetime calculations that the major correlation, at least in simple metals like sodium, occurs with the conduction electrons, and we can leave out the core electrons. Thus the problem is reduced to positrons interacting with the Fermi distribution of electrons, and we can invoke the modern many-body techniques to compute the effective mass. Utilizing a Thomas-Fermi screened Coulomb interaction (appropriate for sodium) to compute the positron self-energy in the lowest (second) order, we have found the effective mass to be 1.3 times the bare mass, a significant change in the right direction, though still well below the observed value. If the present experimental value of Stewart turns out to be correct, a definite indication is given that strong coupling calculations would be necessary to get any reasonable agreement.

Since the methods of calculation are quite well known, only an outline will be given. Following Bardeen,[5] we attempt to compute the wavefunction correct to first order in the wave vector $\mathbf{k}$, which gives the energy correct to $0(\mathbf{k}^2)$, the linear term vanishing by symmetry. The coefficient of the $\mathbf{k}^2$ term gives the effective mass. The wavefunction of the positron is written as

$$\psi(\mathbf{x}) = e^{i\mathbf{k}\cdot\mathbf{x}}[u_0(r) + i\mathbf{k}\cdot\mathbf{x}v(r)] \tag{5}$$

Substituting

$$u_0(r) = \frac{R}{r}, \qquad v(r) = \frac{P}{r^2} - \frac{R}{r} \tag{6}$$

R satisfies an s-wave equation

$$\frac{d^2R}{dr^2} + \frac{2m}{\hbar^2}(E_0 - V(r))R = 0 \tag{7}$$

with the boundary condition $(dR/dr)_{r_s} = R(r_s)/r_s$, corresponding to $(du_0/dr)_{r_s} = 0$ on the Wigner-Seitz sphere. This determines the ground state energy E_0. P satisfies a p-wave equation with the same energy E_0,

$$\frac{d^2 P}{dr^2} - \frac{2}{r^2} P + \frac{2m}{\hbar^2} (E_0 - V(r)) P = 0 \tag{8}$$

There is one solution of this equation finite at the origin; its scale factor is fixed by the boundary condition that $v(r_s) = 0$ or $P(r_s) = r_s R(r_s)$. One can now integrate (7) and (8) numerically, and the total energy, correct to $0(k^2)$, is

$$E = E_0 + \frac{\hbar^2 k^2}{2m} \alpha \tag{9}$$

where α is given by

$$\alpha = r \left[\frac{r}{p} \frac{dP}{dr} - 1 \right]_{r_s} \tag{10}$$

and $r = (4\pi/3) r_s{}^3 [u_0(r_s)]^2$ is the ratio of the s-wave function at the radius to its mean value in the Wigner-Seitz sphere. The reciprocal of α gives the effective mass.

For the potential we have

$$V(r) = \frac{Ze^2}{r} - \sum_{i=1}^{Z} \int \frac{e^2}{|\mathbf{x} - \mathbf{y}|} |\phi_i(\mathbf{y})|^2 \, d\mathbf{y} \tag{11}$$

The ten wavefunctions of the inner core electrons were taken to be the atomic wavefunctions, as given by Kennard and Ramberg,[6] and the conduction electron wavefunction is that given by Callaway.[7] The differential equations were solved by Hartree's method[8] numerically. No great numerical accuracy was attempted since the effective mass was anticipated to be small. We obtained a ground state energy 0.07 atomic units and an effective mass 0.93 m_e with an accuracy of about 10%, confirming our anticipations.

As for the self-energy effects due to the electrons, we use the standard many body techniques. The second order self-energy, calculated to the order $\mathbf{k}^2$, which is the leading term as $k \to 0$, comes out to be

$$\begin{aligned}
E^{(2)}(k) = \text{const} &- \frac{k^2}{2m} \left[\frac{32\alpha^2 r_s{}^2}{3\pi^2 k_s{}^2 (4 + k_s{}^2)} + \frac{4\alpha^2 r_s{}^2}{3\pi^2} \right. \\
&\times \int_0^2 \frac{q^2 \, dq}{(q^2 + k_s{}^2)^2} \left(\frac{1}{q} \ln(1 + q) + \frac{2}{1 + q} \right) \\
&\left. + \frac{4\alpha^2 r_s{}^2}{3\pi^2} \int_2^\infty \frac{q \, dq}{(q^2 + k_s{}^2)^2} \left(\ln \frac{q + 1}{q - 1} - \frac{4q}{q^2 - 1} \right) \right]
\end{aligned} \tag{12}$$

The irrelevant constant causes a shift of the chemical potential; the parameter r_s is defined by the number density n of electrons in metals (a_0 is the Bohr radius)

$$n = \frac{1}{\frac{4\pi}{3} a_0^3 r_s^3} \tag{13}$$

and the screening parameter k_s is given by

$$k_s = 0.82 \, r_s^{1/2} \tag{14}$$

Numerical quadrature gives $m^* \approx 1.3 \, m_e$. The fact that the band mass is negligibly different from one suggests that the effective mass is essentially determined by r_s as in (12). It might well be that the variation of the effective mass as a function of r_s will "parallel" that of the decay rate which also depends essentially on r_s.

Greater numerical accuracy in the above calculations and their extension to strong coupling limits are now being planned.

REFERENCES

1. Stewart, A. T., and J. B. Shand, *Bull. Am. Phys. Soc.* Ser. II, **10**, 21 (1965).
2. Majumdar, C. K., *Phys. Rev.* (to be published); Thesis, Univ. of California, La Jolla, 1965.
3. Lee-Whiting, G. E., *Phys. Rev.* **97**, 1557 (1955).
4. Dresselhaus, G., *J. Phys. Chem. Solids* **1**, 14 (1956).
5. Wigner, E. P., and F. Seitz, *Phys. Rev.* **43**, 804 (1933); J. Bardeen, *J. Chem. Phys.* **6**, 367 (1938).
6. Kennard, E., and E. Ramberg, *Phys. Rev.* **46**, 1034 (1934).
7. Callaway, J., *Phys. Rev.* **123**, 1255 (1961).
8. Hartree, D. R., "The Calculation of Atomic Structures." Wiley, London and New York, 1957.

Positron Mean Lives in Liquid and Solid Mercury*

John D. McGervey

Western Reserve University, Cleveland, Ohio

Angular correlation measurements of annihilation radiation from liquid and solid mercury have shown that the relative size of the "tail" in the distribution is much greater in the solid than in the liquid.[1] The results were interpreted as giving the fraction of positrons annihilating with core electrons in each phase, on the assumption that the tails consist entirely of core annihilations. But it is clear from calculations presented at this conference that some portion of the tails is caused by annihilation of valence electrons. The mean life measurement presented in this paper should help to resolve the problem.

The mean lives were measured with a time to amplitude converter whose resolution (full width at half maximum) is 0.35 nsec for the Co^{60} gamma rays. The first source used was $Na^{22}Cl$, deposited inside a stainless steel envelope which was sealed and mounted in a column of mercury. Because a fairly large tail in the lifetime distribution cast some doubt on the accuracy of the first results, another source was prepared. By electrolysis of a salt solution, the Na^{22} (about 2 μCi) was mixed directly with 2 cm^3 of mercury, forming a sodium amalgam. Since the total sodium concentration in this amalgam is only about 0.02 at.-%, the positron lifetime in the amalgam should not be perceptibly different from that in pure mercury. The lifetime distributions obtained with this source had a tail intensity of only 1-2%, so that subtraction of the tail changes the logarithmic slope of the main curve by at most 3%.

The mercury container was a stainless steel tube, $^1/_4$ in. in diameter. This tube projected from the bottom of a stainless-steel can which held the coolant (liquid nitrogen or a dry ice-alcohol mixture). The entire assembly was surrounded with styrofoam.

Typical lifetime distributions are shown in Fig. 1. Both solid and liquid were run several times, for 1000 or more minutes each time, with consistent results. In the figure, channels containing fewer than 50 counts were grouped together in order to facilitate fitting of the

*This work was supported in part by the U.S. Atomic Energy Commission.

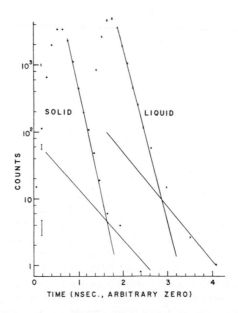

Fig. 1. Positron lifetime distributions in liquid mercury (25° C) and solid mercury (−190° C).

tail. As indicated above, the method of determining the tail is not
critical.

The mean lives in the main component are 1.65×10^{-10} sec in
the liquid and 1.38×10^{-10} sec in the solid, with an error of about
5% in each case. The major source of error is slight nonlinearity
in the time to amplitude conversion, which produces some uncertain-
ity in the calibration. This of course does not greatly affect the accuracy in the ratio of the mean lives. The calibration was checked
by measurement of the mean life in aluminum; the result, 1.9×10^{-10}
sec, is in agreement with the result of Bell and Jørgensen.[2]

The decay constant $\lambda = 1/\tau$ is therefore 6.1 nsec^{-1} in the liquid
and 7.2 nsec^{-1} in the solid. If one uses the fractions reported by
Gustafson et al.[1] to separate these into core- and valence-electron
annihilations, one obtains the following partial decay constants λ_c
and λ_v in nsec^{-1}:

	Liquid	Solid
λ_c (core)	3.7	5.4
λ_v (valence)	2.4	1.8

One should expect λ_c to be greater in the solid than in the liquid, for in the disordered structure of the liquid it is easier for the positron to avoid the positively charged cores. In the liquid, the positron wavefunction is large between widely spaced cores and small between cores which are close together, and the net overlap with the core wavefunctions is thus smaller than in the solid structure.

It is significant that both values of λ_v listed above are much smaller than that given by the calculation of Kahana.[3] Kahana's result gives $\lambda = 3.8$ nsec^{-1} for the annihilation rate of a positron in a free-electron gas whose density equals the valence electron density in mercury. Of course, this value is not directly applicable to mercury, because the effect of zone boundaries on Kahana's enhancement factor is not known. The discrepancy does give another indication, however, that the fraction of annihilations with valence electrons has been greatly underestimated.

Figure 2 illustrates how great such an underestimate can be. The angular distribution shown there was obtained in our laboratory; it fits

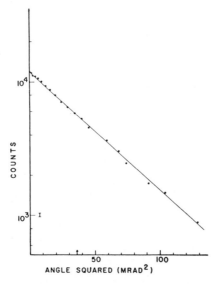

Fig. 2. Angular correlation of annihilation radiation from positrons in molybdenum (polycrystalline). The logarithm of the number of counts is plotted vs. the square of the angle to illustrate the fit to a Gaussian. The arrow indicates the angle corresponding to the Fermi energy.

a Gaussian rather well at all angles. The technique used in Reference 1 would therefore indicate that the fraction of annihilations with valence electrons is zero! Clearly, in cases such as this, it is necessary to make careful theoretical calculations of the shape of the distributions from core and valence electrons before one can separate the contribution of one from the other.

REFERENCES

1. Gustafson, D. R., A. R. Mackintosh, and D. J. Zaffarano, *Phys. Rev.* **130**, 1455 (1963).
2. Bell, R. E., and M. H. Jørgensen, *Canad. J. Phys.* **38**, 652 (1960).
3. Kahana, S., *Phys. Rev.* **129**, 1622 (1963).

Positron Annihilation in Liquid Mercury and Bismuth

R. N. West and N. E. Cusack

University of East Anglia, Norwich, England

The study of the angular correlation of the photons from the annihilation of positrons in solid metals has been found to show some general features of the electron momentum distributions in those metals.

The purpose of our experiments was to investigate the momentum distributions in liquid metals by comparing the angular distributions for solid and liquid in each case. In particular, it was desired to investigate the "smearing" of the Fermi Cutoff described by other workers.[1,2]

The apparatus was the normal parallel slit system, the slits subtending half a milliradian in the vertical or z-direction. The samples were contained in an open tray with their free surface presented to the source so as to keep background counts to a minimum. As the source was likely to be subjected to high temperatures, attack by liquid metals, and repeated evacuation, considerable attention was paid to the selection of a suitable material. The source used consisted of an active glaze containing 5 mc of Na^{22} fused to the face of a ceramic disc. This source can be subjected to temperatures up to 900°C, and is physically strong. The counting equipment is a simple fast coincidence system using Avalanche transistors. Although the system has good stability, as an added precaution against drifts in the electronics, the moving counter was cycled over its 30 mrad range every twelve hours.

It was decided to repeat the work of Gustafson, Mackintosh, and Zaffarano[1] on solid and liquid mercury to test the apparatus. The results for both solid and liquid, corrected for resolution and for the finite lengths of the slits, are shown in Fig. 1. The presentation and analysis of the results is identical to that used by the previously mentioned experimenters.[1] The distributions have been folded about their centroids, and normalized so that the coincidences at large angles, for both solid and liquid, lie on the same Gaussian function. The area under this Gaussian, the shape of which should not change appreciably on melting, is assumed to be due to core annihilations.

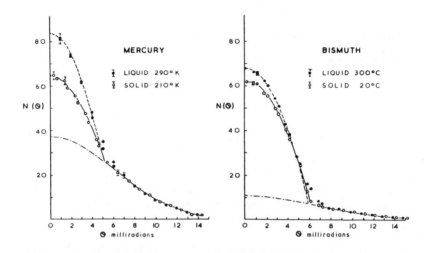

Fig. 1. The angular distributions of the annihilation photons in mercury and bismuth. The experimental results have been folded about the centroids of the distributions.

The remaining portions of each curve are then assumed to be due to annihilations with the conduction electrons. If the areas under these curves are truly proportional to the relative number of annihilations with each class of electron, it is seen that there is enhancement of the conduction electron annihilations in the liquid. In the solid the area of the Gaussian is 75% of the total distribution. In the liquid it is reduced to 65%.

The parts of the distributions assumed due to conduction electrons have been fitted with least squares parabolas to the nine central points. These are shown, with the Gaussian as abscissa, in Fig. 2. The parabola for the solid cuts off at an angle $\theta_F = 5.27 \pm 0.1$ mrad compared to one calculated on the basis of the free-electron theory with $\theta_F = 5.26$. The liquid data, however, deviate significantly from a parabola at large angles. This has been interpreted as a blurring of the Fermi surface, attributable to scattering by the disordered structure. At present we have no better explanation than this. Following Gustafson et al., we assume that the probability of occupancy of a state k is given by

$$P(k) = A \left\{ \exp[\,(k^2/k_f{}^2 - 1)/\Delta\,] + 1 \right\}^{-1}$$

where Δ is a parameter which described the blurring of the Fermi surface. The angular distribution for this function can be shown to be

$$N(\theta) = (1 - \theta^2/\theta_F^2) + \Delta \ln \{\exp[(\theta^2/\theta_F^2 - 1)/\Delta] + 1\} \quad (1)$$

As shown in Fig. 2, a good fit to the data is obtained if Δ is taken as 0.20, and $\theta_F = 5.08$ mrad. The free-electron value is 5.19 mrad. The difference between these values is of the same order as the possible error, and is probably not significant. If the uncertainty in k is taken as the difference between the values for which $P(k)$ is $1/6$ and $5/6$, respectively, δk is found to be approximately 20% of k_F. This implies a mean free path of about 7 Å.

These results for mercury are in agreement with those reported by Gustafson et al.,[1] the accuracy of the two experiments being similar.

The corrected distributions for liquid and polycrystalline bismuth are also shown in Fig. 1. Exactly the same analysis has been carried out on these results. In the solid, the area under the Gaussian is 29% of the whole distribution. In the liquid it is 28%. This effect, although much smaller than that in mercury, is nevertheless believed to be significant. Although the core contribution for bismuth is considerably smaller than that for mercury, the shapes are indistinguishable. This is probably due to the similarity of the cores of the two metals.

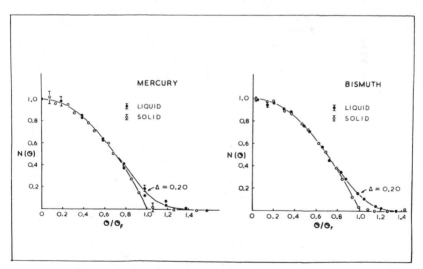

Fig. 2. The angular distributions of photons attributed to annihilation with the valence electrons, normalized to the value at $\theta = 0$. The curves are plots of Eq. (1), using the experimental values of θ_F quoted in the text. For the solid data, $\Delta = 0$ in both materials.

The parabolic parts of the curves are shown in Fig. 2. As before, the data for the solid agree with the free-electron parabola, the value of θ_F obtained (6.19 mrad) being within 1% of the calculated value. For the liquid, θ_F is found to be 6.00 mrad, compared to a calculated 6.27 mrad. The smearing observed is of the same order as in liquid mercury, giving a mean free path of about 6 Å. As bismuth contracts on melting, θ_F would be expected to increase on melting, whereas it appears to be 4% smaller. A similar effect has been observed in gallium.[3]

It is interesting to enquire whether this is a real effect or whether it is due to the method of analysis of the results. We are unable to think of any plausible core distribution that when used instead of a Gaussian would remove the effect. It might be that the high-momentum components are not due to core electrons, but to valence electrons. If we take the extreme case in which the whole distribution is due to valence electrons, and fit the smeared parabola formula, this would still not bring θ_F any nearer the free-electron value. The similarity of the Gaussians in mercury and bismuth gives further support to the belief that these are indeed a good approximation to the core annihilation functions. If this is so, an alloy of these two metals should give a core distribution approximating to the same Gaussian. If a significant proportion of the Gaussian in the pure metals were due to high momentum components from the valence electrons, it would be surprising if the shape were retained in the alloy.

The distribution curve for a liquid alloy containing two atomic parts of mercury to one of bismuth has been measured. These proportions were chosen so as to give three valence electrons per atom. The experimentally determined θ_F for the alloy is found to be 5.56 mrad. This is exactly equal to a value of θ_F calculated for three free electrons per atom. It is interesting to note that although the free electron value is not found in liquid bismuth, it appears to be valid in the alloy.

The high momentum parts of the distribution do indeed lie on the same Gaussian as the pure metals. Nevertheless, we believe that the distinction between core and valence electron contributions to annihilation will never be made clear in the absence of more theoretical calculations. Systematic calculations of core annihilation distributions are at present being undertaken by Borland at the National Physical Laboratory.

REFERENCES

1. Gustafson, D. R., A. R. Mackintosh, and D. J. Zaffarano. *Phys. Rev.* **130**, 1455 (1963).
2. Stewart, A. T., J. H. Kusmiss, and R. H. March, *Phys. Rev.* **132**, 495 (1963).
3. Gustafson, D. R., and A. R. Mackintosh. *Phys. Letters* **5**, 234 (1963).

Momentum Distribution of Photons from Positrons Annihilating in Lithium-Ammonia Solutions*

P. G. Varlashkin and A. T. Stewart

University of North Carolina, Chapel Hill, North Carolina

INTRODUCTION

Alkali metals dissolve readily in liquid ammonia forming solutions with metallic characteristics attributable to the solvated electrons, i.e, the electrons donated to the solution by the metal atoms. Unlike a metal, however, the electron density of a metal-ammonia solution may be varied over a wide range by simply changing the concentration of the solute metal. Further, the observed electrical and thermal conductivities imply that the electrons are almost as free as conduction electrons in a metal.

We have undertaken to investigate the momentum distribution of photons from positrons annihilating in solutions of varying concentration. If the electrons are free at the time of annihilation we would expect to see a narrow central parabolic distribution superimposed upon a background characteristic of positrons annihilating in ammonia. On the other hand, the possibility of forming positronium in a dilute electron gas has been pointed out.[1]

EXPERIMENTAL

Lithium-ammonia solutions were formed in a stainless steel cell by condensing ammonia in on top of a small piece of lithium. The solution concentration was determined by weighing the small piece of special high purity lithium in a dry argon atmosphere and transferring it to the stainless steel cup in argon. After evacuation of the argon, a measured amount of doubly distilled sodium dried ammonia was distilled into the cup. The temperature of the cup ($-57°C$) was controlled by being thermally connected to a dry-ice and acetone bath by a large copper bar.

*Work supported in part by the National Science Foundation and the Advanced Research Projects Agency.

313

Metal-ammonia solutions are unstable in the presence of trace contaminants. Solution decay proceeds via the reaction $M + NH_3 \rightarrow MNH_2 + \frac{1}{2} H_2$. Several metals are known or suspected to be catalysts for the decomposition reaction. Although lithium-ammonia solutions are the most stable of the alkali metal-ammonia solutions, metal-ammonia experiments are customarily conducted in glassware, while the experiments reported herein had to be performed with a stainless steel cell. Consequently, solution vapor pressure was monitored during each experiment. The constancy of the solution vapor pressure indicated no detectable hydrogen evolution over a period of $2\frac{1}{2}$ days. This is taken to imply that there is no significant solution decomposition during the course of a data run. The total data acquisition time for each of the solutions reported herein was about 12 hr. The photon angular distribution was measured once every 4 hr. Each individual 4-hr scan was automatically plotted. In no case have we detected any difference between the angular distribution obtained in the first scan and any of the succeeding scans.

A source of positrons, Cu^{64}, was mounted about $\frac{1}{2}$ in. above the surface of the solutions. The solution chamber was placed between the pole pieces of a magnet which could be used to focus the positrons on the specimen. The angular resolution of the apparatus was about 0.3 mad, full-width at half maximum.

RESULTS AND DISCUSSION

The data from positron annihilation in pure liquid ammonia are shown in Fig. 1. They resemble the usual broad momentum distribution characteristic of non-metals and show some evidence of a low intensity narrow peak often associated with positronium formation. Liquid ammonia was examined both in the presence and absence of a magnetic field. Although the effect is slight, the distribution is noticeably more sharply peaked in the presence of a magnetic field. This is to be expected if the magnetic field converts appreciable amounts of orthopositronium into parapositronium.

Similar magnetic field dependency measurements were made on a concentrated lithium-ammonia solution. In the case of the solution, the magnetic field caused no visible effect.

The momentum distribution from positron annihilations in lithium-ammonia solutions is much more narrow than that of pure liquid ammonia (See Fig. 2). The full width at half maximum is about 3 mrad compared with about 7 mrad for pure ammonia. The data of Fig. 2 were taken in a 9.3 kG magnetic field.

The addition of lithium to ammonia produces at least two striking effects. First, the pure ammonia and the solution curves are completely different in shape. Over no region do the curves have the same slope, and consequently, no change in scale factor will cause

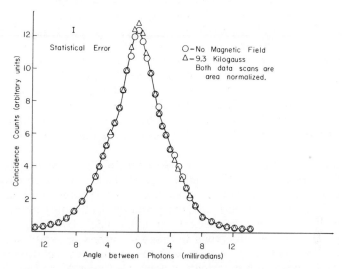

Fig. 1. Angular correlation of photons from positrons annihilating in liquid ammonia with and without a magnetic field.

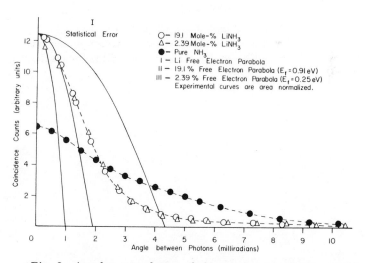

Fig. 2. Angular correlation of photons from positrons annihilating in liquid ammonia and in lithium-ammonia solutions. Also shown are the angular distributions one would expect for positrons annihilating with free electrons in a gas of the same electron concentrations as existed in the solutions.

a portion of the curves to be coincident. Even at large angles (high momentum) the solution- and pure-ammonia curves have different rates of change of slope, and consequently, no curve fitting and accompanying extrapolation to determine core contribution may be performed. The data for the metallic solutions therefore appear to contain no component corresponding to annihilations in pure ammonia. Second, there is no apparent concentration dependence. The two concentrations illustrated differ by a factor of eight, and the resultant free electron Fermi energies by almost a factor of four. The densities used in computing Fermi energy are those reported by Jolly.[2]

As can be seen from the data presented in Fig. 2, even for concentrations as low as 2.39% and as high as 19.1%, the momentum distribution shows no sign of dependence upon free electron density. The previously measured transport properties of metal-ammonia solutions are all strongly concentration dependent over this range. The presence of free electrons in these solutions is established almost beyond question. The failure of the angular correlation data to reveal a momentum distribution dependent upon Fermi energy is puzzling, and must mean that the positron forms some sort of bound state which is independent of the solution concentration over the reported range.

REFERENCES

1. Held, A., and S. Kahana, *Can. J. Phys.* **42**, 1908-13 (1964).
2. Jolly, W. L., Metal-ammonia solutions, in "Progress in Inorganic Chemistry" (F. A. Cotton, ed.), Vol. 1, p. 244. Wiley (Interscience), London and New York, 1959.

Positron Lifetimes in Metal - Ammonia Solutions[*]

W. E. Millett, L. H. Dieterman,† and J. C. Thompson

The University of Texas, Austin, Texas

Lifetime measurements on liquid lithium-ammonia solutions at $-65°C$ as a function of lithium concentration are reported here. Before discussing these results we will first consider some of the physical characteristics of such solutions and attempt to arrive at a mechanism for positron decay in such solutions.

Ammonia has a tetrahedral structure and therefore has a permanent electric dipole moment. The nitrogen-hydrogen bond in NH_3 is of sufficient strength that it is not ruptured when electrons or singly charged ions are present in the liquid. Furthermore, the dipole moment is large enough to ionize a neutral lithium atom, but obviously not large enough to bind another ammonia molecule against thermal agitation. If neutral lithium is added to pure liquid ammonia the singly charged lithium ions and the electrons, formed by ionization, each act as strong centers of long-range attraction for the ammonia molecules. The number of NH_3 molecules clustered around each charge center is determined by the magnitude of the electric moment, the temperature of the liquid and the type of packing. If μ_0 is the electric dipole moment and $\mathbf{E}$ is the electric field at the dipole, the potential energy of the dipole is $-\mu_0 \cdot \mathbf{E}$. Let us assume that all of the charge of the ammonia molecule is contained within its radius $a_0 = 1.5$ Å. For convenience, assume that the molecules of the cluster have a simple cubic structure with one lattice point containing either an electron or a positive ion. Now consider the cluster to contain only those molecules whose centers lie within a sphere of radius r_0. The magnitude of the average radial component of the electric field at a distance $r_0 + 2a_0$ from the charge center will be $\bar{E}_r = e/(r_0 + 2a_0)^2$ and the average potential energy of an ammonia molecule at this distance from the center of the cluster will be $-\mu_0 e/(r_0 + 2a_0)^2$. Let us say that if $\mu_0 e/(r_0 + 2a_0)^2 < \frac{3}{2} kT$, this outermost ammonia will not

[*]Research assisted by the Office of Naval Research, the National Science Foundation and the R. A. Welch Foundation.

†NASA Trainee.

be bound. For the cubic lattice assume $r_0 = 2na_0$, where n is an integer greater than unity, so $n = 4$ at $T = 208°K$. The approximate number of ammonia molecules n_0 in such a cluster is obtained from

$$f \frac{4\pi}{3} [(2n + 1)a_0]^3 = (n_0 + 1) \frac{4\pi}{3} a_0{}^3$$

where f is the packing fraction for the crystalline structure assumed. For the calculation here $n_0 = 360$. Thus a single neutral lithium added to pure liquid ammonia will ionize and form a positive and negative macroion, which involve a total of about 720 ammonia molecules. These two macroions will then become bound to form a macromolecule having a binding energy of about $e^2/[2(2n + 1)a_0] = 0.11$ eV, and an electric dipole moment

$$\mu = 2(2n + 1)a_0 \, e = 130 \times 10^{-18} \text{ scon. cm.} = 100 \, \mu_0$$

The binding energy of antiparallel macromolecules is about four times the binding of antiparallel ammonia molecules, but this is still presumably less than $^3/_2 kT$ at $T = 208°K$. The lithium concentration at which only macromolecules are present (they all have n layers of ammonia molecules) will be designated by Cn. At concentrations greater than C_n, ionization of lithium will continue to take place if

$$\frac{\alpha \mu^2}{(a + (2n + 1)a_0)^3} \geq \frac{\alpha \mu_0{}^2}{(a + a_0)^3}$$

which is satisfied for the cases $n = 4,3,2,1$. At concentrations just above C_n (where $4 \geq n \geq 2$), macroions of two, and essentially only two different sizes, will be present in the solution, $r_0 = 2na_0$ and $r_0 = 2(n - 1)a_0$. Minimum energy conditions restrict the existence of partially filled shells and restrict the macromolecules to those formed of macroions of the same size. At concentrations above C_1 the configurations that are stable must be sought with more care. Since the data here are not detailed in this concentration range, this part of the problem will not be discussed further. The critical concentrations of interest here are

$$C_4 = 1 \text{ Li}/750 \text{ NH}_3 = 0.13\% \text{ mole fraction}$$

$$C_3 = 1 \text{ Li}/350 \text{ NH}_3 = 0.29\% \text{ mole fraction}$$

$$C_2 = 1 \text{ Li}/128 \text{ NH}_3 = 0.78\% \text{ mole fraction}$$

$$C_1 = 1 \text{ Li}/26 \text{ NH}_3 = 3.8\% \text{ mole fraction}$$

The discussion given above may come as a shock to those familiar with the literature of metal ammonia solutions. There are several divergent theories and a treatment based on Coulomb's law for the interaction of electric charges seemed to be not out of place.

A positron in pure liquid ammonia will either annihilate directly or form a macroion. If the structure of the macroion is simple cubic, as assumed before, the positron will be bound in a box about 3 Å across and surrounded by six nearest ammonia molecules. The end of the ammonia molecule having the hydrogen atoms will be furthest from the positron. Therefore, in this bound state, the positron annihilates essentially only with one of the six (sp^3) hybridized orbital electrons of the nitrogen. Those positrons that annihilate directly will also most likely annihilate with the (sp^3) hybridized orbitals of nitrogen because of the strong dipole-charge interaction. The long lifetime is associated with the long lifetime in the bound state.

When lithium is added, the macromolecules are attracted to the positron macroion. This results in a greater overlap of the electron and bound positron wavefunctions, and thus an increased annihilation rate. As the lithium concentration is increased, the external pressure on the positron macroion will increase, and there is the possibility that the crystalline structure of the macroion will change abruptly, giving rise to an abrupt change in the annihilation rate. Another, and probably more significant, factor is the one due to the decrease in size of the macroions with concentration. This, however, should not give rise to any abrupt changes.

The figure is a plot of the probability of annihilation per unit time for the long component as a function of lithium concentration up to

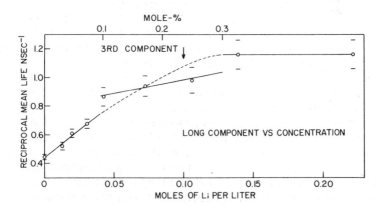

Fig. 1. A plot of the annihilation rate of the long component vs concentration in moles of lithium per liter and mole per cent of lithium. The errors are standard deviation. The arrow is approximately at the concentration at which a third component in the decay scheme appears.

TABLE I
Annihilation Rates for the Long Component
and Their Fractions for the Concentrations[a]

Mole-%	$1/\tau_2$ Nsec^{-1}	f_2 in %
0	0.45	28
0.03	0.52	25
0.047	0.61	24
0.072	0.67	25
0.10	0.87	21
0.17	0.94	15
0.25	0.98	14
0.33	1.16	14
0.53	1.16	14
0.73	1.12	14
1.22	1.07	13
3.0	1.08	13
9.5	1.01	14

[a]The bars to the left, between concentrations, indicate the location of the critical concentrations C_4, C_3, C_2, and C_1.

0.53 mole-%, i.e., up to $C_2 > C > C_3$. The error bars are generous since they represent standard deviation rather than probable error. The question of whether the breaks at about 0.1 and 0.3 mole-%
are real is being reinvestigated at the present time. If the breaks
are taken to be real and the graph as indicated by the solid lines, the
ratio of annihilation rates at the first break is 1.18 if it is at 0.1
mole-% or 1.25 at 0.072 mole-%, and for the second break it is 1.09
at 0.33 mole-% and 1.17 at 0.25 mole-%. The ratio of number of
nearest neighbors for body-centered cubic to simple cubic is 1.33
and for face-centered to body-centered is 1.5. It will be interesting
to know if these breaks are indeed real.

The table shows the annihilation rates for the long component and
the fraction of the long component for the lithium concentrations. The
bars between and to the left of the concentrations indicate the positions of C_4, C_3, C_2, and C_1. The fraction decreases with C up to C_4
and then stays about constant. This is in agreement with the model
proposed, since the time for formation of a positron macroion is
longer for $C > C_1$, and thus the chance for direct annihilation to
take place is greater. This of course results from the fact that the
NH_3 molecules have much greater mobility than the macromolecules.

Use of Zeeman Splitting in Positronium as a Means of Polarization Analysis in an Experiment on the g Factor of the Free Positron*

A. Rich and H. R. Crane

The University of Michigan, Ann Arbor, Michigan

ABSTRACT

The highly efficient method of positron polarization analysis, based on Zeeman splitting in positronium, is being used in a measurement of the positron g factor. A brief description of the experiment, and the derivation of a general equation which describes the polarization detector, are presented. It is shown that in some experimental situations, approximations to the general equation that have been used in the past can lead to erroneous values of positron polarization.

1. INTRODUCTION

Recently, several groups have attempted to measure the polarization ($\mathbf{P}$) of positrons emitted from radioactive sources and in μ decay. The technique used in all cases has been to form positronium in a magnetic field ($\mathbf{B}$), and then measure the relative intensity difference between delayed annihilation γ's ($2R$) for field up and field down.

Our group at the University of Michigan is using this method of polarization analysis (subsequently called the $\mathbf{P} \cdot \mathbf{B}$ effect) in an attempt to measure the g factor anomaly of the free positron. A brief account of the experiment will be found in Section 2. During the course of our work we calculated R in its most general form so that we might maximize it with respect to all its parameters. Since a general formula for R has not yet appeared in the literature, we have included its derivation in Section 3.2. Evaluation of the result showed that approximations to the general formula that were used

*This work was supported by the United States Atomic Energy Commission.

in the past can lead to erroneous values of positron polarization in certain experiments. A discussion of this point, as well as some preliminary results of the g factor experiment, are included in the last section.

2. THE POSITRON g FACTOR EXPERIMENT

The method we are using to measure the positron[1] g factor may be described as follows: A 0.1 μsec, 200 keV ($P = v/c = 0.7$) bunch of positrons is selected from the continuous emission of a 600 mCi Co^{58} source. These are trapped in a betatron-shaped magnetic field (B_t = 222 gauss), and held for a predetermined length of time (up to 40 μsec). The bunch is then ejected from the trap, extracted from the solenoid, and focused so as to enter a plastic scintillator placed in a magnetic field (**B**) of 13 kG. This sequence is repeated at 32 kc/sec. The fraction of the bunch which annihilates into γ rays in any given time interval after entry depends upon **P · B** (Section 3.2). Thus a plot of delayed coincidence beam rate/positron beam rate vs trapping time is a cosine curve whose angular frequency is the difference between the orbital angular frequency (ω_c) and the spin precession angular frequency (ω_s). This is related to the g factor through the equation[2]

$$a = \frac{m_0 c}{e B_t} \omega_D \qquad (1)$$

where $a = (g/2 - 1) = g$ factor anomaly; $\omega_D = \omega_s - \omega_c = 2\pi$ times the difference frequency; and m_0, c, e have the usual meaning. Thus the anomaly "a" is measured directly. Corrections to Eq. (1) of order 0.07% for the parameters of the present experiment, have been obtained by Ford and Hirt.[3] They will be applied when necessary.

It may be noted here that Mott scattering could in principle be used as a polarization analyzer. Unfortunately, its low detection efficiency (10^{-5}), coupled with the low intensity which can be obtained from a radioactive source, makes its use impractical in this experiment. For instance, only 1,000 trapped positrons per second can be obtained from a 100 mCi source after beam reductions due to (i) angle and energy collimation, and (ii) consideration of the limited time the trap is open, as compared to its dead time.

3. THE POLARIZATION DETECTOR

3.1 Ground State Ps in a Magnetic Field

The eigenvalues and eigenstates of the Hamiltonian for n = 1 Ps in a static magnetic field may be most easily found by diagonalizing the magnetic perturbation $(\mu_0[\boldsymbol{\sigma}_P - \boldsymbol{\sigma}_e] \cdot \mathbf{B})$ in the singlet triplet representation. The results are shown in Table I, which includes decay rates as well. Since only the $m = 0$ states are affected by $\mathbf{B}$, the $m = \pm 1$ states have not been included.

3.2 General Analysis of the P · B Effect

In this section we will present equations which describe the following experimental situation. At time $t = 0$, a thermalized beam of positrons, of polarization $\mathbf{P}$, forms Ps in a solid placed in a magnetic field, $\mathbf{B} = \hat{z}B$. The polarization is defined as

$$\mathbf{P} = \langle \boldsymbol{\sigma} \cdot \hat{\mathbf{e}} \rangle_{\text{Max}} \, \hat{e}_0 = \frac{(N_\uparrow - N_\downarrow)}{(N_\uparrow + N_\downarrow) = N_0} \, \hat{e}_0 \qquad (2)$$

where $\hat{e}_0$ = a unit vector in the direction in which the expectation value "$\langle \; \rangle$" of $\boldsymbol{\sigma} \cdot \hat{e}$ is a maximum, $N_\uparrow$, $N_\downarrow$ = the number of positrons in the beam with spins parallel, antiparallel to $\hat{e}_0{}^4$, and N_0 = the total number of particles in the beam. The initial Ps states and their respective populations are

$$\text{State:} \quad \psi^{\uparrow\uparrow} = \psi_{1,1} \qquad \psi^{\uparrow\downarrow} \qquad \psi^{\downarrow\downarrow} = \psi_{1,-1} \qquad \psi^{\downarrow\uparrow}$$

$$\text{Population:} \quad \frac{N_\uparrow}{2} \qquad \frac{N_\uparrow}{2} \qquad \frac{N_\downarrow}{2} \qquad \frac{N_\downarrow}{2}$$

with a representative state written in terms of Pauli spinors given as

$$\psi^{\uparrow\downarrow} = \begin{pmatrix} \cos\dfrac{\theta}{2} \; e^{-i\varphi} \\[2mm] \sin\dfrac{\theta}{2} \end{pmatrix} \begin{pmatrix} -\sin\dfrac{\theta}{2} \\[2mm] \cos\dfrac{\theta}{2} \; e^{+i\varphi} \end{pmatrix} \qquad (3)$$

where $\cos\theta = \hat{e}_0 \cdot \hat{z}$. The phase factors, $e^{\pm i\varphi}$, go out when probabilities are computed, and will be dropped at this point.

These states may be expanded in terms of the eigenstates of Table I, which are assumed to represent Ps in a solid, as $(\hbar = 1)$:

$$\begin{aligned}
\psi^{\uparrow\downarrow} = \; &\psi_{1,0}' \, \exp\left[-\left(iE_{1,0}' + \frac{\Lambda_{1,0}'}{2}\right)t\right]\left[b \sin^2\frac{\theta}{2} - a \cos^2\frac{\theta}{2}\right] \\
&- \psi_{0,0}' \, \exp\left[-\left(iE_{1,0}' + \frac{\Lambda_{0,0}'}{2}\right)t\right]\left[b \cos^2\frac{\theta}{2} - a \sin^2\frac{\theta}{2}\right] \\
&+ \tfrac{1}{2}\sin\theta\,[\psi_{1,0} - \psi_{1,-1}]\,\exp\left[-\left(iE_{1,0} + \frac{\Lambda_{1,0}}{2}\right)t\right]
\end{aligned} \qquad (4)$$

TABLE I

Field Perturbed Ground State Ps $(m = 0)$

State $(\psi_{L,m})$	Energy	Decay rate
$\psi'_{0,0} = \dfrac{1}{(1+y^2)^{1/2}}(\psi_{0,0} + y\psi_{1,0})$	$E'_{0,0} = \dfrac{(E_{0,0} + E_{1,0}) - \Delta(1+x^2)^{1/2}}{2}$	$\Lambda'_{0,0} = \dfrac{1}{1+y^2}(\Lambda_{0,0} + y^2\Lambda_{1,0})$
$\psi'_{1,0} = \dfrac{1}{(1+y^2)^{1/2}}(\psi_{1,0} + y\psi_{0,0})$	$E'_{1,0} = \dfrac{(E_{0,0} + E_{1,0}) + \Delta(1+x^2)^{1/2}}{2}$	$\Lambda'_{1,0} = \dfrac{1}{1+y^2}(\Lambda_{1,0} + y^2\Lambda_{0,0})$

Notes:

(a) Unprimed energies eigenstates and decay rates refer to $B = 0$.

(b) $\psi_{0,0} = 1/\sqrt{2}\,(\uparrow\downarrow - \downarrow\uparrow)$; $\psi_{1,0} = 1/\sqrt{2}\,(\uparrow\downarrow + \downarrow\uparrow)$; $E_{0,0} = -\frac{1}{2}\alpha^2$; $E_{1,0} = \frac{2}{3}\alpha^2$; $\Lambda_{0,0} = 8\times10^9$; $\Lambda_{1,0} = 0.5\times10^9$; α^2 (h Ry) = 0.72 mv; $\uparrow$, $\downarrow$ implies positron $\binom{1}{0}$, electron $\binom{0}{1}$.

(c) $\Delta = E_{1,0} - E_{0,0}$; $X = (4\mu_0 B)/\Delta$; $y = X/[1 + (1 + X^2)^{1/2}]$.

where

$$a = \left(\frac{1 - \epsilon}{2}\right)^{1/2}, \qquad b = \left(\frac{1 + \epsilon}{2}\right)^{1/2}, \qquad \epsilon = X(1 + X^2)^{-1/2}$$

Similar expansions hold for the other states.

The number of Ps atoms that survive through time t is then given by

$$N(\theta, t) = \int d^3r \sum_{\text{spins}} \left\{ \frac{N_\uparrow}{2} [(\psi^{\uparrow\uparrow})^\dagger(\psi^{\uparrow\uparrow}) + (\psi^{\uparrow\uparrow})^\dagger(\psi^{\uparrow\uparrow})] \right.$$

$$+ \frac{N_\downarrow}{2} [(\psi^{\uparrow\uparrow})^\dagger(\psi^{\uparrow\uparrow}) + (\psi^{\uparrow\uparrow})^\dagger(\psi^{\uparrow\uparrow})] \right\}$$

$$= \frac{N_0}{4} [2 \exp[-\Lambda_{1,0}t] + \exp[-\Lambda'_{1,0}t] + \exp[-\Lambda'_{0,0}t]$$

$$- P\epsilon \cos\theta (\exp[-\Lambda'_{1,0}t] - \exp[-\Lambda'_{0,0}t])] \tag{5}$$

This equation describes the $\mathbf{P \cdot B}$ effect in full generality. To analyze experiments which use the effect, the experimental parameter $R(\theta_1, \theta_2, t_1, t_2)$ is often introduced. Its general definition is

$$R(\theta_1, \theta_2, t_1, t_2) = \frac{[N(\theta_1, t_1) - N(\theta_1, t_2)] - [N(\theta_2, t_1) - N(\theta_2, t_2)]}{[N(\theta_1, t_1) - N(\theta_1, t_2)] + [N(\theta_2, t_1) - N(\theta_2, t_2)]} \tag{6}$$

i.e., R is half the relative intensity difference between the observed delayed Ps decays for $\cos^{-1}(\hat{e}_0 \cdot \hat{z}) = \theta_1$ and then θ_2. Substituting Eq. (5) into Eq. (6) yields

$$R = \frac{P\epsilon(\beta' - \alpha')(\cos\theta_1 - \cos\theta_2)}{4\alpha + 2(\alpha' + \beta') + (\beta' - \alpha')P\epsilon(\cos\theta_1 + \cos\theta_2)} \tag{7}$$

where

$$\alpha = (\exp[-\Lambda_{1,0}t_1] - \exp[-\Lambda_{1,0}t_2])$$
$$\alpha' = (\exp[-\Lambda'_{1,0}t_1] - \exp[-\Lambda'_{1,0}t_2])$$
$$\beta' = (\exp[-\Lambda'_{0,0}t_1] - \exp[-\Lambda'_{0,0}t_2])$$

In the usual experiments $\theta_1 = 0$, $\theta_2 = \pi$ (B reversed) so that

$$R = \frac{P\epsilon(\beta' - \alpha')}{2\alpha + (\alpha' + \beta')} \tag{8}$$

This reduces to the well-known expression $R = -\frac{1}{3}P\epsilon$ if coincidence timing considerations, and the magnitude of B, permit us to set $\beta' \ll \alpha'$ and $\alpha' = \alpha$.

To include the effect of a finite coincidence circuit resolving time, described by a prompt curve $Q(t)$ normalized to unit area, the probability distribution

$$f(\theta, t) = -\frac{1}{N_0}\frac{dN}{dt}, \quad t > 0; \qquad f(\theta, t) = 0, \quad t < 0$$

should be folded with $Q(T - t)$.[5] The result is then the experimentally observed distribution $F(T)$, which, when integrated over the range of T used, gives ΔN the number of coincidence counts that should be observed as

$$\Delta N(\theta, T_1, T_2) = N_0 \int_{T_1}^{T_2} F(T)\,dT = N_0 \int_{T_1}^{T_2} dT \int_0^\infty dt\, f(\theta, t) Q(T - t)$$

(9)

where $T_2 - T_1$ is the interval of the annihilation time spectrum in which ΔN is recorded.

4. CONCLUSIONS AND RESULTS

The question of just what approximations can be made in $f(\theta, t)$, before it is substituted into Eq. (9), may be answered only when the relevant parameters $(B, Q, T_1, T_2, \ldots)$ are known. In general, however, the approximation $\alpha' = \alpha$ will break down rather badly at $B \approx 20$ kG. For a typical Q(fwhm ≈ 1 nsec), use of the simple equation $P = 3R/\epsilon$ may result in values of P, half as large as would be obtained from the exact equation.

When Eq. (9) is evaluated, using the parameters that characterize the present g factor experiment, we find

$$\frac{\Delta N}{N_0} = [0.35 \pm 0.05][1 - (0.02 \pm 0.005)\cos\theta] \tag{10}$$

This implies an efficiency[6] of 10% as compared to .001% for Mott scattering while the amplitude of the cosine curve, (.02), is about $1/2$ what we would expect from Mott scattering. Because of the low-beam current available (Sec. 2), it is clear that in our application the $\mathbf{P} \cdot \mathbf{B}$ effect is far superior to Mott scattering as a positron polarization detector.

In the experimental work completed to date we have determined the positron g-factor anomaly to 1%. Our result[8] is $a = 0.001\,168 \pm 0.000\,011$ or expressed in powers of $\alpha = e^2/hc$, $a = \alpha/2\pi + (1.2 \pm 2)\times \alpha^2/\pi^2$. This is in agreement with the experimental and theoretical values of the electron anomaly which are[7]

$$a_{\text{exptl.}} = 0.001\,159\,622 \pm 0.000\,000\,027 = \frac{\alpha}{2\pi} - (0.327 \pm 0.005)\frac{\alpha^2}{\pi^2}$$

$$a_{\text{theoret.}} = 0.001\,159\,615 = \frac{\alpha}{2\pi} - 0.328\frac{\alpha^2}{\pi^2}$$

The amplitude of the cosine curve was 0.014 ± 0.003, in good agreement with the prediction 0.02 ± 0.005 of Eq. 10. The experimental error quoted is statistical and is estimated by the method of maximem likelihood.[9] Error in the theoretical prediction of the amplitude is due to (i) uncertainty in the shape of $Q(t)$, (ii) uncertainty in the various lifetimes and fractional intensities, (iii) uncertainty in locating the peak of Q ($t = 0$) due to counting statistics and (iv) coincidence circuit jitter during a run. Since $P = 0.7$ was used in the calculation of R, we conclude that there is little depolarization between emission of the positron and formation of Ps.

ACKNOWLEDGMENTS

We wish to thank Professor R. R. Lewis, Professor G. Weinreich, and Professor K. M. Case, for several stimulating discussions of the theory of the experiment. Dr. D. T. Wilkinson contributed a great deal of help during the first stages of the investigation.

REFERENCES

1. See D. T. Wilkinson and H. R. Crane, *Phys. Rev.* **130**, 852 (1963), for the latest electron g factor determination. This paper also contains references to previous work.
2. Mendlowitz, H., and K. M. Case, *Phys. Rev.* **97**, 33 (1955).
3. Ford, G. W., and C. W. Hirt, University of Michigan, 1961 (unpublished).
4. If the density matrix is used to describe the polarized beam the resulting equations are unchanged.
5. Bay, Z., V. P. Henri, and H. Kanner, *Phys. Rev.* **100**, 1197 (1955). This reference also lists conditions which must be satisfied by the coincidence system in order that the folding give the correct experimental distribution.
6. Efficiency is defined as $\frac{1}{2}$ the term $[\frac{1}{4} \int_{T_1}^{T_2} dT \int_0^\infty dt\, Q(T - t) \times$ $\{\Lambda'_{1,0}\, e^{-\Lambda'_{1,0} t} + \Lambda'_{0,0}\, e^{-\Lambda'_{0,0} t}\}]$ appearing in Eq. 9, and represents essentially that fraction of all decays affected by the magnetic field and observed in delayed coincidence. The extra factor $\frac{1}{2}$ is due to the loss of about 50% of the positrons which decay by direct annihilation without forming Ps.
7. See Ref. 1.
8. Details of the calculation will appear shortly in *Phys. Rev. Letters*.
9. Parratt, L. G., "Probability and Experimental Errors in Science" (Wiley, New York, 1961), Chap. 3.

Theory of Positron Lifetime in Solid Argon[*]

E. J. Woll, Jr.

Carnegie Institute of Technology
Pittsburgh, Pennsylvania

An approach is suggested which is expected to prove useful for calculation of electron-positron wavefunctions for simple insulating solids. The approach yields a wavefunction showing some effect of correlation. The method is based on the Born-Oppenheimer treatment of molecules.[1] Application is made to the case of solid argon. The lowest-order approximation to the correlated wavefunction in argon is estimated; this estimated wavefunction is then used to calculate positron lifetime and angular distribution of annihilation radiation.

The Hamiltonian which governs the motions of the electrons with a positron in a solid can be written

$$H = \sum_i H_e(\mathbf{x}_i) - \sum_i \frac{e^2}{|\mathbf{x}_i - \mathbf{y}|} + H_p \mathbf{y}$$

where the first term, a sum over single electron Hamiltonians, would be appropriate in the absence of the positron (under the assumption that electron-electron interactions can be treated in the Hartree approximation.) The third term includes the positron kinetic energy, and the potential felt by the positron at position $\mathbf{y}$ due to the nuclei in the solid.

The electron-positron wavefunction sought is the ground state solution of the Schrödinger equation

$$H \Psi_k (\{\mathbf{x}_i\}, \mathbf{y}) = E_k \Psi_k (\{\mathbf{x}_i\}, \mathbf{y})$$

The present treatment makes use of the solutions of a Schrödinger equation for electrons in the presence of a *fixed* positive charge, namely,

$$\sum_i \left[H_e(\mathbf{x}_i) - \frac{e^2}{|\mathbf{x}_i - \mathbf{y}|} \right] \Phi_A(\{\mathbf{x}_i\}; \mathbf{y}) = \mathcal{E}_A(\mathbf{y}) \Phi_A(\{\mathbf{x}_i\}; \mathbf{y})$$

[*]Supported in part by the National Science Foundation.

329

The solutions Φ_A, paramatrized by $\mathbf{y}$, are many body electron wavefunctions. These functions are Slater determinants, made up of single electron wavefunctions, which are solutions of the single electron Hamiltonian in the presence of a fixed charge, while the energy $\mathcal{E}_A(\mathbf{y})$ is the sum of the occupied single particle energies.

The complete electron-positron wavefunction is expanded in a series of the functions Φ_A, with coefficients which depend on $\mathbf{y}$.

$$\Psi_k(\{\mathbf{x}_i\}, \mathbf{y}) = \sum_A \chi_k^{(A)}(\mathbf{y}) \, \Phi_A(\{\mathbf{x}_i\}; \mathbf{y})$$

The hope of the present work is that the lowest term in this sum, corresponding to the electron ground state, will dominate the sum. This hope is grounded in the fact that a finite energy is necessary to cause electron excitation.

The coefficients $\chi_k^{(A)}$ satisfy the set of equations

$$E_k \, \chi_k^{(A)}(\mathbf{y}) = [H_p(\mathbf{y}) + \mathcal{E}_A(\mathbf{y})] \, \chi_k^{(A)}(\mathbf{y})$$
$$- \sum_B [\nabla_y \chi_k^{(B)} \cdot (\Phi_A | \nabla_y | \Phi_B) + \tfrac{1}{2} \chi_k^{(B)} (\Phi_A | \nabla_y^2 | \Phi_B)]$$

In the case where the first term in the sum for Ψ_k is dominant, however, the correlated electron-positron wavefunction can be approximated as the product wavefunction $\chi_k^0 \Phi_0$, where χ_k^0 satisfies

$$[H_p(\mathbf{y}) + \mathcal{E}_0(\mathbf{y}) - \tfrac{1}{2} (\Phi_0 | \nabla_y^2 | \Phi_0)] \, \chi_k^0(\mathbf{y}) \approx E_k \, \chi_k^0(\mathbf{y})$$

This is a Schrödinger equation, soluble at least numerically for the "positron wavefunction" χ_k^0, providing the energy $\mathcal{E}_0$ and the electron wavefunction Φ_0 are known.

Because the electrons are tightly bound, it is appropriate to find the required energies and wavefunctions using low-order perturbation theory. Up to second order, the energy is given by

$$\mathcal{E}_0(\mathbf{y}) = \mathcal{E}_0^0 - \left(\Phi_0^0 \, \Big| \sum_i \frac{e^2}{|\mathbf{x}_i - \mathbf{y}|} \Big| \, \Phi_0^0 \right)$$
$$- \sum_{A \neq 0} \left(\Phi_0^0 \, \Big| \sum_i \frac{e^2}{|\mathbf{x}_i - \mathbf{y}|} \Big| \Phi_A^0 \right) \frac{1}{\mathcal{E}_A^0 - \mathcal{E}_0^0}$$
$$\times \left(\Phi_A^0 \, \Big| \sum_j \frac{e^2}{|\mathbf{x}_j - \mathbf{y}|} \Big| \Phi_0^0 \right) + \cdots$$

where the superscript zero has been used to designate unperturbed energies and wavefunctions. The second term is the usual Hartree attraction of the electrons for the positron. The third term is an attraction due to virtual polarization of the electrons by the positron.

It is this attraction which can be expected to produce an effect due to correlation, even in the lowest order approximation to the electron-positron wavefunction.

The potential due to virtual polarization of the electrons can be estimated by assuming that all excited states have the same energy. The sum over intermediate states then is simply a completeness sum. (The estimate thus does not require a knowledge of the excited-state electron wavefunctions.) Using the tight binding approximation, the effective polarization potential is reducible to

$$v_p \approx -\frac{1}{\Delta} \sum_{\mathbf{R}} \left[\sum_{\alpha} \left(\alpha \left| \frac{e^4}{(\mathbf{x} - \mathbf{y} + \mathbf{R})^2} \right| \alpha \right) \right. $$
$$\left. - \sum_{\alpha} \sum_{\alpha'} \left| \left(\alpha \left| \frac{e^2}{|\mathbf{x} - \mathbf{y} + \mathbf{R}|} \right| \alpha' \right) \right|^2 \right]$$

where the sum on $\mathbf{R}$ runs over lattice sites, α, α' are atomic wavefunctions, and Δ is the approximate energy gap.

The term $\frac{1}{2}(\Phi_0| \nabla_y^2 |\Phi_0)$ is of higher order than V_P, and is neglected in the present estimate.

The total potential, including polarization, seen by the lowest order positron wavefunction is plotted in Fig. 1 for the case of solid argon. For this case, the atomic wavefunctions taken are those of Hartree

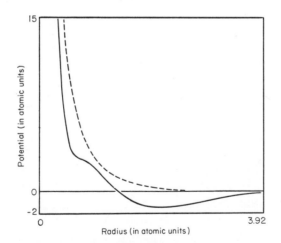

Fig. 1. The total potential seen by the positron, including repulsion by the atomic cores, Hartree attraction by the outer electrons and attraction due to virtual polarization of the outer electrons is given by the solid line. For comparison, the dashed line shows the potential seen by the positron in the absence of polarization.

and Hartree,[2] and the energy gap used is taken from the work of Knox and Bassani[3] to be

$$\Delta = 0.405 \text{ atomic units}$$

The ground-state positron wavefunction is found by numerical integration of the Schrödinger equation, with the assumption that the unit cell can be replaced by a sphere (of radius 3.92 atomic units in argon) with the radial derivative of the wavefunction zero at the edge of the sphere. The resulting wavefunction is shown in Fig. 2.

The lifetime of the positron against two-quantum decay is given, essentially, by the integral of the square of the electron-positron wavefunction, evaluated where the electron and positron coordinates are equal. Using the positron wavefunction shown in Fig. 2, with the unperturbed ground-state electron wavefunction, the result for the inverse lifetime is

$$1/\tau_1 = 19 \times 10^8/\text{sec} \quad \text{with polarization}$$

On the other hand, the result calculated ignoring polarization is

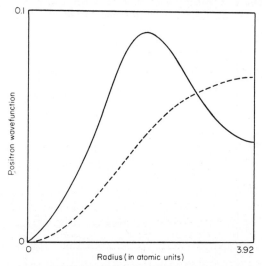

Fig. 2. The ground-state positron wavefunction (normalized to one over the unit cell) is given by the solid line. For comparison, the dashed line shows the wavefunction calculated in the absence of polarization. (Note that this wavefunction is a slight correction of the work reported by Rose and DeBenedetti in Ref. 5.)

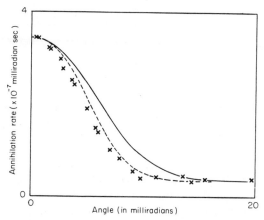

Fig. 3. The angular distribution of annihilation radiation, calculated using the wavefunction
of Fig. 2, is given by the solid line. For comparison, the dashed line shows the angular distribution calculated in the absence of polarization. (Note that this angular distribution is a
slight correction to the work reported by Rose
and DeBenedetti in Ref. 5.)

$$1/\tau_2 \ = \ 5.7 \times 10^8/\text{sec} \quad \text{without polarization}$$

and the experimental inverse lifetime, measured by Liu and Roberts,[4]
is

$$1/\tau \ = \ 23 \times 10^8/\text{sec} \quad \text{experimental}$$

The present theory, though somewhat crude, therefore produces a
quite significant improvement in the agreement with experimental
lifetime values.

The angular distribution of annihilation radiation has also been
calculated, using the techniques of Rose and DeBenedetti.[5] The result of this calculation is shown in Fig. 3. Agreement with experiment in this case is noticeably worsened, in comparison with the calculation which ignores polarization.

It seems possible, though unfortunate, the approximations which
are appropriate for calculation of the lifetime are inappropriate for
calculation of the angular distribution; the converse has long been
known to be true. However, it should be pointed out that the approximations made in calculating V_p should produce an overestimate;
thus, the lowest order effect may be smaller than calculated. In this
case, it would be necessary to add to the lowest order wavefunction,

terms which corresponded to excited electron wavefunctions, in order to reproduce experimental lifetimes. This will have the effect of narrowing the angular distribution, thereby improving agreement with experiment.

REFERENCES

1. As described, for example, in L. I. Schiff, "Quantum Mechanics," p. 289. McGraw-Hill, New York, 1949.
2. Hartree, D. R., and W. Hartree, *Proc. Roy. Soc. (London)* **A166**, 450 (1938).
3. Knox, R. S., and F. Bassani, *Phys. Rev.* **124**, 652 (1961).
4. Liu, D. C., and W. K. Roberts, *Phys. Rev.* **132**, 1633 (1963).
5. Rose, K. L., and S. DeBenedetti, *Phys. Rev.* **138**, A927 (1965).

The Lifetimes of Positronium in Polymers Irradiated by Gamma Rays

Girish Chandra, V. G. Kulkarni, R. G. Lagu, and B. V. Thosar

Tata Institute of Fundamental Research, Bombay, India

INTRODUCTION

The slow component (τ_2) of the life-time of the positrons annihilating in certain solids is in general attributed to the decay of the triplet state of the positronium atom into two photons either by a pickoff process or by triplet to singlet conversion induced by the presence of paramagnetic free radicals. As τ_2 is sensitive to the structure of the solid in which the positrons annihilate, some information regarding certain features of the state of the solid can be obtained using positron annihilation phenomena as a probe. The present paper reports the variation of τ_2 in Teflon and Polyethylene (both long chain polymers) as a function of the dose of gamma irradiation to which these samples are subjected. The results obtained are qualitatively interpreted in terms of the damage caused to the structure of these polymers by gamma irradiation.

EXPERIMENTAL SETUP

A thin source of Na^{22} deposited on a thin mylar film $(\sim 400 \mu g/cm^2)$ was sandwiched between two discs (2 mm thick) of the material. The delayed coincidence spectrum between the 1280 keV nuclear gamma ray and the 511 keV annihilation gamma ray was recorded on a Nuclear Data 512 channel analyzer. The conventional slow-fast coincidence set up using a bridge type time to amplitude converter,[1] 2 × 2 in. NaI(Tl) crystals coupled to RCA 6810A photomultiplier tubes was employed. The resolution of the prompt curve was 1 nsec (half width at half maximum), and the range of linearity was about 30 nsec. The coincidence spectra for unirradiated (Normal), and irradiated samples were alternately recorded, for short intervals of time in different quadrants of the multichannel analyzer, until good statistics were obtained. A straight-line fit (on a logarithmic scale) for points on the slow component was obtained by the method of least squares, after applying a correction for chance coincidence. The half lives measured for the normal samples, 3.5 ± 0.2 nsec for Teflon and 2.0 ± 0.2 nsec for Polyethylene, were in good agreement with the values reported in literature.

RESULTS

Figures 1 and 2 show the experimental results for Teflon and Polyethylene, respectively. In curve B of Fig. 1, the percentage decrease in the value of τ_2, plotted on Y axis is taken as a measure of the degree of quenching of the ^3S state. The concentration of free radicals, as well as the degree of quenching, at first increases with radiation dose up to about 4.5 megarads. At higher doses, however, the concentration of free radicals tends to saturate around a value of 1.9×10^{18} spins/cc, while the degree of quenching reaches a maximum of about 35% and then decreases. It is interesting to note that the saturation of free radical concentration and the reversal in quenching occur around the same dose value (~4.5 megarads). Curve A in Fig. 1 is reproducible even a month after irradiation, indicating the stability of the free radicals produced in Teflon.

In the case of irradiated Polyethylene, the value of τ_2, as compared to that in unirradiated sample, at first increases rapidly and then tends to attain a constant higher value up to a dose of 9 megarads. The percentage increase in τ_2 is plotted as a function of radiation dose in Fig. 2. No EPR signals could be detected in the irradiated Polyethylene samples in the range of radiation doses (0-9 megarads) studied. Thus no stable free radicals were produced in this material.

DISCUSSION

The absence of free radicals in Polyethylene could be attributed to rapid cross linking. That the cross linking is not observed in Teflon may be due to the fact that the distortion of the $\begin{smallmatrix} C & & C \\ & \diagdown C \diagup & \end{smallmatrix}$ bond angle from the tetrahedral angle (109.5 to 116°) would reduce the stability of such a system which is under tension.[2] The effect of gamma irradiation on Polyethylene would be to reduce the degree of crystallinity as a result of cross linking.

Teflon[5]

Let N_0 be the number of sites per cm³ in unirradiated Teflon where positronium atoms formed in the triplet state are quenched by the normal surroundings and decay with a decay constant $\lambda^0 (\lambda^0 \sim 1/\tau_2^0)$. The breaking of both C — F and C — C bonds in irradiated Teflon has been reported in literature.[2-4] The breaking of C — F bond creates a

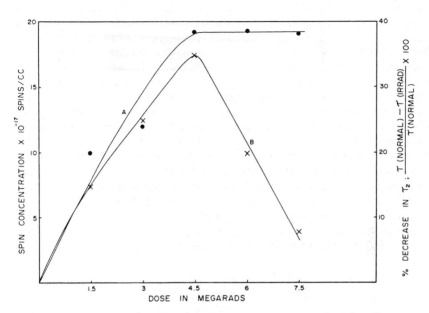

Fig. 1. Curves showing the spin concentration in irradiated Teflon.
(A) The degree of quenching (% decrease in τ_2). (B) The degree of quenching versus the dose of gamma irradiation.

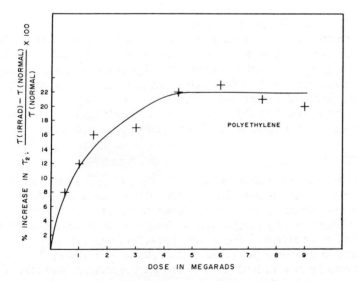

Fig. 2. Curve showing the per cent increase in τ_2 in irradiated Polyethylene versus the dose of gamma irradiation.

vacancy at the site of the fluorine atom, while the breaking of $C - C$ bonds leaves a gap at the site of the bond scission due to the contraction along the Teflon chain. The free radicals and the gaps are thereafter created in a mutual neighborhood. Let the number of such free radical sites per cm^3 be S_1 where the positronium atom would be rapidly quenched due to the presence of an unpaired electron in its vicinity. Let $\lambda' (> \lambda^0)$ be the decay constant for this process. The saturation of spins above 4.5 megarads indicates a process of recombination of free radicals which will pair off the unpaired electrons to form recombination bonds, but would leave the gaps unaffected. Let S_2 be the number of such recombination sites per cm^3 where the positronium decays with a decay constant $\lambda'' (< \lambda')$. $\lambda'' = \lambda^0$ as there is no significant difference between the two types of sites N_0 and S_2 as far as a quenching mechanism is concerned. Now the relative numbers of positronium atoms annihilating at these three different types of sites will be equal to $N_0 : S_1 : S_2$.

Let λ_{eff} be the measured decay constant, then

$$\lambda_{eff} = \frac{N_0 + S_2}{N_0 + S_1 + S_2} \lambda^0 + \frac{S_1}{N_0 + S_1 + S_2} \lambda'$$

and

$$\Delta \lambda = \lambda_{eff} - \lambda^0 = \frac{S_1}{N_0 + S_1 + S_2} (\lambda' - \lambda^0)$$

where N_0, λ' and λ^0 are constants.

For small doses of irradiation, S_2 is small and increases slowly compared to S_1. $\Delta \lambda$ is therefore sensitive only to S_1 and hence increases with S_1, i.e. with the dose. For doses larger than 4.5 megarads S_1 becomes constant (saturates) while S_2 increases rapidly with the dose. Hence $\Delta \lambda$ decreases with further irradiation.

Thus the curve B in Fig. 1 is explained qualitatively on the basis of creation and recombination of free radicals in Teflon.

Polyethylene

If polyethylene is conceived as consisting of small microcrystals mixed with the low density disordered regions, the positronium atom experiencing strong repulsive exchange forces from high density regions is likely to stay comparatively longer in disordered regions. According to Charlesby[6] the x-ray diffraction spectra indicate that the nature of disorder produced in Polyethylene, irradiated to very large doses by pile radiation, is to reduce the number and size of the microcrystals. The irradiation of Polyethylene would, therefore, increase the size of the disordered regions. The lifetime τ_2 is shown to be proportional to the volume of the potential well representing the low density disordered regions.[7] The increase in τ_2 observed in our experiments may thus be due to the increase in the size of the amorphous regions which is equivalent to overall reduction in the degree of crystallinity in irradiated Polyethylene.

ACKNOWLEDGMENT

The irradiation mentioned in this paper was carried out at the Atomic Energy Establishment Trombay, India. The authors are thankful to Drs. C. R. Kanekar and P. G. Nair for taking the EPR spectra for Polyethylene.

REFERENCES

1. Chandra, G., *Nuovo Cimento* **31**, 297 (1964).
2. Charlesby, A., "Atomic Radiation and Polymers," Chap. 20. MacMillan (Pergamon), New York, 1960.
3. Rexroad, H. N., and W. Gordy, *J. Chem. Phys.* **30**, 399 (1959).
4. Kusumoto, H., *J. Phys. Soc. (Japan)* **15**, 867 (1960).
5. Chandra, G., V. G. Kulkarni, R. G. Lagu, A. V. Patankar, and B. V. Thosar, *Phys. Letters* **16**, 40 (1965).
6. Charlesby, A., "Atomic Radiation and Polymers," Chap. 13. MacMillan (Pergamon), New York, 1960.
7. Wilson, R. K., P. O. Johnson, and R. Stump, Phys. Rev. **129**, 2091 (1963).

Positronium Formation in Certain Metal Oxides*

J. H. Kusmiss and A. T. Stewart

University of North Carolina, Chapel Hill, North Carolina

The angular correlation of the γ-ray pairs resulting from the annihilation of positrons in CaO, MgO, and ZnO has been previously measured.[1] It was found that the results for CaO seemed to depend on the particle size of the poly-crystalline specimens; a narrow component of low intensity appeared in the angular correlation data for coarse crystalline samples. This paper reports the outcome of angular correlation experiments on the above-mentioned oxides in an oxygen atmosphere. In addition, we have made measurements on polycrystalline Al_2O_3, both in vacuum and in O_2 at atmospheric pressure.

The angular correlation curves for ZnO powder in vacuum and in O_2 are shown in Fig. 1. The large narrow component which appears when the specimen is in O_2 is indicative of the decay of singlet positronium. If positronium were being formed in the bulk of the ZnO specimen the half width of the narrow peak implies the existence of large "holes" of size 10-20 Å in the crystal lattice. If all of the positronium atoms which are formed were converted to the singlet state in the presence of O_2, however, we would expect at most a four-fold increase in the relative intensity of the narrow component over the vacuum case. The observed increase is apparently much larger than this. Oxygen is known to enhance the formation of positronium, at least in gases.[2] We conclude that positronium is being formed either in the gas-filled interstices of the powder specimen or on the surface of the powder particles, and subsequently, annihilating in the gas.

The angular correlation results we obtain for Al_2O_3 powder in vacuum and in O_2 at atmospheric pressure are similar to those obtained by Løvseth.[3] A narrow component of approximately 10% relative intensity is present in the angular distribution for the sample in vacuum. In the presence of O_2, the relative intensity of the narrow component increases to about 25%. These results are in agreement with the results of Løvseth, except that our specimens were

*Partially supported by a grant from the National Science Foundation.

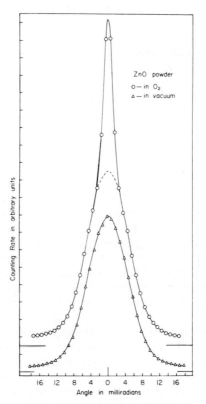

Fig. 1. Two-photon angular correlation data for ZnO powder in vacuum and in oxygen.

crystalline (as verified by x-ray diffraction), whereas Løvseth reported his samples to be completely amorphous. We conclude from our results that the narrow peak in vacuum is caused by the annihilation of singlet positronium which is being formed either in holes or on the surface of the bulk material. Some of the narrow peak may be due to triplet positronium if conversion to the singlet state is taking place by some means. We attribute the added intensity of the narrow peak in O_2 to the formation of additional positronium because of the presence of the gas, as in the case of ZnO.

The angular correlation data for three types of MgO specimen in vacuum or O_2 are depicted in Figure 2. The curve for MgO powder in vacuum is considerably narrower than that for single-crystal MgO in vacuum; this suggests that a certain amount of narrow component is present for the powder but that the narrow component cannot be resolved, i.e., it blends into the broad part of the angular distribution.

When the powder specimen is placed in O_2, however, the presence of
a narrow component becomes apparent (see Fig. 2, left). The angular
correlation results for single-crystal MgO are unaffected when the
experiment is repeated in an O_2 environment (Fig. 2, lower right),
but the angular distribution for a coarse crystalline powder specimen in O_2 is somewhat narrower than that for a large single crystal
in O_2 (Fig. 2, upper right). The results for MgO are consistent with
the interpretation adduced in the case of ZnO and Al_2O_3, namely, that
positronium is formed on or near the surface of a finely divided specimen in vacuum, and that the presence of O_2 causes an increased
amount of positronium formation either on the surface of the powder
particles or in the gas-filled spaces between them.

The results for CaO do not fit in completely with the picture we
have presented above. CaO powder in O_2 and CaO crystal chips in
O_2 give identical angular correlation distributions which are very
sharply peaked, though the narrow component which undoubtedly is
present in both cases cannot be separated from the broad underlying
distribution. The angular correlation curves obtained for specimens
in vacuum varied considerably in half-width and shape, the broadest
curve being obtained for a powder specimen and the narrowest for a
specimen composed of coarse crystalline chips. Results were not

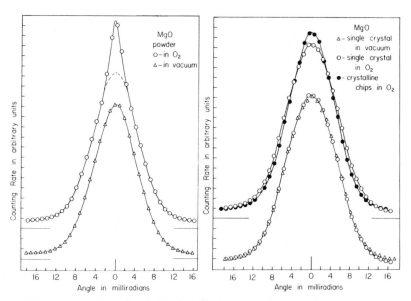

Fig. 2. Two-photon angular correlation data for various types of MgO
specimen in vacuum or in oxygen.

reproducible from week to week and seemed to depend on the history of the sample. The propensity of CaO for absorbing water vapor and CO_2 is well known, and we suggest that more careful experiments, ruling out the presence of adsorbed gases on the surface of the specimen, must be made before the angular correlation results for metallic oxides are fully understood. There is also a lack of agreement between lifetime measurements made by different workers[4,5] on these materials.

We should like to acknowledge the assistance of J. J. Donaghy, J. B. Shand, G. M. Beardsley, S. M. Kim, and T. M. Patterson in carrying out the experiments we have reported in this paper. We are indebted to Professor J. C. Morrow of the Chemistry Department of the University of North Carolina for supplying us with an x-ray diffraction photograph and also for a helpful discussion.

REFERENCES

1. Kusmiss, J. H., J. B. Shand, J. J. Donaghy, and A. T. Stewart, *Bull. Am. Phys. Soc.* **9**, 238 (1964).
2. Heinberg, M., and L. Page, *Phys. Rev.* **107**, 1589 (1957).
3. Løvseth, Jørgen, *Phys. Norvegica* **1**, 145 (1963).
4. Bussolati, C., and L. Zappa, *Phys. Rev.* **136A**, 657 (1964).
5. Weisberg, H., and S. Berko (private communication).

Anomalous Long Annihilation Mean Lives of Positrons in Some Ionic Crystals

Robert Paulin and Georges Ambrosino

Institut National des Sciences et Techniques Nucléaires
Saclay, France

ABSTRACT

We have studied the annihilation life-time spectrum of positrons in different ionic crystals with the help of a classical "fast-slow" experimental device. We have found in some oxides (Al_2O_3, BeO, MgO) the same long mean life ($\cong 5.1 \pm 0.1 \times 10^{-8}$ sec) with 12% intensity and in two fluorides (F_2Mg, F_2Ca) a little shorter but less abundant mean life ($\cong 3.3$ and 4.2×10^{-8} sec, respectively). These results compared with measured 3γ annihilation probabilities, however, do not permit one to determine the nature of the bound-state created (orthopositronium or positronium bound with a negative ion).

EXPERIMENTAL PROCEDURE AND RESULTS

The time amplitude converter used gives a good linear response in time, better than 3%, over a range of 60 nsec, and a full width at half-maximum of 1.2×10^{-9} sec for the Co^{60} prompt curve. With the source used ($= 5\mu C$ of Na^{22} deposited between two aluminum foils of 1.5 mg/cm^2) the ratio of random to peak coincidences is less than 2×10^{-4}. The source is mixed into the multicrystalline powder (chemical purity for analysis), previously compressed by hand. This assembly is enclosed in a tight container of thin-walled Plexiglas.

The half-lives are measured by the semilogarithmic slope method (as shown in Fig. 1) from which the mean lives shown in Table I are deduced.

These results clearly show the formation of two bound-states of the positron in various oxides and some fluorides. One of these bound-states was already mentioned by Bussolati in alkaline earth oxides.[1]

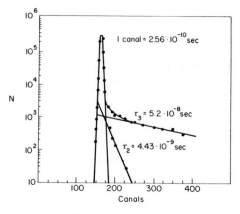

Fig. 1. Time spectrum in BeO.

TABLE I

Sample	$\tau_2 \times 10^{-9}$ sec	I_2 (%)	$\tau_3 \times 10^{-8}$ sec	I_3 (%)
BeO	4.4 $\pm$ 0.4	1.1	5.2 $\pm$ 0.1	11.2
MgO	5.7 $\pm$ 0.4	1.1	5.1 $\pm$ 0.1	10.9
CaO	2.2 $\pm$ 0.4	2	1.4 $\pm$ 0.2	1.3
BaO	—	—	—	—
ZnO	$\cong 2.6$	0.1	2.6 $\pm$ 0.2	0.4
CdO	—	—	1.44 $\pm$ 0.3	0.1
B_2O_3	1.66 $\pm$ 0.2	30	—	—
Al_2O_3	3.32 $\pm$ 0.2	3	5.17 $\pm$ 0.1	13
Fe_2O_3	—	—	—	—
La_2O_3	—	—	3.2 $\pm$ 0.2	0.4
Cr_2O_3	—	—	—	—
CrO_3	—	—	—	—
ClNa	5.0 $\pm$ 0.4	0.3	—	—
F_2Mg	3.7 $\pm$ 0.4	1.7	3.32 $\pm$ 0.1	5.65
F_2Ca	2.4 $\pm$ 0.4	2.7	4.2 $\pm$ 0.2	2.5

TABLE II

Sample	$\tau_2 \times 10^{-9}$ sec	I_2 (%)	$\tau_3 \times 10^{-8}$ sec	I_3 (%)
Al_2O_3 at 200° C	4.43 $\pm$ 0.4	2.7	4.6 $\pm$ 0.1	14.7
Al_2O_3 compressed	5.2 $\pm$ 0.4	3.5	6.3 $\pm$ 0.1	14
MgO compressed	3.7 $\pm$ 0.4	1.1	5.3 $\pm$ 0.1	8.5
F_2Mg compressed	3.3 $\pm$ 0.4	2.5	4.95 $\pm$ 0.2	3.5

LOCALIZATION OF THE BOUND STATE

To be sure that the very long mean lives observed do not result from orthopositronium formation in gases absorbed into the powder, as suggested by Kohonen for alumina, experiments have been made after heating alumina at 200°C for half an hour.[2]

One can see on Table II that this treatment of the powder does not affect the slow component.

The muticrystalline nature of the sample suggests moreover the possibility of free orthopositronium formation in the intervals between the powder grains. To reduce these interstices we made powder pills with a 11,000 kg/cm^2 press.

The results (Table II) show that the slow component is very little altered.

So it seems that the bound states observed arise from positron annihilation within the crystals.

DISCUSSION

The very long mean lives measured allow us to think that the most stable bound state is positronium-like; either orthopositronium or positronium bound with a negative ion.

Assume that orthopositronium is created; it will have a probability p_3 to decay through a 3γ emission, and a probability p_2 to decay through a 2γ emission by conversion from triplet to singlet state or "pickoff." The measured mean life, τ, therefore reflects this double possibility. One can write

$$p_{2\gamma} + p_{3\gamma} = 1$$

now $p_3 = \tau/\tau_3$ with $\tau_3 = 1.39 \times 10^{-7}$ sec, and $\tau \cong 5.1 \times 10^{-8}$ sec for Al$_2$O$_3$, BeO, MgO; so $p_3 \cong 1/3$ and $p_2 \cong 2/3$.

Let P be the produced quantity of orthopositronium; there will be $P/3$ which will decay with 3γ emission. The measured intensity of the slowest bound state is about 12% for the three mentioned oxides. From the energy distribution[3] of 3γ rays and the width of the detection energy-band (0.25 − 0.51 MeV) one can estimate the 3γ to 2γ detection efficiency ratio to be $1/2$ or so.

The measured percentage (0.12) is therefore made with $2/3$ double and $1/6$ triple decays. The orthopositronium quantity should be $P = 6/5 \times 0.12 = 0.144$, about 14% of all positrons which annihilate. The triple decay probability must be about $0.144 \times 1/3 = 0.048 \cong$ 5%, which seems to be the same order of magnitude as the values measured in alkaline-earth oxides.[1] By comparing the γ spectrum of MgO and Al$_2$O$_3$ with that of BaO we confirm that in these two samples the 3γ annihilation probability is clearly superior to that of the baryte. Thus the hypothesis of orthopositronium formation would seem confirmed though theoretically impossible in ionic crystals. On the other hand, from closely studying the results published by Bussolati it appears that the value of p_3 in BeO is three times that of MgO. In other words, the conversion rate from triplet to singlet or "pickoff" annihilation being three times more important in MgO, the long mean life must be observed three times shorter. However, the values we measured in these two oxides are almost the same, thus positronium formation seems denied.

The possibility remains of more complicated positron bound states with the negative ion. In the case of oxides (Al_2O_3, BeO, MgO) the very close values of mean lives and intensities suggest the formation of a bound state with an oxygen ion (Oe^- e^+)$^-$ which would appear to be similar to the hydroxide ion OH^-. But to observe the same mean life of about 5×10^{-8} sec in three oxides we must assume either that this "oxypositronium" ion freely annihilates in singlet state, or that its triplet life is much longer than that of orthopositronium, and that it decays by conversion or "pickoff." Neither of these two hypotheses seems attractive, for the strong probabilities of 3γ annihilation in these samples would not be explained. In addition, it is difficult to imagine the nature of a bound state formed with fluoride ion. Finally, a life-time measurement made with aluminum hydroxide ($Al_2(OH)_6$), in order to verify that the presence of the hydroxide ion prevented oxypositronium formation was not quite conclusive. If the very long component is largely suppressed, another bound state with shorter life appears ($\cong 1.3 \times 10^{-9}$ sec) in rather large quantities (8%).

CONCLUSION

It seems difficult to reconcile the results of mean life and 3γ decay probability measurements. Other experiments are necessary to clear up the nature of this bound state.

The presence of another bound state with shorter mean life (Ref. τ_2, I_2 in Table I) does not make easier the interpretation.

We point out at last the surprising abundance of the single bound state measured in B_2O_3.

REFERENCES

1. Bussolati, C., and L. Zappa, *Phys. Rev.* **136A**, 657 (1964).
2. Kohonen, T., *Ann. Acad. Scient. Fennicae* **AVI**, 130 (1963).
3. Ore, A., and J. L. Powell, *Phys. Rev.* **75**, 1696 (1949).

Search for an Electric Field Effect in Teflon and Polyethylene*

T. M. Patterson and A. T. Stewart

University of North Carolina, Chapel Hill, North Carolina

An electric field effect in the long lifetime (τ_2), and intensity of the long lifetime (I_2), has been reported in two papers by Bisi, Bisi, Fasana, and Zappa[1] and by Bisi, Fasana, and Zappa.[2] In Teflon, I_2 was found to be decreased approximately 30% by a uniform electric field of 100 kV/cm, and in polyethylene, approximately the same amount with a field of 50 kV/cm. τ_2 was decreased approximately 10% in both materials by a field of 100 kV/cm. No explanation has been proposed for this effect, and for this reason, we thought it of interest to measure the angular correlation of the 2-photon decay in the same materials with comparable electric fields.

The narrow component found in the angular correlation curves of most amorphous materials is believed to result mostly from thermalized singlet positronium annihilation, and the broad component, to result from free positrons and triplet "pickoff" annihilation. Any change with electric field in the relative abundance of positronium formation, or in triplet to singlet conversion rate, should therefore be observed as a change in the narrow component relative to the broad component.

The experimental apparatus consisted of the standard long slit detectors with an angular resolution of 0.5 mrad (FWHM). The samples were commercially obtained in the form of thin sheets approximately 0.010 in. thick. A thin layer of silver (approximately 1000 Å) was evaporated on both upper and lower surfaces so that the samples formed the dielectric of thin parallel plate capacitors whose plates were transparent to positrons from the Cu^{64} source. The samples were positioned about a centimeter beneath the source, the field in all cases being in the same direction as the motion of the incident positrons.

Figure 1 shows the two sets of data for Teflon obtained with no field and with a field of 118 kV/cm. The data were normalized to

*This work supported in part by the National Science Foundation and the Advanced Research Projects Agency.

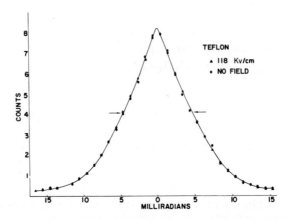

Fig. 1. Angular correlation of 2-photon annihilation in Teflon with and without electric field. Areas normalized up to points indicated by arrows.

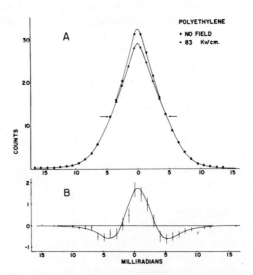

Fig. 2. (A) Angular correlation of 2-photon annihilation in polyethylene with and without electric field. Areas normalized up to points indicated by arrows. (B) Plot of differences between field off and field on angular correlation curves in polyethylene, normalized to equal total areas.

equal partial areas on the wings, including the area up to the arrows. Only slight change, if any, is observable within the experimental error. Figure 2A shows the results for polyethylene with the same normalization as in Fig. 1. A definite decrease in the narrow component with a field of 83 kV/cm is noted. The decrease in area amounts to approximately 5% of the total area of the field off curve. Figure 2B is a plot of the difference between field off and field on for angular correlation curves in polyethylene normalized to equal total areas.

REFERENCES

1. Bisi, A., F. Bisi, A. Fasana, and L. Zappa, Phys. Rev. **122**, 1709 (1961).
2. Bisi, A., A. Fasana, and L. Zappa, Phys. Rev. **124**, 1487 (1961).

Positronium Annihilation in Water and Ice down to −144°C by Angular Correlation Measurements[*]

P. Colombino, B. Fiscella, and L. Trossi

Istituto di Fisica dell'Università, Turin, Italy and
Istituto Nazionale di Fisica Nucleare, Sezione di Torino
Turin, Italy

We report some results of measurements of angular correlation in 2γ, on the water-ice system at different temperatures. The sample temperature was held constant to less than 0.4°C for long time periods by refrigerant Peletier batteries, or by a liquid nitrogen setup.

All the experimental angular distribution curves have been normalized by giving the curves a standard height where the breadth was 8 mrad (see Fig. 1). In each curve, the θ = 0 point was arbitrarily set on the centroid position.

Such a normalization makes evident that at every temperature, and in both states, all the curves coincide in the $|\theta| \geq 4$ mrad ranges. Once this fact is established, the said normalization permits also the comparison of curves limited to the central part for the sake of obtaining greater details.

In Fig. 1 are plotted three curves (4, −15, and −117°C), normalized with this method, while in reference 1, in order to visualize the progress of curves vs. temperature t, we have plotted a set of curves with the centers displaced along the horizontal axis in positions corresponding to the experiment's temperature. From these curves and from others not reported here, we can observe that a decrease in temperature in the range from −4 to −18°C, results in no significant change, apart from a slight enhancement of the narrow component.

A sudden change appears instead when passing from −18C to −25°C. Below −25°C the central peak is very sharp and clearly separable from the remainder of the curve.

Most data were obtained with a $Na^{22}Cl$ source ($\cong$3 mC), covered by a thin mica foil. At very low temperatures, in order to avoid damage to this source, a Cu^{64} source was used. In every case annihilation was obtained by bombarding the upper surface of the samples.

[*]This work was partly supported by Consiglio Nazionale delle Ricerche.

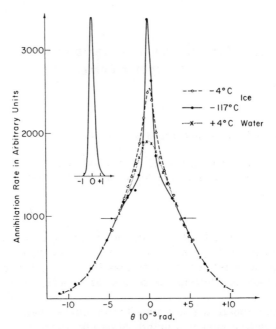

Fig. 1. Angular distribution in water +4° C, ice
−4° C, and ice −117° C. Arrows show standard
height where breadth is 8 mrad. Angular resolution
is also shown.

As previously stated, in the central zone the curves differ one from
another, depending on sample temperature, while in the outer zone
($|\theta| \geq 4$ mrad), they coincide at any temperature in the range from
22 to −117°C. This may give rise to the rather spontaneous hypothesis that the so-called broad component keeps its shape unaltered,
while on the contrary, the "narrow component" seems to change in
shape.

Therefore, the normalization adopted puts well in evidence the
various curve components, making easy their separation.

We are of course aware that the components of different curves
are altered in their relative intensities. Account of this fact is taken
in our calculations by indirectly recurring to a normalization in area
when necessary.†

The common broad component was evaluated from atomic functions by Fourier transformation. We have considered 2s and 2p

†For detailed calculations and bibliography, see "Study of Positronium in
Water and Ice from 22 to −144° C by Annihilation Quanta Measurements."[1]

electrons of H_2O, annihilating with positrons practically at rest. In the wavefunction of these electrons, the component coming from the two hydrogen atoms was neglected, the positron being repelled by the positive charge existing in the neighborhood of each hydrogen atom. Consequently, the resultant wavefunction was similar to that of an oxygen atom, and was approximated by a linear combination of hydrogen-like wavefunctions ψ_{2s} and ψ_{2p} with a proper effective charge number $Z - s$.

The percentage b_t of this component in the curves at +4, -15, and 117°C was 92.1, 85.2, and 87.5%, respectively. Such values lead directly to the Ps formation rate at the corresponding temperatures (in fact, neglecting the conversion process $^3S \rightarrow {}^1S$ the percentage of the narrow component, to which contribute para-Ps atoms only, is $1/4$ of the previous rate). In Table I we report the Ps formation rate found in such a way, and the $4/3\ I_2$ values coming from time distribution measurements for comparison.

In addition, from b and I_2 values, one could derive the amount of ortho-Ps, p_{tc} converted to para-Ps before the annihilation process:

$$p_{tc} = \frac{1 - b - (1 - \tau_s/\tau_2)I_2/3}{1 + \tau_s/3\tau_2} \tag{1}$$

Unfortunately, the error in b_t and I_2 are too large to say that p_{tc} at various temperatures is zero or not. But if it exists, it must be less than 2.67% in water and 4.04% in ice (see Table II).

From the analysis of a wide series of experimental results, and from other considerations, we were induced to deal with what remains of the experimental curves after subtraction of the broad component, as being due to the contribution of two different components.

The narrower of these components becomes more and more pronounced as the temperature decreases, but vanishes in the liquid phase. It was calculated theoretically, considering para-Ps atoms as a gas and allowing it to diffuse and thermalize within the ice lattice, until a Maxwellian distribution of velocities is reached.

The other component, which is a little broader, was simply worked

TABLE I

Positronium Formation Rates in H_2O at 4, -15, and $-117°$ C
by τ_2 Measurements and Angular Correlation Method;
b is the Broad Component Intensity

%	$4/3\ I_2$ (Brandt et al.)[2]	$4/3\ I_2$ (Fabri et al.)[3]	$4(1 - b)$ (from this work)
p4	33.3 ± 6.7	37.3 ± 2.67	31.6 ± 3.7
p-15	60.0 ± 6.7	56.0 ± 4.0	59.1 ± 3.2
p-117			49.0 ± 3.5

TABLE II

Numerical Values of the Probability p_{tc} of $^3S \rightarrow {}^1S$ Conversion Process in H_2O at 4, -15, and $-117°$ C, According to Formula (1)[a]

%	I_2 and τ_2 (Brandt et al.)[2][b]	I_2 and τ_2 (Fabri et al.)[3]
$(p_{tc})4$	0.25 ± 2.41	-0.74 ± 1.53
$(p_{tc})-15$	1.66 ± 2.35	2.27 ± 1.77
$(p_{tc})-117$	-0.45 ± 1.86 (?)	-0.16 ± 1.80 (?)

[a]The last values of the second column were derived by using arbitrarily the I_2 and τ_2 values given at $-15°$ C.

[b]Brandt et al.[2] give I_2 values for ice without specifying temperature.

out by subtracting the theoretical broad component from the water curve.

According to this idea, we tried to approximate the various experimental curves by combining the three components with variable intensities. This was always possible in the temperature range of investigation, and the graphs constructed in such a manner agreed surprisingly well with the experimental ones.

Thus we may attribute the water-ice effect to an increase in Ps rate formation in ice, which causes an enhancement of the narrow component at the loss of the broad one. The modification of the curves at the state transition is made even more evident by a slight narrowing of the peak that may be attributed to some *para*-Ps atoms that undergo complete thermalization. This thermalization mechanism seems to increase when the ice temperatures goes from -18 to $-25°$C, where the narrowest component becomes prominent. This would be in agreement with the increased number of hydrogen bonds, which may offer more energy loss chances to particles to be slowed down. Many properties of ice undergo a notable change in the range from 0 to $-50°$C.

REFERENCES

1. Colombino, P., B. Fiscella, and L. Trossi, *Nuovo Cimento* **38**, 707 (1965).
2. Brandt, W., S. Berko, and W. W. Walker, *Phys. Rev.* **120**, 1289 (1960).
3. Fabri, G., E. Germagnoli, I. F. Quercia, and E. Turrisi, *Nuovo Cimento* **30**, 21 (1963).

Magnetic Quenching of Positronium in Water

G. *Fabri*

Laboratorio C.I.S.E., Milan, Italy

E. *Germagnoli*

Istituto di Fisica dell'Università, Parma, Italy

G. *Iaci, I. F. Quercia, and E. Turrisi*

Istituto di Fisica dell'Università, Catania, Italy

In order to learn a little more about the possibility of investigating the structure of water by means of positron annihilation and formation of positronium atoms, in recent years, a series of measurements has been performed,[1-5] observing the effect of a magnetic field quenching the triplet state of positronium in water.

The first measurements were performed by observing the modifications of angular distribution of the 2-γ annihilation in ice and water, due to an external magnetic field. Those measurements showed that the quenching effect of the magnetic field was much smaller in ice than in water.[1,5] We concluded that some unknown process was to be taken into account for understanding the observed behavior.

At this time we started a series of experiments observing directly the quenching effect of a magnetic field on the τ_2 component of the positronium lifetime in water.

We shall refer here to the measurements carried out in water at $20°C \pm 1°C$, by comparing the delay curves without and with the magnetic field. The effect of the magnetic field is estimated, according to a method proposed by Bisi et al.,[6] from the ratio $R(H)$ between the areas subtended by the delay curves from a given value of the delay t^* to $t = \infty$. The value of t^* has been chosen in such a way as to avoid any contribution of events involving the short lifetime τ_1. The definition of $R(H)$ is given by

$$R(H) = \left[\frac{\int_{t*}^{\infty} I_{2\gamma}(t)\, dt}{\int_{0}^{\infty} I_{2\gamma}(t)\, dt}\right]_{H} \bigg/ \left[\frac{\int_{t*}^{\infty} I_{2\gamma}(t)\, dt}{\int_{0}^{\infty} I_{2\gamma}(t)\, dt}\right]_{H=0}$$

Experimental values of $R(H)$ with $t* = 3.5$ nsec in water are reported in Fig. 1 vs. the applied magnetic field.

If positrons, before annihilating in water, form atoms of positronium, the external magnetic field mixes triplet and singlet positronium states. The observable consequence of such a mixing is that some of the triplet positronium atoms are switched into the singlet state and annihilate with the short lifetime of this state; in this way, the number of decays with the longer lifetime τ_2 is decreased by the magnetic field.

By supposing the positronium is formed in the ground state, the mixing effect can be calculated, and a simple formula can be derived for the expected shape of the function $R(H)$.

Calling $\Gamma = \gamma_3 + \gamma_1 (M_z/\hbar\omega_0)^2$, the decay constant of the state formed by the linear combination of the eigenfunctions of the singlet and the triplet $m = 0$ substate, the only one mixed by the magnetic field, we can introduce a "magnetic lifetime"

$$\tau_H = \frac{1}{2\Gamma}$$

which depends on the free positronium atom decay constants:

$$\gamma_3 = 3.7 \times 10^6 s^{-1} = \text{triplet decay constant}$$

$$\gamma_1 = 4 \times 10^9 s^{-1} = \text{singlet decay constant}$$

and on the ratio

$$\frac{M_z}{\hbar\omega_0} = \frac{e\hbar}{mc}\frac{H}{\hbar\omega_0}$$

where H is the external magnetic field and $\hbar\omega_0$ is the ground-state fine-structure splitting constant of the positronium atom.

An approximate formula for $R(H)$ is given by

$$R(H) = \frac{2}{3} + \frac{1}{3}\frac{\tau_H}{\tau_2 + \tau_H} e^{-(t*/\tau_H)}$$

More sophisticated calculations carried out by Bisi et al.,[6] and by Fabri et al.,[3] give more approximate expressions for the function $R(H)$ (see curves plotted in Fig. 1 and 2). All these expressions agree quite well with the value of $R(H)$ found experimentally in various substances like Lucite and Teflon,[6] but they do not agree at all with the values found experimentally for water at 20°C as is shown in Fig. 1. Of course, by introducing suitable hypotheses, it

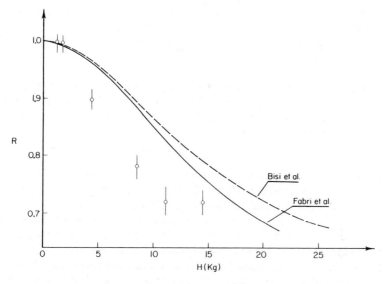

Fig. 1. Magnetic quenching of 2-photon long-lived component in water at 20° C.

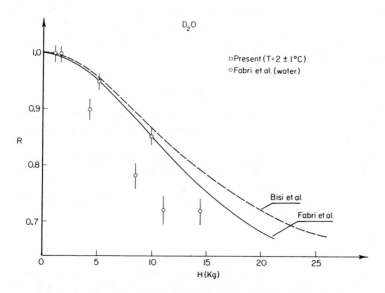

Fig. 2. Magnetic quenching of long-lived component in water at 20° C, and heavy water at 25° C.

is possible to obtain a calculated curve in agreement with the experimental points; for instance, we could assume that in the ratio

$$\frac{e\hbar}{mc}\ \frac{H}{\hbar\omega_0}$$

the value of the fine structure splitting energy $\hbar\omega_0$ is different from the free positronium atom value of 8.34×10^{-4} eV. Assuming this hypothesis tentatively, the value of the fine structure energy, best fitting experimental results is

$$\hbar\omega_0 = 5 \times 10^{-4} \text{ eV}$$

The same value fits satisfactorily a quenching curve, obtained by measuring the increasing of the 2-photon counting rate in water at 20°C, as a function of the magnetic field.[3]*

At present we are performing measurements of $R(H)$ in heavy water.[4] Preliminary results are shown in Fig. 2; it is very clear that in this case the experimental points fall on the expected theoretical curve. In this case the measured temperature was 25 ± 1°C. As a check, at the same time, we have taken repeated measurements of $R(H)$ in water at this temperature. Experimental points are given in Fig. 1; they also fall on the theoretical curve, far away from the experimental points obtained for water at 20°C in our previous measurements.

At present we are carefully checking the possible origin of the discrepancy between the values found for $R(H)$ in water in the two different series of measurements which are largely out of statistical errors. Particularly, we are investigating a possible temperature effect between 10 and 30°C.

REFERENCES

1. Iaci, G., I. F. Quercia, and E. Turrisi, *Nuovo Cimento* **24**, 746 (1962).
2. Fabri, G., E. Germagnoli, I. F. Quercia, and E. Turrisi, *Nuovo Cimento* **30**, 21 (1963).
3. Fabri, G., G. Poletti, and G. Randone, *Phys. Rev.* **135**, A80, (1964).
4. Iaci, G., M. Lo Savio, I. F. Quercia, and E. Turrisi (work in progress).
5. Colombino, P., (private communication).
6. Bisi, A., A. Fiorentini, E. Gatti, and L. Zappa, *Phys. Rev.* **128**, 2195 (1962).

*During the conference Goldanskii showed that taking into account both the variation of $\hbar\omega_0$ and of the singlet decay constant λ_1, of the distorted positronium, the best fit can be reached with $\hbar\omega_0 \approx 3 \times 10^{-4}$ eV and $\lambda_1 \approx 2 \times 10^{11}$ sec^{-1}.

Momentum Distribution of Singlet Positronium in Certain Organic Liquids

W. E. Millett

University of Texas, Austin, Texas

The angular correlation of two photon annihilation radiation from liquid benzene and normal heptane has been measured with apparatus employing cylindrical geometry, the data was corrected for instrument resolution, and then analyzed to determine $N(p)$ vs p.[1] This paper describes how the momentum distribution of singlet positronium in these liquids was obtained. The analysis was carried out in terms of the momentum distributions of diamond, graphite, and hydrogenic $1S$. For convenience, all distributions were plotted as ln $N(p)$ vs ln p. A shift of one curve relative to another along the ordinate is equivalent to a change of scale or relative fraction, and a shift along the abscissa is equivalent to a change of effective charge.

Since the carbons in both graphite and benzene have trigonal (sp^2) orbitals in the plane of the ring and p orbitals normal to the plane of the ring, it seems reasonable to make a comparison of the high momentum contribution of these two materials. This is most easily done with the log N vs log θ shown in Fig. 1. The agreement of these two distributions at high momenta is very good without shifting the curves relative to one another. The difference between the two curves, indicated by the plus signs, is now compared with the hydrogen $1S$ for nuclear charge $Z = 0.70$. The difference between these two curves is indicated by the circled points. This remaining contribution is presumably due to singlet positronium annihilating in flight.

A similar analysis was carried through for normal heptane. In this case, however, the carbon structure was more like that of diamond so the momentum distribution in diamond was fitted at high momenta. To do this it was necessary to shift the diamond curve to lower momenta by 1.25 to 1.0 which would be equivalent to multiplying the momentum scale in diamond by 0.8. The high momentum contribution of the difference curve is now fitted with a hydrogenic $1S$ with $Z = 0.57$. The difference curve from this analysis of the distribution for normal heptane is the broken line curve in Fig. one. The agreement of the functional form of these two curves is good.

Figure 2 is a plot of $N(p)$ vs p for benzene and the decomposition determined from the analysis described above. The relative fractions of the parts to the whole are also indicated. The singlet positronium distribution amounts to 13% of the total distribution, which is in fair agreement with the value expected from the half-life data. The analysis of normal heptane indicated 11% single positronium as compared to $\frac{1}{3}$ (37%) from the half-life data.

Let us denote the momentum distribution of the positronium at the time of formation by $f(\mathbf{p})$. If positronium did not annihilate or breakup until it was thermalized, it would have a momentum distribution designated by $g(\mathbf{p})$. If the annihilation of the positronium occurs at a time t after formation, the momentum distribution of the two photon annihilation radiation will, according to first-order transport theory, be

$$\rho(\mathbf{p},t) = Af(\mathbf{p})e^{-\lambda_0 t} + Bg(\mathbf{p})(1 - e^{-\lambda_0 t})$$

where λ_0 is the reciprocal of the thermalization time. After integration over time

$$\rho(\mathbf{p}) = A \frac{\lambda}{\lambda_0 + \lambda} f(\mathbf{p}) + B \frac{\lambda_0}{\lambda_0 + \lambda} g(\mathbf{p})$$

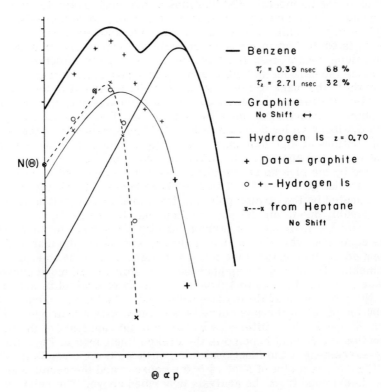

Fig. 1. Plot of log $N(\theta)$ vs log θ for benzene.

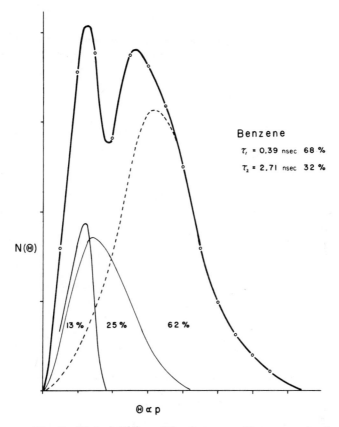

Fig. 2. Plot of $N(\theta)$ vs θ for benzene. The per cent relative areas are indicated on the graph.

where λ is the probability of annihilation of singlet positronium per unit time.

Figure 3 is a plot of $\rho(\mathbf{p})$ vs $\mathbf{p}$ for singlet positronium, as obtained from the normal heptane data. This curve can be broken down into one part which is gaussian and another part which is flat out to 2 mrad. The thermalization time may be determined from the relative areas which turns out to be $3/2\lambda \doteq 0.2$ nsec.

If this analysis is acceptable, it will be necessary to modify an assumption introduced by Ore.[2] He assumed that "the probability that a positron shall be left with a definite energy, as a result of the last inelastic collision suffered by this particle, is the same for all energies below the first excited state." The results obtained here indicate that it is $\rho(\mathbf{p})$ which should be the same for all $\mathbf{p}$ below that which corresponds to the first excited state.

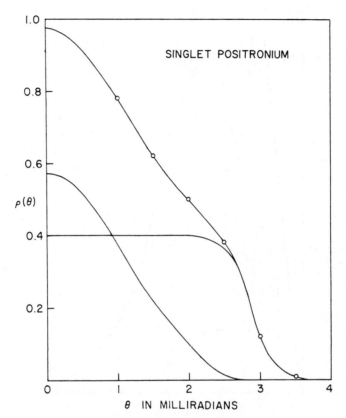

Fig. 3. Plot of $\rho(\theta)$ vs θ for singlet positronium formed in benzene. The gaussian shaped
curve is indeed gaussian and represents the function g **(p)**, while the flat curve represents f **(p)**.

REFERENCES

1. Millett, W. E., and R. Castillo-Bahena, *Phys. Rev.* **108**, 257 (1957).
2. Ore, A., Universitetet i Bergen Årbok 1949, Naturvitenskapelig
   rekke, Nr. 9, 1 (1949).

Positronium Quenching by Paramagnetic Species in Solutions

G. J. Celitans and John Lee

New England Institute for Medical Research
Ridgefield, Connecticut

Oxygen, nitric oxide, and other paramagnetic species rapidly quench triplet Ps formed in liquids with kinetics displaying all the features of diffusion controlled reactions. Previously reported observations[1] in this regard have been improved and extended.

The effect of quencher concentration $[Q]$ on the long-lived positron lifetime (k^{-1}) in water, and a number of organic liquids studied, is expressible in terms of a bimolecular reaction equation,

$$k = k_0 + k_q [Q]$$

where k_0 is the "pickoff" rate and k_q, constant for all $[Q]$, depends on the macroscopic viscosity (η) of the solvent, as predicted by the Debye relationship for a fast reaction where the rate limiting step is the rate of transport together of the reactants

$$k_q = 8RT/3000 \, \eta \quad M^{-1} \sec^{-1}$$

This is shown in Fig. 1, where k_q for oxygen quenching of Ps is plotted against the reciprocal of the viscosity for a number of liquids at room temperature. The slope of the line, however, is about twice that predicted by the Debye equation, and this is interpreted as "slip" of the Ps in contact with the medium.[2] The scatter of points about the line is significant, particularly for the case of water, and probably lies in deviation from the simple Debye relationship, such as the possibility of slip flow.

The temperature dependence of k_q is in the expected relationship shown by the Arrhenius plots for oxygen, nitric oxide, and paramagnetic Cr(III) ion quenching in Fig. 2.

The Debye equation also predicts that the temperature coefficient for the reaction velocity should be approximately the same as for viscosity, and it is seen from Table I that this is indeed the case, the

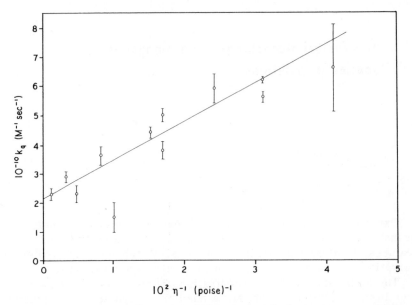

Fig. 1. Viscosity effect of the rate constant k_q for oxygen quenching of Ps.

activation energy E_A for Ps quenching by oxygen, nitric oxide, and paramagnetic Cr (III) ion being of the same magnitude as that for viscosity E. The viscosity control of the quenching of Ps is further indicated by the magnitude of the values for k_q, which on a simple gas kinetic picture should be much greater than 10^{12} $M^{-1} sec^{-1}$, at least for nitric oxide, which has a quenching cross section of the same order as the geometrical cross section in the gas phase. The implication of these results is that the gas kinetic model is not valid for Ps in liquids, as is the case also for molecular species.

The results may be explained by assuming the Ps to be formed in a cage in the liquid, and its reaction rate being controlled by the transport rate of this cage. If one assumes this cage to have the classical diameter of the Ps atom (1.06 Å), then from the measurements of the diffusion rate of oxygen, D_{O_2} in these same liquids,[3] the diffusion rate of the Ps cage D_{Ps} may be estimated from the Smoluchowski equation:

$$k_q = \frac{4\pi N^0}{1000} (D_{O_2} + D_{Ps}) (r_{O_2} + r_{Ps})$$

where N^0 is the Avogadro number. The estimates of D_{Ps} are in Table II where the radius of the oxygen molecule r_{O_2} is assumed to be

TABLE I

Activation Energies, E_A (Kcal/mole)
for Oxygen, Nitric Oxide and Chromium (III) Ion,
Compared with the Activation Energies for Viscosity, E[8]

Solvent	Quencher	E_A	E
n-Butanol	O_2	3.0	4.4
Ethanol	O_2	2.9	3.2
Ethanol	NO	2.5	3.2
Pyridine	Cr (III)	2.8	2.3
Acetone	O_2	2.3	1.6
n-Hexane	O_2	1.2	1.6
n-Pentane	NO	1.0	1.5
Diethyl ether	O_2	1.4	1.4

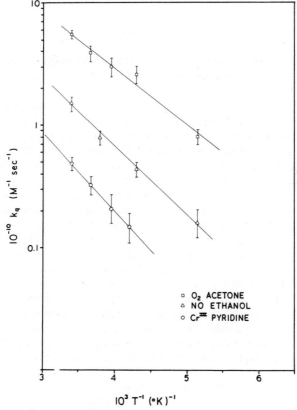

Fig. 2. Temperature dependence of the rate constant k_q for oxygen, nitric oxide and chromium (III) ion quenching of Ps.

TABLE II

Diffusion Coefficients for Ps in Liquids Calculated from the Smoluchowski Equation and the Measured Diffusion Coefficients of Oxygen in These Same Liquids.[3] These are Compared with the Diffusion Coefficients for Ps Calculated from the Stokes-Einstein Equation D'_{Ps}

Liquid	$10^5 D_{O_2}$ (cm^2 sec^{-1})	$10^5 D_{Ps}$ (cm^2 sec^{-1})	$10^5 D'_{Ps}$ (cm^2 sec^{-1})
Acetone	9.0	19.6	12.6
n-Heptane	5.6	25.1	9.9
Benzene	5.7	17.2	6.2
Ethanol	3.9	14.8	3.4
n-Octanol	1.6	10.4	0.5

2 Å. It is to be noted that the values calculated from the Stokes-Einstein equation,

$$D = kT/6\pi\eta r$$

are several times smaller, which is also to be found in the case of oxygen,[3] where it is explained by the breakdown of the Stokes-Einstein condition.

The lifetime curves are analyzed by fitting them to a two-component exponential relationship. Examination of the short lifetime shows that it is an average of a very short lifetime, presumably that for decay of Ps (^1S) and one of about 0.5 nsec, probably representing the annihilation of free positrons. If the curves really contain three exponential components, these quenching results can be shown to be substantially unaltered; the absolute values of the lifetimes are reduced, however, in some cases by as much as 10%. Also an observed enhancement[4] of the long-lifetime intensity by oxygen and nitric oxide in some liquids cannot be attributed to interference by a middle component, and must arise from increase in Ps formation, which does not affect the first equation, since formation and quenching are sequential, not competitive processes.

The absence of an enhanced narrow component in the angular distribution of the annihilation photons, which is believed to originate from Ps (^1S) annihilation, observed by Kerr et al.[5] for oxygen in hexane, rules out triplet to singlet conversion as the quenching mechanism. The quenching is probably by a chemical process:

$$Ps + O_2 \rightarrow PsO_2 \longleftrightarrow e^+ O_2^-$$

the e^+ annihilating in the oxygen electron cloud as if it were being "picked-off," thus not contributing to the narrow component of the angular distribution. The analogy with ordinary chemistry is strong, since oxygen is well known as a powerful one-electron acceptor. It would be expected that the nitric oxide mechanism would be the same, and this should be verified by angular correlation measurements.

Other paramagnetic species are expected to behave in a similar way and show similar quenching rate constants. For example, using the results of Berko and Zuchelli,[6] the quenching constant for the free radical diphenylpicrylhydrazyl quenching of Ps (^3S) in benzene can be estimated as 2.2×10^{10} M^{-1} sec^{-1}; this is only slightly lower than the corresponding constant for nitric oxide, $(3.1 \pm 0.3) \times 10^{10}$ M^{-1} sec^{-1}, or oxygen, $(4.4 \pm 0.2) \times 10^{10}$ M^{-1} sec^{-1}, quenching in benzene. Paramagnetic ions have a quenching rate constant in the range 10^9–10^{10} M^{-1} sec^{-1} in aqueous solution,[7] since in this medium they are highly solvated and move very slowly. For a non-aqueous, weakly complexing solvent, such as pyridine, which has about the same viscosity as water, the rate constants would be expected to be much higher, because of the relative lack of ion solvation. Preliminary results indicate that this is the case. The rate constant for Cr(III) quenching of Ps in aqueous solution[7] is 1.8×10^9 M^{-1} sec^{-1}, whereas in pyridine the rate constant increases to $(4.6 \pm 0.4) \times 10^9$ M^{-1} sec^{-1}. Studies are continuing of the rate constants and activation energies of other paramagnetic ions in aqueous and nonaqueous solutions.

The interpretation of the present results may be summarized by saying that Ps is trapped in a solvent cage and quenching occurs on every encounter with the quencher molecule or ion, since there may be several hundred collisions in each encounter. This picture of Ps in liquids is analogous to that for the free electron in this environment. This diffusion-controlled situation limits the amount of useful information about Ps reaction mechanisms, which may be obtained from these studies.

ACKNOWLEDGMENT

We thank S. Berko and H. Linchitz for discussion of this work.

REFERENCES

1. Lee, J., and G. J. Celitans, *J. Chem. Phys.* **42**, 437 (1965).
2. Osborne, A. D., and G. Porter, *Proc. Roy. Soc. (London)* **A284**, 9 (1965).
3. Ware, W. R., *J. Phys. Chem.* **66**, 455 (1962).
4. Lee, J., S. J. Tao, and G. J. Celitans, These Proceedings.

5. Kerr, D. P., A. M. Cooper, and B. G. Hogg, *Canad. J. Phys.* **43**, 963 (1965).
6. Berko, S., and A. J. Zuchelli, *Phys. Rev.* **102**, 724 (1956).
7. Goldanskii, V. I., V. G. Firsov, and V. P. Shantarovich, *Dokl. Academy Nauk USSR* **155**, 363 (1964); R. E. Green and R. E. Bell, *Canad. J. Phys.* **36**, 1684 (1958).

Positronium Formation in Gases and Liquids

John Lee, S. J. Tao, and G. J. Celitans

New England Institute for Medical Research, Ridgefield, Connecticut

Using simple energetic considerations, Ore derived limits between which the fraction of positrons stopping in a monatomic gas such as argon should form positronium (Ps).[1] The calculation of a maximum formation likelihood is, however, predicated on the assumption that the last positron-molecule collision above the ionization potential leaves the positron with any energy up to the ionization potential of the molecule with equal probability. This assumption is open to question since large collision resonances are expected in the regions above the ionization potential of the molecule,[2] and these could present a heavy bias on the kinetic energy of the scattered positron. The "Ore gap" region may be relatively underpopulated or overpopulated depending on the relative dispositions of these resonances. The relevance of these arguments would be strengthened by observation of formation fractions greater than the maxima predicted using the simple Ore theory. Unfortunately, although such cases do exist in the older literature,[3] the results are open to question since they depend on a simple positron decay scheme whereas the situation is now known to be quite complex. Recent observations show that the positron lifetime spectrum in gases is nonexponential.[4-7] In the case of the monatomic gases where the first electronic excitation level fell clearly above the threshold level for Ps formation, the estimation of a formation minimum appears, on the face of it, unambiguous. However, more complicated species fail to show effects of an increasing number of electronic and vibrational levels in the Ore gap region, and in some cases, even a negative value is predicted for the formation minimum. The Ore model may be sufficient for the monatomic gases, as supported by the studies of mixtures of argon and krypton, etc.[8] Although some attempts have been made to apply it to solids and liquids, one must still question the interpretation of the ionization potential, the Ps formation energy and the threshold for Ps formation in these environments. The picture is further complicated by the observation of resonance phenomena for annihilation of positrons in gases at energies below the threshold for Ps formation.[9] Figure 1 demonstrates that the annihilation rate exhibits a

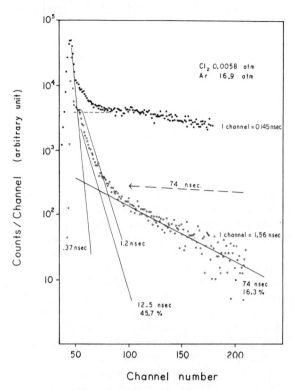

Fig. 1. Positron annihilation lifetime curve in a chlorine argon mixture showing the nonexponentiality of the decay. The upper curve is a high-resolution expansion of the first 10 nsec of the main lower curve.

strong time dependence, since the decay is obviously neither simply exponential nor the sum of exponentials. The shortest and longest lifetimes are due to self-annihilation from the two Ps states. The time-dependent annihilation rate $\lambda(t)$ is due to the combination of the energy dependence of the annihilation rate and the nonnegligible slowing down time of either free positrons or Ps. Both the shape of the distribution of positron or Ps energies and the individual positron energy will change with time, and a time-dependent rate of annihilation will result if the molecule has a resonance for annihilation at specific positron energies. Fig. 1 demonstrates the existence of at least two separate resonance groups in the case of chlorine-argon mixtures. The shape of this curve will, of course, depend markedly on composition, pressure, etc. The first resonance group, which is the one at longer times, is attributed to free positrons. Many theoretical calculations have failed to predict the existence of resonance scattering or annihilation. A suggestion has been made that it is the result of bound states of Ps or positron attachment.[7],[10] However, a detailed analysis of $\lambda(t)$ shows that a resonance group may contain more than one resonance at energies below 1 eV,[9] but present theory makes it difficult to imagine the existence of more than one bound state at these low energies. Further theoretical explanation is required. Electron scattering cross-sections have been calculated in the past by assuming the nonrelativistic Schroedinger equation. Recent calculations for scattering of Dirac particles[11] indicate that it might be useful to see if this same relativistic treatment predicts the presence of annihilation resonances.

The second resonance group which occurs at shorter times may be attributed to Ps compound formation, such as in a reaction

$$Ps + Cl_2 \rightarrow PsCl + Cl$$

which requires a threshold energy of 0.5 eV. This being true, the annihilation lifetime of the third component, τ_3, in Fig. 1, may not be just a simple constant.

Liquids usually display considerable Ps formation, although a simple Ore gap does not exist. We have observed an increase in the intensity (I_2) of the long lifetime annihilations, interpreted as an enhancement of Ps formation, by the addition of oxygen or nitric oxide to a number of liquids at room temperature. We have already demonstrated the diffusion controlled nature of Ps reactions with these agents,[12] postulating that Ps is transported through the liquid in a solvent cage, and that reaction occurs with every encounter of the Ps cage and quencher cage. Immediately upon formation, the Ps will find itself within a cage containing the parent radical ion or its primary decomposition products as well as the other solvent molecules. The amount of Ps that appears in the long-lived component will therefore be governed by the rate at which the newly formed Ps and the parent radical ion can diffuse away from each other. The overall I_2 will be a ratio of this diffusion rate, and the overall rereactivity of the Ps and parent radical ion. This latter will depend on the chemical nature of the molecule from which the radical ion derives. As well as quenching the Ps after being formed, O_2 and NO are shown in Fig. 2 to enhance the long-lived intensity I_2. This action is probably by competitive scavenging of the parent radical ion by oxygen or nitric oxide so as to reduce the probability of rereaction with the Ps. Since these are all reactive species, this rapid scavenging reaction should be diffusion controlled, and indeed Fig. 2 demonstrates

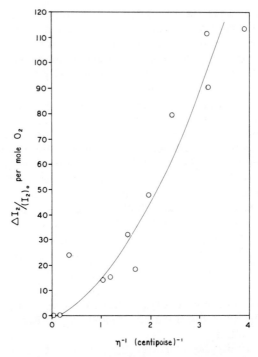

Fig. 2. Relationship of the ability of oxygen and nitric oxide to enhance the intensity of long-lived positrons (I_2) with the inverse viscosity (η^{-1}) in a number of liquids at room temperature.

that the enhancement of I_2 is a function of liquid viscosity, a classical feature of diffusion-controlled reactions. Also activation energies for the enhancement appear to be low and of the same magnitude as for viscosity of these liquids, again indicating diffusion control. Figure 2 also shows that in the case of the less viscous liquids, such as hexane, an I_2 of up to 75% is possible, implying that most of the positrons are forming Ps, although the Ps is then rapidly quenched by the oxygen. Other radical scavengers are also being examined. Unfortunately, most of these scavengers are also very reactive with the Ps, which is itself an elementary free radical so that as I_2 is being enhanced, τ_2 is being shortened until a point is reached when instrumental resolution does not allow I_2 to be estimated with any certainty. Resolution is being improved in this case to verify that I_2 does indeed saturate at 75%. It may also be possible that in liquids resonance effects may be playing a part as in gases, although this is not likely if the Ps and positrons are rapidly thermalized. It is not unlikely that reactive agents such as oxygen and nitric oxide can influence the formation rate, even in the small concentrations that are shown in Fig. 2, since they are known to have long range interactions in liquids. Viscosity would not be expected to play a part with this effect, however.

It is concluded that in gases the Ore theory becomes less useful, not only because of the wide formation limits it predicts, but because of the complications of resonance effects. In liquids, the diffusion controlled nature of Ps reactions demonstrates the predominance of the solvent cage which present evidence suggests may play a part in Ps formation as well.

REFERENCES

1. Ore, A., Univ. i Bergen Årbok Naturvitenskap. rekke Nr. 9 (1949).
2. Mott, N. F., and H. S. W. Massey, "The Theory of Atomic Collisions," 2nd ed., Oxford Univ. Press, London and New York, 1949.
3. Marder, S., V. W. Hughes, C. S. Wu, and W. Bennett, *Phys. Rev.* **103** 1258 (1956).
4. Tao, S. J., J. Bell, and J. H. Green, *Proc. Phys. Soc. (London)* **83** 453 (1964).
5. Falk, W. R., and G. Jones, *Canad. J. Phys.* **42** 1751 (1964).
6. Paul, D. A. L., *Proc. Phys. Soc. (London)* **84** 563 (1964).
7. Osmon, P. E., *Phys. Rev.* **138**, B216 (1965).
8. Gittelman, B., Ph.D. Thesis, Massachusetts Institute of Technology, Dept. of Physics, 1958.
9. Tao, S. J., *Phys. Rev. Letters* **14** 935 (1965).
10. Goldanskii, V. I., and Y. S. Sayasov, *Phys. Letters* **13** 300 (1964); Soviet Physics JETP **20** 1339 (1965).
11. Fradkin, D. M., T. A. Weber, and C. L. Hammer, *Ann. Physik* **27** 338 (1964).
12. Celitans, G. J., and J. Lee, these Proceedings.

Positron Annihilation in Liquefied Gases*

C. V. Briscoe and A. T. Stewart

University of North Carolina, Chapel Hill, North Carolina

INTRODUCTION

The annihilation of positrons in liquid gases other than helium has been studied very little. Paul[1] has measured the time distribution of positron decays in nitrogen and in argon, and has observed two components as is customary in amorphous nonconductors. Liu and Roberts[2] have also measured lifetimes in hydrogen, nitrogen, and oxygen. In addition, Basina et al.[3] have published some data on the angular correlation of photons from positron annihilation in hydrogen. This paper presents data on the distribution of momentum of photons from positrons annihilating in the liquids hydrogen, oxygen, nitrogen, neon, and argon. Except for oxygen, the results show a momentum distribution which appears to be the sum of two separate distributions, a narrow one which shows up as a central peak and a much broader one. The angular distribution for oxygen shows no narrow component at all. The intensity of the narrow component in the other gases is compared with existing data on positronium formation. The width of the narrow component is discussed in terms of the bubble picture of positronium in certain liquids. We have not yet completed our analysis of the wide components of these measurements.

EXPERIMENTAL

The source of positrons was two copper foils mounted parallel to the long slit detectors and about $1/_{16}$ in. apart. The liquid specimen was defined by lead slits close to the cryostat with about 0.025 in. gap. The apparatus measured angles by moving one detector only. The moving slit close to the cryostat was always slightly larger than the fixed specimen-defining slit in order that the volume of specimen did not change with angle. The detectors were about 20 feet away and subtended an angle at the specimen of about 0.2 mrad. The overall resolution of the apparatus had a width (FWHM) of 0.3 mrad. All data were collected at the normal boiling point of the various liquids.

*Work supported in part by the National Science Foundation and the Advanced Research Projects Agency.

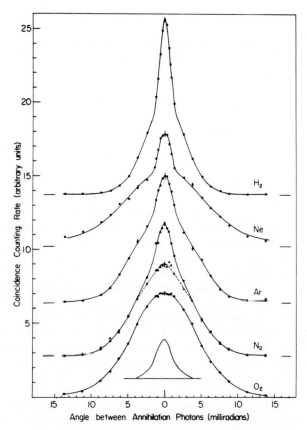

Fig. 1. The angular distribution of photons from
positrons annihilating in several liquefied gases. The
statistical accuracy is indicated by the error bars on
some of the points. Two sets of data are shown for
liquid nitrogen. The circles represent data for nitrogen of 99.998% purity, and the triangles for nitrogen at
99.5% purity. The inset shows the difference.

RESULTS

Figure 1 shows the angular distribution of radiation from positrons
annihilating in the several liquid gases. It is obvious that all results
show a narrow component except the data for oxygen. We show two
sets of data for nitrogen. The set without the narrow peak was obtained in liquid nitrogen of 99.5% purity. The set with the narrow
peak was obtained in liquid nitrogen of 99.998% purity. The small
insert shows the difference between these two nitrogen data sets.

DISCUSSION

We first compared the intensities of the narrow components with other observations of the fraction of positrons which have a long lifetime. These data are collected in Table I. The nice agreement which we pointed out for helium does not appear so clearly for the other gases. Since, as we have seen, a small amount of oxygen causes the narrow peak to disappear in liquid nitrogen, it may be that quite small traces of oxygen can cause the discrepancy seen in the data for argon and nitrogen. However, there should be no oxygen contamination of our neon and hydrogen specimens, and we note that the neon peak intensity is about the same as for helium. The results for hydrogen, however, are more perplexing. In spite of the narrowness of the broad component and the attendant difficulty of effecting as unambiguous a separation of components as for some other gases, it seems most unlikely that we have overestimated the intensity by a factor of 2. The problem of positronium formation in these liquids clearly needs further study.

Secondly, concerning the narrow component: Following Ferrell,[4] let us assume that a bubble is formed by the repulsion between a positronium atom and the atoms or molecules of the liquid. The size of the bubble is determined by minimizing the total energy of surface tension[5] of the bubble plus the zero-point energy of the contained

TABLE I

	Liu and Roberts			Paul			Present work
	Lifetime $(10^{-9}$ sec)		Intensity (%)	Lifetime $(10^{-9}$ sec)		Intensity (%)	3 × intensity of narrow component (%)
	τ_1	τ_2	I_2	τ_1	τ_2	I_2	
H_2	0.92	28.6					36 ± 7.2
		31^a	18^a				
N_2	0.56	10.8			11	15	$23\,^{+4.6}_{-2.3}$
		9.3^a	11^a				
O_2	0.45						
	0.12^a	0.495^a	64^a				
Ne							16 ± 1.6
Ar		5.8^a	5.5^a		7	7	$22\,^{+4.4}_{-2.2}$
He	1.9	88			90	15	15 ± 1.5

^{a}W. K. Roberts, private communication.

TABLE II

	Observed width (FWHM) of narrow component in milliradians (%)	"Bubble" diameter in angstrom units	
		From width of narrow component	From surface tension
He	$0.8 \pm 5\%$	52	44 (4.2°K) 33 (1.7°K)
H_2	$1.3 \begin{array}{l} + 15\% \\ - 5\% \end{array}$	33	21
Ne	$1.7 \begin{array}{l} + 10\% \\ - 5\% \end{array}$	24	17
N_2	$1.8 \begin{array}{l} + 10\% \\ - 5\% \end{array}$	23	15
Ar	$2.1 \begin{array}{l} + 10\% \\ - 5\% \end{array}$	19	14

positronium atom. This calculation yields the bubble diameters which are listed in Table II. We have also calculated the size of a spherical square well potential which would yield a momentum distribution for zero point motion of the same width as the observed narrow components. The values are also shown in the table. In all cases except helium at 4.2°K the bubble obtained from surface tension measurements is about $^2/_3$ the size of the bubble obtained from the observed momentum of zero point motion in a spherical square well. Part of this small discrepancy may be due to the fact that the walls of a real bubble are somewhat penetrable.

The results for oxygen are different from the other liquids studied. The lack of a narrow component implies that there is no free singlet positronium in the liquid. Yet positrons annihilating in gaseous oxygen show nearly 50% positronium formation as seen in both lifetime and two photon angular correlation experiments.[6,7,8,9] A possible explanation may lie in the formation of some fast annihilating bound state, possibly $(e^+ e^-)O_2$ as suggested by Paul.[10] Furthermore this state is presumably stable enough to capture positronium out of the liquid nitrogen and thus quench its narrow component.

REFERENCES

1. Paul, D. A. L., *Canad. J. Phys.* **36**, 640 (1958).
2. Liu, D. C., and W. K. Roberts, *J. Phys. Chem. Solids* **23**, 1337 (1962); *Phys. Rev.* **130**, 2322 (1963); Phys. Rev. **132**, 1633 (1963).

3. Basina, A. S., K. A. Baskova, B. S. Dzhelepov, and M. A. Dolgoborodova, *Izv. Akad. Nauk. SSSR, Ser. Fiz.* **22**, 968 (1958).
4. Ferrell, R. A., *Phys. Rev.* **108**, 167 (1957).
5. The values used for surface tension were obtained from *A Compendium of the Properties of Materials at Low Temperature (Phase 1)*,   Part 1. Properties of Fluids, Victor J. Johnson, General Editor. Released by Office of Technical Services, U. S. Department of Commerce, Washington, D. C.
6. Page, L. A., and M. Heinberg, *Phys. Rev.* **106**, 1220 (1957).
7. Obenshein, F. E., and L. A. Page, *Phys. Rev.* **125**, 573 (1962).
8. Celitans, G. J., and J. H. Green, *Proc. Phys. Soc. (London)* **83**, 823 (1964).
9. Heinberg, M., and L. A. Page, *Phys. Rev.* **107**, 1589 (1957).
10. Paul, D. A. L., *Canad. J. Phys.* **37**, 1059 (1959).

Positron Annihilation in Liquid Helium*

A. T. Stewart and C. V. Briscoe

University of North Carolina, Chapel Hill, North Carolina

INTRODUCTION

Measurements of lifetimes of positrons decaying in liquid helium[1,2] have shown three components which are interpreted as being due to triplet positronium [about 15%] free positron annihilation [about 80%], and a small component in the prompt peak probably due to singlet annihilation. To account for the long life of triplet positronium, Ferrell[3] has postulated that the positronium atom can exist in a bubble by virtue of the exchange repulsion of the positronium electron with the electrons of the helium atom. Some angular correlation measurements[4,5] have also been made. White, Gacii, and MacKenzie[5] obtained a narrow peak which led them to agree with the conclusion of Paul and Graham[1] that about 17 to 20% of the positrons in helium form positronium. We have made high resolution angular correlation measurements and have indeed obtained a very narrow component of intensity about 5%. If this narrow component is interpreted as due to singlet positronium, this supports the above conclusion that about 20% of positrons in helium form positronium.

EXPERIMENTAL

The source of positrons was two copper foils mounted parallel to the long slit detectors and about $1/8$ of an inch apart. The detectors were about 20 feet away and subtended an angle at the specimen of about 0.2 mrad for most runs and 0.15 mrad for the high resolution experiment. The apparatus varied the angle between the photons by moving one counter only. The liquid helium specimen was defined by a fixed lead slit close to the cryostat with a gap of about 0.050 in. and about 0.025 in. in the high resolution experiment. A moving slit close to the cryostat was always slightly larger than the fixed slit which defined the specimen in order that the volume of the specimen

*Supported in part by the National Science Foundation and the Advanced Research Projects Agency.

did not change with angle. The overall resolution of the apparatus had a full width at half maximum of 0.4 mrad; and for the higher resolution run, 0.25 mrad. Most of the data were collected at 4.2°K and part of one run was also made below the lambda point at about 1.7°K. The low temperature was obtained simply by pumping on the liquid helium. No other changes were made in the apparatus.

RESULTS

Figure 1 shows our measurements of the angular correlation between the photons from positrons annihilating in liquid helium. The inset shows the data for the narrow peak at two different temperatures. It can be seen that there is no difference in this component. Although it is not shown, there was no change in the broad component either. The narrow peak is clearly separable from the broader distribution, and its intensity is about 5%. The results obtained in

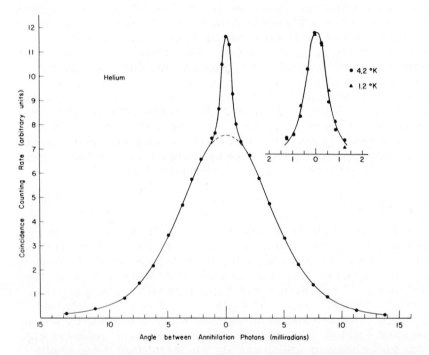

Fig. 1. The angular distribution of photon pairs from positrons annihilating in liquid helium. The insert shows the narrow peak on an expanded horizontal scale. There was no observable difference in the data for helium between 4.2 and 1.7°K. The total coincident counts in the peak was greater than 12,000.

the high resolution experiment are not shown. The only observable difference from the data of Fig. 1 was a slight reduction in the width of the narrow component. Depending upon the method of separating the narrow and broad components, the full width at half maximum of the narrow component is between 0.92 and 0.85 mrad for the lower resolution run and between 0.87 and 0.80 mrad for the higher resolution run. When the effect of apparatus resolution is removed, these figures become 0.81, 0.75, and 0.83, 0.76 mrad, respectively. The average is 0.79 ± 0.05 mrad.

DISCUSSION

The intensity of the narrow component is expected to be the sum of "thermalized" singlet positronium and converted triplet positronium atoms. Since the electrons of helium atoms are in a saturated shell, there seems little likelihood of conversion taking place so we can assume the narrow peak is primarily singlet positronium in equilibrium with liquid helium. If so, the observed 5% intensity agrees well with the interpretation of Paul and Graham,[1] and we conclude with them that about 20% of the positrons in helium form positronium.

To explain the long lifetime of triplet positronium in liquid helium Ferrell[3] proposed that the positrons be contained in a bubble in the liquid. The size of the bubble is determined by minimizing the total energy of surface tension of the bubble plus zero-point energy of the positronium atom. This yields a bubble diameter in helium of about 44 Å at 4.2°K. If we assume the bubble is spherical, our observed width of 0.8 mrad corresponds to the momentum of a positronium atom in a bubble of diameter about 52 Å, in fairly good agreement with Ferrell's model (see Table I). Our data at 1.7°K show a narrow peak with the same width, and hence imply the same bubble diameter. On the other hand, at 1.7°K, the surface tension is much larger and the predicted bubble diameter is 33 Å, a decrease of 25%. A change of 10% would have been easily detected.

TABLE I
Bubble Diameters

°K	Surface tension[6] dynes/cm	Predicted diameter (Å)	FWHM of narrow component (mrad)	Diameter from narrow component (Å)
4.2	0.10	44	0.8	52
1.7	0.325	33	0.8	52

There is another difficulty with the bubble picture. Ferrell accounts for the long positronium lifetime on the basis of pickoff annihilation with the atoms of the vapor inside the bubble. The increase in vapor pressure in going from 4.2° up to the critical point would decrease the long lifetime by about 60% on this basis. Daniel and Stump[7] observed only about a 15% decrease in the lifetime in going from the normal boiling point to near the critical point. Thus, in spite of the obvious approximate validity of the bubble picture which is presented in this paper and in the accompanying paper on other liquid gases, a more detailed picture has now become necessary.

Paul and Graham point out that most (80%) of the positrons annihilate in a "free" state. Thus the angular distribution should be characteristic of the electrons of helium atoms perturbed by the presence of a positron. The broader component of our angular distribution data has a width which is approximately $2/3$ of the width of the momentum distribution of electrons in a free helium atom. This narrower distribution might be expected for two separate reasons. If the positron is forced to annihilate with only electrons of the outer part of the helium atom the photon momentum would be less than the average of the electrons. Secondly, electron-positron correlations would probably result in a narrower momentum distribution. We have not yet compared our data with any calculations of wavefunctions involving correlations.

REFERENCES

1. Paul, D. A. L., and R. L. Graham, *Phys. Rev.* **106**, 16 (1957).
2. Wackerle, J., and R. Stump, *Phys. Rev.* **106**, 18 (1957).
3. Ferrell, R. A., *Phys. Rev.* **108**, 167 (1957).
4. Basina, A. S., K. A. Baskova, B. S. Dzhelepov, and M. A. Dolgoborodova, *Izv. Akad. Nauk. SSSR, Ser. Fez.* **22**, 968 (1958).
5. White, C. G., P. Gacii, and I. K. MacKenzie, *Bull. Canad. Assoc. Phys.* **19**, No. 3, 68 (1963).
6. Allen, J. F., and A. D. Misener, *Proc. Cambridge Phil. Soc.* **34**, 299 (1938).
7. Daniel, T. B., and R. Stump, *Phys. Rev.* **115**, 1599 (1959).

Positron Lifetimes in Low Temperature Helium Gas*

T. M. Kelly† and *L. O. Roellig*

Wayne State University
Detroit, Michigan

It is well known that the positron lifetime spectra in argon gas exhibits a definite shoulder after the prompt peak.[1,2] Recent measurements in other noble gases have indicated that such a shoulder may also be present in helium at room temperature.[3] In this paper results are presented of studies made at 4.2°K and pressures from $1/2$ to 1 atm, which clearly demonstrates the existence of a shoulder in helium gas. In contrast to previous results, an exponential decay is observed on the top of the shoulder. Also for the first time, a hump is noticed at the inflection point of the shoulder.

Due to the spatial limitations of the low temperature apparatus, the helium gas was contained in a brass cylinder of 1.25 in. in diameter. The positrons from a Na^{22} source were moderated by a brass foil in order to increase the number of positrons stopping in the gas. We estimate that about 13% of the positrons annihilated in the gas. The annihilation γ-rays were detected by Pilot B plastic scintillators, mounted on 56AVP photomultiplier tubes. A time-to-amplitude converter of the type described by Simms which had a range of 300 nsec and a resolving time of 3.5 nsec (full width at half maximum) was used for the lifetime measurements.[4]

Figure 1 shows typical delayed coincidence spectra for the gas at 4.2°K, and pressures from approximately 1 to $13/16$ atm. Note that the shoulder region is characterized by the exponential decay on the top of the shoulder (τ_2), followed by a hump, a decay with lifetime (τ_3), and a shoulder width (T). At pressures less than $3/4$ of an atmosphere, the hump and lifetime τ_3 were obscured by the background, and hence only a single lifetime, τ_2, was observed. The results of these lifetime measurements are summarized in Table I.

The observation of a hump at 4.2°K indicates that there is an abrupt change in the annihilation rate. In fact, for such a change in the annihilation rate, one can obtain the relationship:

*Work supported in part by the National Science Foundation.
†NASA Predoctoral Trainee Fellow.

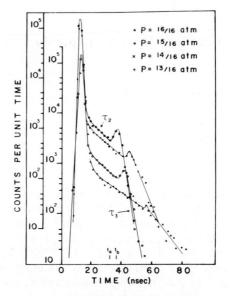

Fig. 1. Positron annihilation
spectra in helium gas at 4.2° K.
Random background and the long
lifetime have been subtracted. The
The lifetimes τ_2 and τ_3 and the
times t_a and t_b are indicated only
for the data taken at $P \cong 16/16$
atm. The ordinate on the left
(right) corresponds to data at
16/16 and 14/16 (15/16 and 13/16)
atm.

TABLE I
Positron Lifetimes in Helium Gas at 4.2° K

P(atm)	ρ (gm/cm$^3 \times 10^{-2}$)	τ_2 (nsec)	τ_3 (nsec)	T(nsec)
16/16	1.68	15.0 ± 1.0	2.7 ± 0.1	25.5 ± 2
15/16	1.57	17.1 ± 1.3	3.5 ± 0.1	30.3 ± 2
14/16	1.37	19.6 ± 1.0	5.1 ± 0.3	35.5 ± 2
27/32	1.31	22.1 ± 1.3	8.8 ± 0.1	39.6 ± 4
13/16	1.23	22.8 ± 1.6	11.8 ± 1.5	40.5 ± 4
12/16	1.10	22.5 ± 0.8	—	—
8/16	0.67	32.9 ± 0.5	—	—

TABLE II
Experimental Results for $\lambda_3/\lambda_2 = (dN/dt)_b/(dN/dt)_a$

P(atm)	λ_3/λ_2	$(dN/dt)_b/(dN/dt)_a$
16/16	6.65	6.35
15/16	4.90	5.1
14/16	3.88	3.78
27/32	2.51	3.3
13/16	1.93	2.5

$$\frac{(dN/dt)_b}{(dN/dt)_a} = \frac{\lambda_3 N_b}{\lambda_2 N_a} \approx \frac{\lambda_3}{\lambda_2} \tag{1}$$

where $(dN/dt)_a$ and $(dN/dt)_b$ can be experimentally determined from the annihilation spectrum at times t_a and t_b (see Fig. 1). Table II shows that our experimental curves satisfy this relation quite well, especially at the higher pressures where the hump is well defined.

Although the width of the shoulder varies with the density of the gas, the product of the shoulder width and the gas density is usually found to be a constant.[1] The density of the gas was computed from the virial equation[5]

$$PV = nRT\left(1 + \frac{nB(T)}{V}\right) \tag{2}$$

If one considers the shoulder width-density product to be a constant, it would have the value $\rho T = 4.8 \pm 0.4 \times 10^{-10}$ (g sec/cm^3). This is shown as curve a in Fig. 2. By assuming elastic collisions with constant cross sections, it is possible to calculate the time it takes a positron to slow down from an initial energy, E_0, to a final energy E.[6] It is found that for a positron emitted from Na^{22} the above value of ρT corresponds to a final energy of $E = 1.4 \pm 0.3$ eV. The de Broglie wavelength of a positron at this energy is $\lambda = 8.1 \pm 0.9$ Å. It is of interest to note that the average interatomic distance for helium gas at 4.2°K and 1 atm is 8.5 Å. This leads one to speculate that the phenomena which is responsible for the hump and the lifetime τ_3 occurs when the de Broglie wavelength of the positron is equal to the interatomic spacing in the gas. The lifetime, τ_3, may be due to positrons annihilating from a quasibound state which consists of an exchange resonance of the positron between two helium atoms. If one makes this assumption, the positron energy at which an abrupt change in the annihilation rate takes place can now be calculated as a function

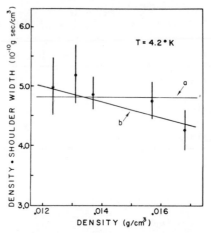

Fig. 2. Variation of density-shoulder width product (ρT) with density for helium gas at 4.2° K. Curve a is for ρT = constant and curve b is the value of ρT for positron de Broglie wavelengths, equal to the average interatomic spacing between helium atoms.

of the density, and hence the value of ρT as a function of density is obtained. The result is shown as curve b in Fig. 2. It is seen that curve b , which contains no adjustable parameters, results in a better fit to the experimental data than curve a.

By extrapolating the shoulder width, T, to the density of liquid helium, one finds that $T = 1.5 \times 10^{-10}$ sec. Hence the shoulder would lie inside the prompt region of the lifetime spectrum, and, therefore, would not be observed. We are led to conclude that the free positron lifetime observed in liquid helium (i.e., the intermediate lifetime, $\tau \simeq 2 \times 10^{-9}$ sec) arises from the same process as the lifetime τ_3 in gaseous helium at 4.2°K.

REFERENCES

1. Tao, S. J., J. Bell, and J. H. Green, *Proc. Phys. Soc. (London)* **83**, 453 (1964).
2. Falk, W. R., P. H. R. Orth, and G. Jones, *Phys. Rev. Letters* **14**, 447 (1965).

3. Osmon, P. E., *Phys. Rev.* **138**, 216 (1965).

4. Simms, P. C., *Rev. Sci. Instr.* **32**, 894 (1961).

5. Kilpatrick, J. E., W. E. Keller, and E. F. Hammel, *Phys. Rev.* **97**, 9 (1955).

6. Tao, S. J., J. H. Green, and G. J. Celitans, *Proc. Phys. Soc. (London)* **81**, 1091 (1963).

The Effect of Some Minor Impurities on the Positron Annihilation Lifetime Spectrum in Argon

S. J. Tao

New England Institute for Medical Research, Ridgefield, Connecticut

and

J. Bell

University of New South Wales, Sydney, Australia

ABSTRACT

The effect of the presence of minor amounts of impurities in argon on the positron annihilation lifetime spectrum is described.

INTRODUCTION

Since the discovery of fine structure in the positron annihilation lifetime spectrum in argon, its existence has been proved beyond doubt by many workers.[1-4] However, quite a few problems associated with the shoulder still remained unsolved. One of them is the discrepancy between the values of the "shoulder-broadness pressure product" in argon reported by different workers. The previous value reported by us was only about 100 nsec atm, which is far below the values of about 275 nsec atm claimed by Paul,[2] and Falk and Jones.[3] Paul has also pointed out that the low values of our measurement might be due to the inclusion of minor amounts of impurities into argon. Meanwhile, after the study of positron annihilation in chlorine, nitrogen, and argon, it has been also discovered that chlorine is a powerful shoulder-narrowing agent.[5] If impurities were introduced into argon gas, the most probable one should be air. In order to clear this point, a series of measurements of positron annihilation lifetime spectra in argon doped with air were made. After the analysis of the $\lambda(t)$ plots, it was concluded

393

that the low value of "shoulder broadness" obtained previously was due to the inclusion of impurities, presumably air. Oxygen is probably responsible for the narrowing of the "shoulder" because of its low-lying electronic excitation levels.

INSTRUMENTAL

Two gas cylinders were used in this work. The one used for obtaining the positron lifetime spectrum in pure argon was made from stainless steel and sealed with lead gaskets. It is 10 in. long and 5 in. in diameter. The other one used in previous work,[1] and for the present series of air-doped argon experiments, was made from aluminum and sealed with rubber O-rings. It is 5 in. long and 3 in. in diameter. The stainless-steel cylinder was cleaned and baked to about 100°C before the filling with gas, but the aluminum cylinder was never cleaned except by evacuation. The surface of the inner wall of the stainless steel was shiny, but although the surface of the inner wall of the aluminum cylinder looked clean, a layer of thick oxide could clearly be seen. The normal procedure for filling gas into the cylinder included evacuation and flushing more than 5 times.

Two high-resolution time-to-amplitude converters were used in this work. The one used for $\lambda(t)$ plots has a resolution of $W^{1}/_{2}$ = 0.5 nsec and a useful range of 25 nsec.[6] The other one used for checking purposes has a resolution of $W^{1}/_{2}$ = 1.2 nsec and a useful range of 360 nsec.[7]

EXPERIMENTAL

$\lambda(t)$ plots of the lifetime spectra were adopted here in analyzing the data. First and third components of the lifetime spectrum were not subtracted in calculating the $\lambda(t)$. It has been found that the subtraction of a third component extrapolated from the tail part by assuming a simple exponential decay does not alter the shape and the value of the $\lambda(t)$ plot significantly. In addition, it is also quite difficult to make a reliable estimation of the first component. Therefore, in order to preserve the integrity of the information contained in the lifetime spectrum it was preferred to calculate the $\lambda(t)$ without subtraction of the first and third components.

A series of measurements of positron annihilation lifetimes at an argon pressure of about 17 atm and air content of 2400, 380, 70, and 15 ppm were made. The $\lambda(t)$ plots of the 380 and 70 ppm air cases are shown in Figs. 1 and 2 as typical examples. After the 15 ppm air run was made the cylinder was flushed several times with argon. A $\lambda(t)$ plot then made was found to lie between that for pure argon and 15 ppm air, making suspect the purity of the argon in the cylinder. A

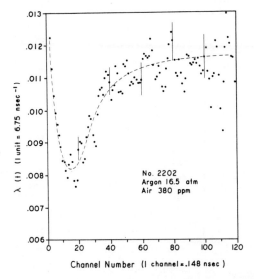

Fig. 1. λ(t) plot for argon with 380 ppm air.

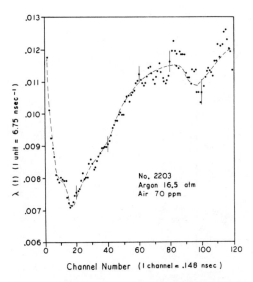

Fig. 2. λ(t) plot for argon with 70 ppm air.

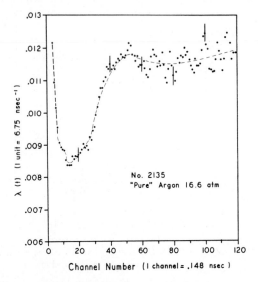

Fig. 3. $\lambda(t)$ plot for "pure" argon in aluminum container.

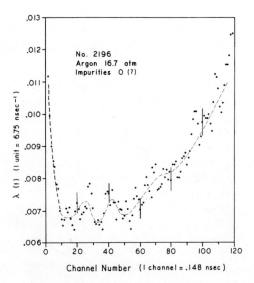

Fig. 4. $\lambda(t)$ plot for pure argon in stainless steel container.

$\lambda(t)$ plot for an old "pure" argon gas stored in the aluminum cylinder is shown in Fig. 2. Two additional ones were made with gases filled in by the old gas-filling procedure. Their $\lambda(t)$ plots were found to be practically the same as the one in Fig. 3. The $\lambda(t)$ plot for the pure argon which was contained in the stainless steel cylinder is shown in Fig. 4.

RESULTS AND DISCUSSIONS

Fine structures exist in these $\lambda(t)$ plots of air-doped argon. However, the data is insufficient for these structures to be traced one by one, as in the case of chlorine argon mixtures. Nevertheless, if we neglect the fine detail and concentrate only on the gross structure, the same procedure used for analyzing the $\lambda(t)$ plots of chlorine argon mixtures[8] may also be employed here.

Three assumptions are made in this analysis. First, the upper cutoff energy of the positron energy distribution at a certain time is sharp. Second, there are relatively sharp and strong annihilation resonances below a certain energy. Third, the energy distribution is relatively flat. Because the value of the upper cutoff energy decreases with time, from the above three assumptions it is expected that $\lambda(t)$ rises sharply at first, reaches a peak at the time when the upper cutoff energy is near the first resonant annihilation energy, decreases after it has passed the resonance and increases again when it approaches the second resonance. By such considerations, a reasonable estimation of values of the resonance energies can be made, provided the scattering process is known.

In a diatomic gas, at such an energy range, inelastic scatterings by molecular excitations are mainly responsible for the energy loss of positrons. There are three types of excitations: electronic, vibrational and rotational. All of them possess distinctive values of minimum energy losses which are also the threshold energies. In the energy range of interest, direct rotational excitation may be neglected due to its low-energy levels. Therefore, we will only consider electronic and vibrational excitations. In general, above the electronic excitation threshold electron excitation is the dominating energy exchange process. Naturally, we may separate the whole energy range into two regions, one above the electronic excitation threshold and one below. It is expected that the positron loses its energy very fast above this threshold because of high value of energy loss in single collision and the high collision cross section, and slowly below the threshold. Consequently, the upper cutoff energy of the positron energy distribution decreases very fast to below the electronic excitation threshold in a diatomic gas. In air, nitrogen has an electronic excitation threshold energy of 8.5 eV which is too high to be effective in the energy range of interest, but oxygen has excitation threshold energies of as low as 1.6 and 1.2 eV. It is no wonder that oxygen in minor quantity is a powerful shoulder-narrowing agent, but not so powerful in large quantities.

If the slowing down time of positrons in pure argon to the main resonance annihilation level and the electronic excitation threshold energy in oxygen are taken as 300 nsec atm and 195 nsec atm, which are equivalent to 0.72 eV and 1.4 eV, respectively, using the scattering cross section evaluated by Teutsch and Hughes,[9] the time positions of the first big hump in these $\lambda(t)$ plots of air-doped argon fit approximately the following semiempirical formula[8]:

$$ T_1 = \frac{195}{p + 1.5 \times 10^5 p_a} + \frac{105}{p + 20\, p_a} $$

where p and p_a are the pressures of argon and air in atmospheres, and T_1 is in nanoseconds. The reason of choosing 20 as the coefficient of p_a in the second term is that it fits well for the "shoulder-broadness pressure products" of Ar-N_2 and Ar-O_2 mixtures at higher pressures.[10]

This formula implies that the average slowing down power of air at positron energies higher than 1.4 eV is 1.5×10^5 times higher than argon, and the average slowing down power of air at energies just below 1.4 eV is only 20 times higher than argon. This, in turn, indicates that the electronic excitation collision cross section of O_2 for positron is about 10 times greater than the elastic cross section of argon, and the average vibrational collision cross section of air for positron is about 10^3 times less than that of electronic excitation. From this formula it can also be shown that the value of T_1 changes very little between p_a = 0.1 to 0.001 atm at a value of about 6 nsec for argon pressure of 17 atm. The lower limit is equivalent to only 60 ppm of air in argon. For argon containing air just below this limit the positions of the fine structures are very sensitive to the amount of impurities present. With such complications it is understandable why "shoulder-broadness pressure product" did not remain constant as claimed by Falk and Jones.[3]

Besides O_2 and Cl_2, acetone vapor has been found to be a powerful shoulder-narrowing agent with attendant fine structure production. Therefore, it is expected that other organic vapors might give the same effect.

From the above argument, it was concluded that the argon in the aluminum cylinder in the previous work was contaminated with oxygen and perhaps organic vapors. The introduction of oxygen into argon gas is attributed to the leakage of air through the O-ring packings during evacuation and the O_2 released from the oxide film of the inner wall of the cylinder.

ACKNOWLEDGMENT

This work was partially supported by USAFOSR Grant No. 62-398, and the authors wish to thank Drs. J. H. Green and John Lee for valuable discussions.

REFERENCES

1. Tao, S. J., J. Bell, and J. H. Green, *Proc. Phys. Soc. (London)* **83**, 453 (1964).
2. Paul, D. A. L., *Proc. Phys. Soc. (London)* **84**, 563 (1964).
3. Falk, W. R., and G. Jones, *Canad. J. Phys.* **42**, 1751 (1964).
4. Osman, P. E., *Phys. Rev.* **138**, B213 (1965).
5. Bell, J., S. J. Tao, and J. H. Green, *Nucl. Instr. Methods*, on press.
6. Bell, J., and S. J. Tao, *Nucl. Instr. Methods*, on press.
7. Tao, S. J., *Phys. Rev. Letters* **14**, 938 (1965).
8. Tao, S. J., to be published.
9. Teutsch, W. B., and V. W. Hughes, *Phys. Rev.* **103**, 1266 (1956).
10. Unpublished data.

The Annihilation of Positrons in Argon

G. Jones and P. H. R. Orth

University of British Columbia
Vancouver, Canada

1. INTRODUCTION

Recent experimental work has indicated that the annihilation of positrons in the noble gases is characterized by a velocity-dependent annihilation rate.[1-4] Subsequent work showed that the observed positron mean lifetime increases when a uniform electric field is applied to the gas.[5] Since the mean velocity of the positrons is increased when an electric field is applied to the gas, these observations indicate that the positron annihilation rate decreases with increasing velocity.

These experimental results should serve as a useful test of the specific velocity dependences of the annihilation and elastic scattering cross sections, calculated in terms of a particular model for the interaction between a positron and a neutral atom.

This paper presents the results of calculations using as a model the scattering of positrons from the Hartree-Fock distribution of electrons in an argon atom including an additional induced dipole-polarization interaction. It is observed that such a model can yield annihilation rates of the same magnitude as the experimental values. Detailed agreement, however, has not yet been obtained.

2. THEORY

For a gas containing N atoms/cm^3, the positron annihilation rate has been shown[7] to be

$$\nu_a = \pi r_0^2 cN \int d^3\mathbf{x} \, |\psi^-|^2 \, |\psi^+|^2 \tag{1}$$

where r_0 is the classical electron radius, and the integral is simply the electron density at the positron averaged over the positron position. If the coulomb distortion of both the atomic electron and the positron wavefunctions is ignored, then use of a plane-wave representation for the positron wavefunction results in the following velocity-independent expression:

$$\nu_a = \pi r_0^2 cNZ \tag{2}$$

where Z is the atomic number of the scattering atom. Inclusion of coulomb distortions necessitates the solution of Eq. (1) by numerical means. In order to emphasize the origin of the velocity-dependence of the theoretical annihilation rate, Eq. (1) may be rewritten in the form:

$$\nu_a(k) = \pi r_0^2 cNZ_{\text{eff}}(k) \tag{3}$$

where $k = (1/\alpha)(v/c)$.

The results presented in this paper were obtained using values of $\nu_a(k)$ and the elastic scattering cross section, $\sigma_s(k)$, calculated by

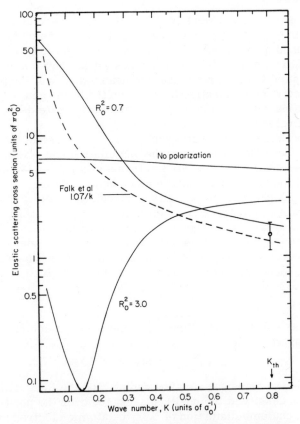

Fig. 1. The dependence of the elastic scattering cross section on the positron wave number, k. The different curves represent different assumed forms of the polarization potential.

solving the Schrödinger equation for the positron using the interaction energy given by Hartree and Hartree.[8] The effect of an additional polarization interaction of the form $-\frac{1}{2}\alpha e^2/[(r^2 + R_0^2)^2]$ was also investigated. The method of solution and the form of the polarization potential are identical to that employed by Massey and Moussa[9] in their treatment of the scattering of positrons. α is the "polarizability" of the neutral argon atom. The numerical value, 11.0 a_0^3, is readily obtained from the dielectric constant of argon. $|\psi^-|^2$ is thus the Hartree-Fock electron density[8] and ψ^+ is the positron wavefunction obtained by solving the Schrödinger equation described above.

The results for the elastic scattering cross section are presented in Fig. 1. The curve labeled "No Polarization" is the result of a solution of the Schrödinger equation in which only the Hartree-Hartree potential was included. The other curves illustrate the effect of including the attractive polarization interaction, with results presented for specific values of the parameter R_0^2. The dashed curve labeled Falk et al., is *not* a solution of the Schrödinger equation, but rather the result of an attempt to empirically fit the experimental time distributions.[5] It is included for comparison only. The experimental point is an estimate of the elastic scattering cross section obtained from studies of the increase in positronium formation when uniform electric fields are applied to a gas.[11,12] It is an average of $\sigma_s(k)$ over a range of k near k_{th}, the value corresponding to the positronium formation threshold.

A plot of Z_{eff} as a function of the positron wave number, k, is presented in Fig. 2. The labeling of the various curves follows that employed in Fig. 1. The curves presented in these two figures correspond to solutions of the appropriate Schrödinger equation for partial waves up to and including $l = 3$.

A comparison is then made to the experimental results by estimating from the results described above, the annihilation rate, λ_a, which should characterize the exponential tail of the experimental time distributions. That is,

$$\lambda_a = 4\pi \int_0^\infty \nu_a(v) v^2 f(v) \, dv \tag{4}$$

where λ_a is the velocity-dependent annihilation rate, $\nu_a(v)$, averaged over the *equilibrium* velocity distribution of the positrons. $f(v)$, the velocity distribution function, is obtained by solving:

$$-\lambda_a f(v) = \frac{1}{V^2} \frac{d}{dv} \left\{ \left[\frac{a^2 v^2}{3\nu_s(v)} + \frac{m}{M} v^3 \nu_s(\nu) \frac{kT}{mv} \right] \right.$$
$$\left. \times \frac{df}{dv} + \frac{m}{M} v^3 \nu_s(\nu) \, f(v) \right\} - \nu_a(v) \, f(v) \tag{5}$$

where $a = eE/m$. This equation, applicable to the equilibrium situation considered here, is a simplified form of the more general time-dependent diffusion equation given by Falk et al.[5] A good approximation to $f(v)$ can be obtained by neglecting the $(\lambda_a - \nu_a)f(v)$ term compared to the diffusion terms. Thus, instead of solving Eq. (5), $f(v)$ may be approximated by solving

$$\left[\frac{a^2 v^2}{3\nu_s(v)} + \frac{m}{M} v^3 \nu_s(v) \frac{kT}{mv}\right] \frac{df}{dv} + \frac{m}{M} v^3 \nu_s(v)\, f(v) = 0 \qquad (6)$$

This approximation is particularly good if $\nu_a(v)$ is nearly constant, and thus equal to λ_a. An estimate of λ_a is then obtained by solving Eq. (4) using within the integrand the approximate $f(v)$ from Eq. (6). An indication of the accuracy of this approximation is illustrated in Fig. 3. The solid line labeled Falk et al., is the dependence of the approximate λ_a as a function of the applied electric field, where the $\nu_a(v)$ and $\sigma_s(v)$ used in these calculations correspond to the dashed curves in Figs. 1 and 2. The dashed line in Fig. 3, however, is the

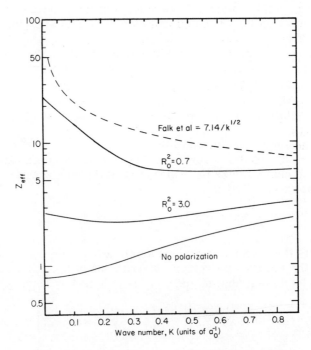

Fig. 2. The dependence of Z_{eff} on the positron wave number, k.

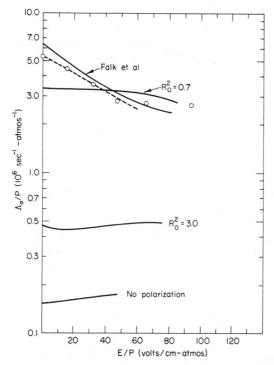

Fig. 3. Theoretical and experimental annihilation rates as a function of the applied electric field. The experimental values are indicated by the open circles.

exact λ_a calculated from the same $\nu_a(v)$ and $\sigma_s(v)$ but using the $f(v)$ obtained by solving Eq. (5).

For the purpose of the preliminary survey described in this paper, all electric-field dependent λ_a values were obtained using the approximation described.

3. RESULTS

The calculated values of λ_a as a function of E/P are illustrated in Fig. 3 for several different forms of the polarization potential. Again the labeling corresponds to that used for Fig. 1. The experimental values of Falk[10] are indicated by the open circles.

The increase in the experimental annihilation rate for E/P values greater than 75 V/cm-atm is interpreted as a reflection of the increase in the positronium formation rate due to the increased fraction of the positron equilibrium velocity distribution, which exceeds the threshold energy for positronium formation. This interpretation is consistent with the discussions of other workers concerning studies of the increased positronium formation when electric fields are applied to the system.[11,12]

4. CONCLUSIONS

It is apparent from Figs. 2 and 3 that the inclusion of a simple polarization potential of the form suggested by Massey and Moussa[9] is sufficient to enhance the theoretical annihilation rate by the factor of about 35 required for agreement with the experimental results. Furthermore, the dependence of Z_{eff} on k is modified to be a decreasing function of k for small k as required by the experimental dependence of λ_a on E/P. The assumed form of the positron-atom interaction fails, however, to yield a good fit to the experimental values. The effect of minor changes in the form of this interaction are being investigated. Further theoretical work in this direction would be useful.

The model assumed in the preceding discussion involves annihilation of a "free" positron moving under the influence of a potential due to the atom with which it interacts. Although it is evident that this model can yield approximate agreement with the experimental results, alternative competing modes of positron annihilation should be examined.

Khare et al.,[13] have shown that it is possible for a positron to form a stable bound state with a helium atom and further suggest that such bound states should be possible with any atom or molecule. Since such a bound state should have a mean lifetime, $\tau < 10^{-9}$ sec, the rate at which such bound states are formed would therefore contribute to the observed annihilation rate. Since theoretical estimates of the cross section for radiative attachment of positrons to atoms are not available, it is interesting to consider the analogous situation for electrons. Results for several atoms (not including argon) presented by Branscombe[14] indicate that electron radiative attachment cross sections of the order of 10^{-23} cm^2 can be expected. The annihilation cross section of thermal positrons in argon, on the other hand, is of the order of 10^{-20} cm^2. If, because of their greater binding energy, the positron radiative attachment cross sections were larger than those associated with electrons, it is apparent that this process could yield a significant contribution to the observed annihilation rate. A quantitative estimate of the magnitude of such cross sections is therefore required before a complete picture of the annihilation of positrons in these gases can be obtained.

ACKNOWLEDGMENT

The authors gratefully acknowledge the generous assistance of A. Fowler and L. Horvath of the U.B.C. Computing Center. Support through a research grant from the National Research Council of Canada is also acknowledged.

REFERENCES

1. Tao, S. J., J. Bell, and J. H. Green, *Proc. Phys. Soc. (London)* **83**, 453 (1964).
2. Falk, W. R., and G. Jones, *Canad. J. Phys.* **42**, 1751 (1964).
3. Paul, D. A. L., *Proc. Phys. Soc. (London)* **84**, 563 (1964).
4. Osmon, P. E., *Phys. Rev.* **138**, B216 (1965).
5. Falk, W. R., P. H. R. Orth, and G. Jones, *Phys. Rev. Letters* **14**, 447 (1965).
6. Jones, G., W. R. Falk, and P. H. R. Orth, paper presented at the IVth International Conference of the Physics of Electronic and Atomic Collisions, 1965.
7. Ferrell, R. A., *Rev. Modern Phys.* **28**, 308 (1956).
8. Hartree, D. R., and W. Hartree, *Proc. Roy. Soc. (London)* **A166**, 450 (1936).
9. Massey, H. S. W., and A. H. A. Moussa, *Proc. Phys. Soc. (London)* **71**, 38 (1958).
10. Falk, W. R., Ph.D. thesis, University of British Columbia, 1965.
11. Marder, S., V. W. Hughes, C. S. Wu, and W. Bennett, *Phys. Rev.* **103**, 1258 (1956).
12. Obenshain, F. E., and L. A. Page, *Phys. Rev.* **125**, 573 (1962).
13. Khare, H. C., P. R. Wallace, G. G. Bach, and A. Chodos, *Canad. J. Phys.* **42**, 1522 (1964).
14. Branscombe, L. M., "Atomic and Molecular Processes," (D. R. Bates), p. 100. Academic Press, New York, 1962.

Positron Formation and Annihilation in Argon-Propane Mixture

C. Y. Leung and *D. A. L. Paul*

University of Toronto, Toronto, Canada

This report has its origins in some work by Dulit, Gittelman, and Deutsch,[1] and two brief unpublished items by one of us.[2,3] In the work of Dulit et al. it was found that the positronium fraction in argon remained essentially unchanged as the partial pressure of a "polyatomic" gas was increased above 0.01%. More recently positron annihilations were briefly studied in liquid argon-liquid propane mixtures[2] and a very few measurement were made, using a 2-quantum correlation technique, of positronium formation in argon and propane gases.[3] We shall describe these experiments briefly since they are not published elsewhere.

The original purpose of the measurements with liquid argon-liquid propane was to attempt to explain the low value of I_2 (orthopositronium intensity) in pure liquid argon which is less than one-third of that in the pure gas. The experiments were lifetime measurements. The liquids were contained in a long-tailed dewar having a Na^{22} source mounted at the bottom of the tail. The source was viewed by 2 in. long NaI(T1) crystals mounted on RCA 6342 photomultipliers. The detectors fed a coincidence circuit which was a 5-channel chronotron, allowing part of the time spectrum to be obtained simultaneously. For positronium intensity studies, five points on the I_2 exponential tail of the decay curves provided good statistical accuracy in fairly short counting periods. Liquid argon was introduced into the Dewar by a technique which avoided the introduction of any oxygen. The argon vapor pressure was then maintained slightly above room temperature so that small ladles of pure liquid propane could be introduced through ports in the Dewar cap, again without letting air into the Dewar. The addition of propane alters the positronium intensity, as shown in Figs. 1, 2.[†] The lifetime also increases 29 ± 2% over the range of the measurements.

---

*E. C. Stevens postgraduate fellow.

[†]The volume of each liquid was measured at its boiling point.

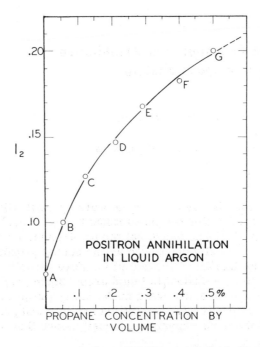

Fig. 1. Orthopositronium intensity in liquid argon at low propane concentrations. The propane volumes correspond to liquid propane at its normal boiling point.

The contrast between the results of Fig. 2 and the report of Dulit et al. stimulated some preliminary measurements by one of us[3] using, basically, the two-quantum angular correlation method of Pond[4] for determining I_2 in gases. Pond used a magnetic field to confine the positrons, but in these later experiments a large gas vessel was used at pressures of less than 1 atm and the counters were placed 20 ft apart (Fig. 3). The orthopositronium fraction is given directly by the number $1 - (N_A/N_B)$ where N_A is the 0.511 MeV coincidence rate in the gas under investigation, and N_B is the rate for a gas of the same stopping power which, however, quenches positronium completely. There are virtually no large corrections which have to be made to the counting rates in this experiment, but rather strong positron sources are required, totaling 10-20 mc, for good statistics. At the time of these experiments, only 600 μc were available, which yielded less than one coincidence per minute.

The results of the experiments are given in Table I. As can be

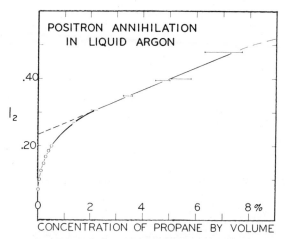

Fig. 2. Orthopositronium intensity in liquid argon
containing higher concentrations of propane. The
ranges of concentration indicated by the bars were
largely due to boil-off of the liquids.

seen, they are subject to large statistical uncertainties, and do not
agree well with the conclusions of Dulit et al.

Our recent measurements have been made with gases compressed
mainly in the range 5-8 atms. The pressure chamber (Fig. 4) is the
same as has been used in some other published work.[5-7] The experiments are lifetime measurements using a simple timesorter circuit,

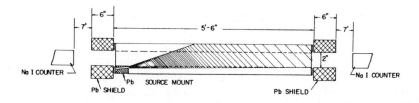

APPARATUS FOR THE MEASUREMENT OF POSITRONIUM FORMATION IN GASES

Fig. 3. Apparatus for the 2-γ correlation determinations of positronium
intensity. The positron sources (Na^{22}) were deposited at the bottom of in-
clined holes drilled in lead blocks. At 0.7 atm of argon gas, the number of
positrons annihilating in the right-hand end window is negligible compared
to the number annihilating in the volume of gas that is viewed by the
counters.

TABLE I

	Over-all positronium percentage	
Substance	Gas	Liquid
argon	35.2 ± 3.5	10 ± 1
argon, 10% propane	52.8 ± 3.7	
argon, 22% propane	45.1 ± 5.0	
propane[a]	43.0 ± 2.7	39 ± 2
ethane[a]	43 ± 4	41 ± 3

[a] The values for the liquids have been given previously.[3]

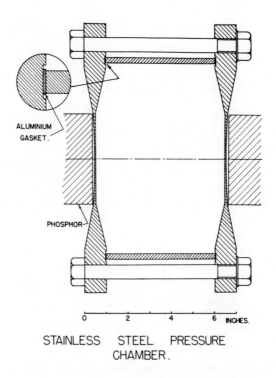

STAINLESS STEEL PRESSURE
CHAMBER.

Fig. 4. Cross section (diameter vertical) of cylindrical pressure chamber for use in the range 0-10 atm. The end windows are tapered in stages to 0.1, 0.06, and 0.05 in., respectively. NaI(Tl) detectors 4 in. in diameter have been used.

consisting basically of a pulse overlap integrator and multichannel analyser. Pulse-height selection inside channels is carried out in the usual way. Our circuit has two features which should be mentioned. First, the 6BN6 which we use as a fast coincidence tube merely provides a negative square overlap pulse at its plate: this signal is fed directly to the grid of a long tailed pair which has the integrator circuit connected to its second plate. The 6BN6 thus cuts off a standing current in the long tailed pair and, since the standing current can be nicely stabilized, little or no drift should arise from the integration. We adopted this method of integration because we found that in a 6BN6, the collector current is never fully switched to the plate: generally only about 65% of the current is transferred under our conditions. The second feature is that our two limited pulses feeding the 6BN6 coincidence tube are of unequal length, namely 2.0 and 1.1 μsec. As a result, there is a saturation-sized integrated pulse corresponding to complete overlap of the longer pulse over the shorter. Some of the random coincidences produce complete overlap giving rise to a sharp peak at the end of the time spectrum. This sharp peak provides a calibration point and any broadening gives a measure of drift. The circuit is calibrated by a method which is described in References 2 and 8. Our calibration delays are RG11/U cables (most of them about 150 nsec long) which have been measured to within ±0.1 nsec.[8]

Our recent data fall into two categories, those requiring a fit of the data to a single exponential curve, and those with double exponentials (i.e., those with small fractions of propane, in which the non-positronium component is not quenched). We have only very recently attempted to analyze the latter.

We emphasize that our results only give relative values of ortho-positronium intensity. Each column of Table II has observed values that depend on (a) the fraction of positrons annihilating in the walls of the vessel, and (b) the relative sensitivity of the annihilation detector to 3-quantum and 2-quantum annihilations. We found much more scatter in the results than was expected from statistics, indicating the need for greater stability in the pulse-height selection channels. Nevertheless, the two sets of data in Table II were fairly consistent and show a decrease in positronium fraction from 0.2 to 1.0% propane. Below 0.2% propane, our data were inconsistent and should be repeated. From 1 to 10% propane the positronium fraction does not vary more than 3.5% of the mean, and unfortunately, our data appear to be scattered rather randomly in this range. At 20% propane the average of two values lies about 3% lower than the mean of the values for the range 1-10%. This result is still inconclusive, but we can say that the steep rise which for the liquid phase continues above 0.1% (Figs. 1,2) is absent with the gas. Since our lifetime

TABLE II

Positronium Fractions in Argon—Propane Gas Mixture

Propane partial pressure (%)	Relative fractions normalized to 1.00 at 0.2% propane[a]	
	Set 1	Set 3
0.1		1.015
0.2	1.00	1.00
0.3	0.98	1.00
0.4	0.945	0.975
0.5	0.96	0.97
1.0		0.95

[a]Set 1 corresponds to a stopping power equal to that of 6000 mm Hg of pure Argon, and Set 3 to 4000 mm Hg of pure argon.

experiments do not yield absolute values of positronium fraction, we favor the 2-quantum angular correlation method for future work.

To obtain reliable measurements of positronium fraction by the 2-quantum method, it is necessary to apply small corrections for the pressure quenching of positronium which is due to pick off. For pure argon, the pressure-quenching coefficient has been given by Celitans and Green[10] and Celitans, Tao, and Green,[11] who obtain the low value (averaged) of

$$(1.9 \pm 0.2) \times 10^{-3} \lambda_0 /atm$$

where λ_0 is the annihilation rate *in vacuo* of orthopositronium. We have measured this coefficient for propane gas (Phillips Petroleum research grade), and obtain the value

TABLE III

Partial pressure of propane (%)	Pressure quenching coefficient (λ_0/atm)
0.2	0.0375
0.4	0.038
1	0.0435
5	0.044
10	0.052

$$(0.104 \pm 0.005) \; \lambda_0 / \text{atm}$$

In the gases of intermediate composition, we obtained the values of Table III, which are good to about $\pm 10\%$. The coefficients of Table III are tending to values, at the lowest partial pressures, which are near that of Duff and Heymann,[12] and the value obtained by Celitans et al.[11] for slightly impure argon.

We have not yet related our data on the positronium fraction in pure propane to that for the mixtures; we need to make a correction for the stopping power, because propane departs appreciably from a perfect gas law at the pressures in question.

DISCUSSION OF LIQUID ARGON—LIQUID PROPANE RESULTS

Below about 2% propane (Figs. 1,2) the propane appears to compete with a mechanism which either selectively removes positronium in a limited energy range or prevents positronium formation. The results could be interpreted on the basis of very rapid resonance pickoff annihilations over a limited energy range above thermal. Thermalization by the propane would remove positronium from the resonance region, so that the long exponential tail would begin to increase in intensity. It was privately suggested by Dr. R. A. Ferrell that this competition might be between the collisional breakup of positronium above 6.8 eV and the rapid slowing of positronium by propane to an energy where it is stable.

In Fig. 2, the extrapolated linear portion of the curve intercepts the I_2 axis at about 24% orthopositronium. This is close to the value for pure argon gas, about as close as one obtains from a similar comparison for other substances (propane, ethane, nitrogen). We do not know whether this fact has any significance.

REFERENCES

1. Dulit, E. P., B. Gittelman, and M. Deutsch, *Bull. Am. Phys. Soc. II*, **1**, XA8 (1956).
2. Paul, D. A. L., Ph.D. Thesis, Queen's University, Kingston, Ontario, 1958.
3. Paul, D. A. L., Unpublished. These results were presented in part at the Canadian Association of Physicists' 14th Congress **10**, 3 (1959).
4. Pond, T. A., *Phys. Rev.* **85**, 489 (1952).
5. Paul, D. A. L., and L. St. Pierre, *Phys. Rev. Letters* **11**, 493 (1953).
6. Paul, D. A. L., *Proc. Phys. Soc. (G.B.)* **84**, 563 (1964).
7. Abid, I., and D. A. L. Paul, *Proc. Phys. Soc. (G.B.)* **86**, 1038 (1965).

8. Graham, R. L., J. S. Geiger, R. E. Bell, and R. Barton, *Nuclear Instr. Meth.* **15**, 40 (1962).
9. Abid, I., M.A. Thesis, Physics Dept., University of Toronto, 1964.
10. Celitans, G. J., and J. H. Green, *Proc. Phys. Soc. (G.B.)* **82**, 1002 (1964).
11. Celitans, G. J., S. J. Tao, and J. H. Green, *Proc. Phys. Soc. (G.B.)* **83**, 833 (1964).
12. Duff, B. G., and F. F. Heymann, *Proc. Roy. Soc. (London)* **270A**, 517 (1962).

Data Analysis in Positron Lifetime Measurement

D. A. L. Paul and P. C. Stangeby

University of Toronto, Toronto, Canada

The lifetime spectra discussed in the previous paper are fitted by least squares, when appropriate, to the formula

$$n = n_1 \, e^{-\lambda_1 t} + n_2 \, e^{-\lambda_2 t} + b \qquad (1)$$

Our experience has been that straightforward fitting, using approximate values of λ_1, λ_2, and the Taylor expansion linear approximation to evaluate corrections to λ_1, λ_2, does not work satisfactorily. There appear to be several contributory causes to this state of affairs: (a) $\exp(-\lambda t)\,(1 - \delta\lambda \cdot t)$ is not a good approximation for $\exp[(-\lambda + \delta\lambda)t]$ at large values of t; (b) even if the initial values of λ_1 and λ_2 were very good choices, it does not seem certain that the corrections $\delta\lambda_1, \delta\lambda_2$, obtained simultaneously, are the most appropriate ones to apply.* We had some success when fitting four of the five parameters and making one correction at a time. The computation then converges slowly on answers which, we think, do not correspond to the minimum in x^2.

More recently, we have studied this problem by evaluating the χ^2 surface as a function of λ_1 and λ_2, making 3-parameter fits which give n_1, n_2, b for fixed λ_1, λ_2. The shapes of the χ^2 surfaces had previously been unknown to us and are illustrated in Figs. 1 and 2. Note in these figures the very different scales which have been used for experimental as opposed to exact generated data. Using exact computer-generated data we have found that in order to preserve significant digits it is desirable to have more than eight significant figures retained for 150 data points, totalling over 100,000 counts. We now use IBM double precision arithmetic (16 figures) for convenience, though twelve-figure accuracy might suffice. The three-parameter fit that determines χ^2 in this method can be made to converge very rapidly on the minimum point of the χ^2 surface. We begin (Fig. 3) with a 3×3 matrix of points in the $\lambda_1 - \lambda_2$ plane, which we

---

*The recent experience of G. J. Celitans (private communication) lead us to believe that this approach can be made to work.

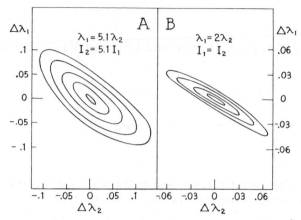

Fig. 1. Contour maps in the λ_1-λ_2 plane of the χ^2 surface. (A) Experimental data; (B) Exact generated data.

hope encloses the "correct" answer. If the middle point of this matrix does not correspond to the lowest of the nine χ^2 values, the matrix is reconstructed with a shift to the lowest χ^2 as center. If no such shift is required, the approximate location of the point of lowest χ^2 is determined using a parabolic fit and a new 3×3 matrix is set up having this "minimum" point at its center, and the previous center as one of the corners. This completes the first iteration. Con-

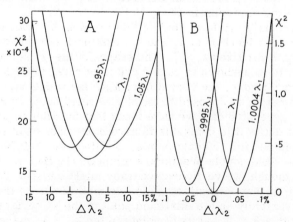

Fig. 2. Sections of χ^2 surfaces at different λ_1, values. (A) Experimental data; (B) Exact generated data.

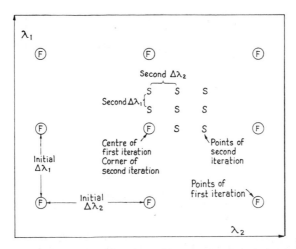

Fig. 3. Curve fitting double exponentials by least squares: the matrices of points (λ_1, λ_2) at the last stage of one iteration and the first stage of the next iteration.

vergence to within 1 part in 10^5 of the ultimate limiting values of λ_1, λ_2 is achieved in three of four iterations. Furthermore, the program is bound to approach a minimum in χ^2, and if this does not correspond to the desired solution, then there must be other minima in the χ^2 surface. So far we have not found any examples of other such minima since we changed to the IBM double precision arithmetic, but there may be ambiguous cases when one of the exponential decays is very weak, or when the two mean lives are almost equal. We think that any difficulties in fitting by this method are due to inherently ambivalent data. If the data do not clearly define two exponentials, one cannot expect an unambiguous answer, and indeed one hopes not to obtain one.

We are still adding some refinements to this program. When this is done, we will be glad to provide copies on request.

ACKNOWLEDGMENTS

This work has been supported by the National Research Council under grant No. A2224 and by the University of Toronto.

Positron Decay in Silicon

G. Fabri, G. Poletti, and G. Randone

Laboratorio Centro Informazioni Studi Esperienze, Milan, Italy

Angular correlation measurements of radiation from positrons annihilating in silicon have been made by Stewart,[1] Agodi et al.,[2] and Colombino et al.[3]

The shape of the experimental curves, substantially an inverted parabola, led to the conclusion that positrons annihilate in silicon with nearly free electrons, belonging to the valence band and to the conduction band, and without formation of bound states. With the aim of deciding whether the annihilations take place mainly with valence or conduction electrons, it seemed worthwhile to compare the delay spectra of annihilations in silicon single crystals with the ones concerning annihilations in the depletion layer of a reverse-biased silicon junction. In this last case, if the mean electric field at the junction is high enough to sweep away electron-hole pairs generated by incoming positrons, annihilations with conduction electrons should become very unlikely.

The positron source (Na^{22}) was deposited by evaporating a $Na^{22}Cl$ hydrochloric solution in a small cavity bored in an n-type silicon single crystal, which was placed in front of the effective area of a surface barrier silicon detector.

A block diagram of the experimental arrangement is shown in Fig. 1. Detectors A and B were NE 102 plastic scintillators, detector C, a surface-barrier silicon junction connected to a fast amplifier, and detecting the positrons.

Pulses from detectors A and B, with suitable amplitude requirements, were fed into a vernier time sorter[4] for delay measurements, the delay spectrum being stored within the first 100 channels of a 200 channel pulse-height analyzer.

Channels A, B, and C are connected to a three-fold fast coincidence, the output of which allows pulses from the time sorter to be stored in the second 100 channels of the analyzer.

The surface barrier detector was prepared with n-type 1800-Ω cm silicon and with a reverse bias of 400 V. The thickness of the depletion layer was about 430 μ. In this case, taking into account the mean electric field strength and electron mobility in silicon, it is possible to conclude that an electron excited to the conduction band

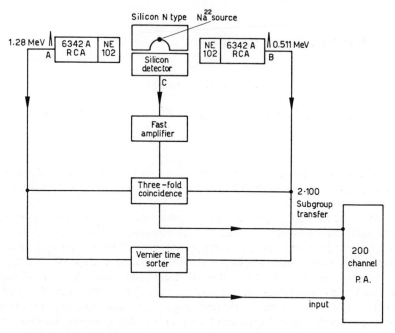

Fig. 1. Block diagram of the experimental arrangement.

by a positron gets away a few microns from the positron itself in a time which is very short in comparison with the annihilation lifetime.

Figure 2 shows the delay curves measured by the described experimental apparatus.

The delay curve, relative to n-type silicon without electric field, shows a complex decay

$$\tau_1 = 2.6 \pm 0.5 \times 10^{-10} \text{ sec;}$$

$$\tau_2 = 1.2 \pm 0.1 \times 10^{-9} \text{ sec;}$$

$$I_2 = 0.026 \pm 0.005.$$

The lack of the tail with the long lifetime (τ_2) is evident in the curve relative to the annihilations in the space charge region of the detector. No evident influence of the electric field on the short lifetime has been observed.

On this ground one can put forward the hypothesis that a long-lived bound state can be formed between positrons and a fraction of the electrons excited to the conduction band by the positrons them-

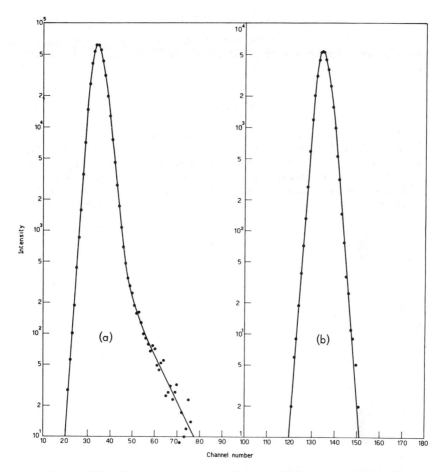

Fig. 2. (a) Delay spectrum of positrons annihilating in n-type silicon single crystal. (b) Delay spectrum of positrons annihilating in the space charge region of a silicon surface barrier detector. 1 channel = 1.41 × 10^{-10} sec.

selves. Of course, this bound state could not be formed in the space-charge region of a surface-barrier silicon detector, where electric field sweeps away the mobile charges.

A similar measurement performed with a p-type silicon single crystal showed a delay curve which was identical to the one obtained with the n-type silicon; as it was expected, the mean concentration of conduction electrons does not influence the annihilation features, supporting the hypothesis that the bound state can be formed only with electrons excited to conduction band by the incoming positrons.

ACKNOWLEDGMENTS

We are indebted to Professor E. Germagnoli for helpful comments, and to Mr. C. Cottini for assistance and advice with regard to the electronic equipment.

REFERENCES

1. Stewart, A. T., *Canad. J. Phys.* **35**, 168 (1957).
2. Agodi, A., I. F. Quercia, and E. Tunisi, *Nuovo Cimento* **33**, 1488 (1964).
3. Colombino, P., B. Fiscella, and L. Trossi, *Nuovo Cimento* **31**, 950 (1964).
4. Cottini, C., and E. Gatti, *Nuovo Cimento* **4**, 1550 (1956); C. Cottini, E. Gatti, and F. Vaghi, *Nuclear Electronics I.A.E.A., Vienna*, V. **1**, 177 (1959)

Author Index

The numbers in parentheses are reference numbers and are included to assist the reader in locating a reference where the author's name is not mentioned in the text. The numbers in boldface refer to the pages on which the complete references are given.

A

Abid, I., 101, **111**, 411(7), **415**, **416**
Adrian, F. J., 179(34), **182**
Agodi, A., 421, **424**
Alichanian, A. I., 17, **49**
Alichanow, A. I., 17, **49**
Allen, J. F., 385(6), **386**
Allison, D. C. S., **111**
Amaldi, E., 103, **111**
Ambrosino, G., 26, **50**, 86, 92(19), **94**
Anderson, C. D., 3, **14**
Argyle, P. E., 20(10), **49**
Arzimovitch, L. A., 17, **49**
Atkins, K. R., 128(16), 130(16), **141**

B

Bach, G. G., 102(22), **111**, 116(9), **125**, 131(18), **141**, 406(3), **407**
Bardeen, J., 302, **304**
Barton, R., 413(8), **416**
Basina, A. S., 377, **381**, 383(4), **386**
Baskova, K. A., 377(3), **381**, 383(4), **386**
Bassani, F., 332, **334**
Bates, D. R., 188, **252**
Batterman, B. W., 67(12), **78**
Bay, Z., 326(5), **327**
Bell, J., 101, 105, 109, **111**, **112**, 114(1), **124**, 186(12), 193, 232, 247(12), **252**, 371(4), **375**, 387(1), 389(1), **390**, 393(1, 5), 394(1, 6), **399**, 401(1), **407**
Bell, R. E., 7, 11, **15**, 22, **49**, 51(5a), 55, **59**, 82, **94**, 143(2), 147, 151, **153**, **154**, 185, 196(2), 198, 215, 229(2, 3), 232(2), 233, 234, 235(102), 237(102), 243(102), 244(102), 245(102), **252**, **255**, 268, **268**, 277(1), **280**, 306, **308**, 369(7), **370**, 413(8), **416**
Bennett, W., 104, **111**, 116(15), 121(15), **125**, 193(22), **252**, 371(3), **375**, 403(11), 406(11), **407**
Bergersen, B., 51, 53, 58, **59**
Beringer, R., 17, 18, **49**
Berko, S., 10(32), 12, 13, 14, **15**, 33(26), 34, **50**, 51, 59, **59**, 62, 63, 67(13, 14), 68, 69(14), 70(14), 72(19), 74(20), 75(20), 76(20), 77(23), **78**, **79**, 138(40), **141**, 143(1), 150, **153**, **154**, 161(13), 162(13), 163(13), 177, **182**, 184(1), 194, 199(30), 200(30), 201(48), 202, 203(48), 204(48), 212(48), 213(30), 214(30, 48), 217(1), 227(48), 230, 231, 232(97), 233(97), **252**, **253**, **254**, 259, 260, **263**, 265(4), **268**, 269(1), 270(1), **275**, 292(7), **295**, 344(5), **344**, 355(2), 356(2), **356**, 369, **370**

Subject Index

*Note: For brevity, expres-
sions like "Angular correlation
of annihilation photon," "Three
photon annihilation rate,"
"Long lifetime," etc., are ab-
breviated as "Angular correlation," "Three photon," "Lifetime," etc.*

A

Alkali halides, see also Hydrides
  angular correlation, 87
  lifetimes, 89
    table of, 90
  nonformation of Ps, 81
  three photon, 92, 226
    table of, 93
Alkali hydrides, angular correlation,
  83
Alkali metals, 10
  lifetime, 11
Alloys, 37
  Li-Mg, 38, 39
Aluminum, single crystal, 33
Angular correlation, see also specific
  materials or class of material,
  e.g., Metals, Al, Oxides, Liquid
  He
  Ar, calculated with polarization, 333
  cylindrical geometry, 63
  derivative of, and phase space den-
    sity, 28
  early history, 17
  Li−NH₃ solutions, 313
  liquefied common gases, 377
  liquid He, 383
  liquid metals, 40-44, 309
  metals, collection of data, 27
  oxides, 341

parabolic shape, 19
solid and liquid Hg and Bi, 309
temperature dependence
  In and alloys, 283
  several metals, 42-44
Annihilation in crystal, theory, 19, 15
  155-181
Annihilation photons, line width, 18
Annihilation rate
  calculation and experiment, 55
  with core and conduction electrons,
    306
  cores, 58
Antiparticles, see Positrons
Argon, 10, 186, 333, 377
  cross sections, 193
Atomic collisions
  with positrons, 113
  with Ps, 113

B

Beryllium, 12, 33
  band gap determination, 291
  calculation of angular correlation,
    34
  single crystal angular correlation,
    291
Bismuth, 11, 309
Bond strength
  Ps−O, 151
  Ps−OH, 152

DATE DUE